COLLECTIVE OSCILLATIONS IN A PLASMA

COLLECTIVE OSCILLATIONS IN A PLASMA

BY

A. I. AKHIEZER, I. A. AKHIEZER, R. V. POLOVIN,

A. G. SITENKO AND K. N. STEPANOV

TRANSLATED BY

H. S. H. MASSEY

TRANSLATION EDITED BY

R. J. TAYLER

THE M.I.T. PRESS

Massachusetts Institute of Technology

Cambridge, Massachusetts

First English edition 1967

Library of Congress Catalog Card No. 66–21113

This is a translation of the original Russian book
Коллективные колебания в плазме,
published by Atomizdat, Moscow, 1964, and
contains corrections and revisions supplied by the authors

Contents

Foreword

THE STUDY of collective oscillations in a plasma is of great interest for many physical and technical problems: the propagation of radio waves in the ionosphere and other plasmas, the radio-emission of stars, the amplification and generation of micro-waves by a plasma, the acceleration of charged particles in a plasma, relaxation in a plasma, plasma diagnostics, high-frequency heating and the containment of a plasma in devices for thermonuclear synthesis, etc.

The present book covers the theory of linear oscillations in a "collisionless" plasma, i.e. in a plasma in which binary collisions have no significant effect on its oscillatory properties. The book discusses three basic problems; the spectra of the natural oscillations, the stability and instability of various particle distributions, and fluctuations in a homogeneous plasma.

The spectra of the eigen oscillations are studied for an equilibrium and for a two-temperature plasma with and without an external magnetic field. The frequencies and decrements of damping caused by resonant interaction of the particles with the field are determined for Langmuir oscillations, non-isothermal sound, modified Langmuir oscillations in a magnetic field, electron- and ion-cyclotron waves and magnetohydrodynamic waves. The problem of the excitation of these waves by external currents is also discussed.

In the case of non-equilibrium plasmas the collective oscillations may be both damped and growing. This phenomenon is particularly clearly manifested when beams of charged particles pass through the plasma. A study of the nature of the oscillations in a non-equilibrium plasma permits us to establish stability and instability criteria for the various particle distributions in a plasma.

This problem is discussed for a free plasma as well as for a plasma located in an external magnetic field.

The book also investigates fluctuations in a plasma. These are linked with such phenomena as thermal emission, wave scattering and transformation and scattering of particles in the plasma. The study of the fluctuations and the connected phenomena—wave scattering and transformation in particular—can be used for plasma diagnostics. Important information on plasma parameters under laboratory conditions may also be provided by direct experimental determination of the correlation functions of the density and fields in the plasma.

CHAPTER I

Spectra of Eigen Oscillations of a Free Plasma†

1. Kinetic Equations

1. Self-consistent Fields

The general approach in the theoretical study of a plasma is based on the use of the kinetic equations defining the distribution functions of its particles. We shall use $F^\alpha(\boldsymbol{v}, \boldsymbol{r}, t)$ to denote the distribution function of plasma particles of a kind α [$F^\alpha\, d^3\boldsymbol{r} d^3\boldsymbol{v}$ is the number of particles of a kind α whose coordinates and velocity components at a point in time t are within the ranges $(\boldsymbol{r}, \boldsymbol{r} + d\boldsymbol{r})$ and $(\boldsymbol{v}, \boldsymbol{v} + d\boldsymbol{v})$]. If $\boldsymbol{E}(\boldsymbol{r}, t)$ and $\boldsymbol{H}(\boldsymbol{r}, t)$ are the electric and magnetic fields acting in the plasma, then the kinetic equation defining F^α can be written in the following general form:

$$\frac{\partial F^\alpha}{\partial t} + \left(\boldsymbol{v} \cdot \frac{\partial F^\alpha}{\partial \boldsymbol{r}}\right) + \frac{e_\alpha}{m_\alpha}\left(\boldsymbol{E} + \frac{1}{c}\,[\boldsymbol{v} \wedge \boldsymbol{H}] \cdot \frac{\partial F^\alpha}{\partial \boldsymbol{v}}\right) + L^\alpha\{F^\beta\} = 0. \quad (1.1)$$

Here the third term defines the variation of the distribution function caused by the action of the fields and the fourth term that caused by the action of binary collisions (e_α and m_α are the charge and mass of particles of a kind α). The fields $\boldsymbol{E}$ and $\boldsymbol{H}$ are caused by external sources and by the particles of the plasma itself, so they

† Editor's Note: In this book the term *free plasma* is used where other authors use the expression *unmagnetized plasma.*

may be called self-consistent. They satisfy the Maxwell equations

$$\left.\begin{aligned}
\operatorname{curl} \boldsymbol{E} &= -\frac{1}{c}\cdot\frac{\partial \boldsymbol{H}}{\partial t};\\
\operatorname{div} \boldsymbol{H} &= 0;\\
\operatorname{curl} \boldsymbol{H} &= \frac{1}{c}\cdot\frac{\partial \boldsymbol{E}}{\partial t} + \frac{4\pi}{c}(\boldsymbol{j}_0 + \boldsymbol{j});\\
\operatorname{div} \boldsymbol{E} &= 4\pi(\varrho_0 + \varrho),
\end{aligned}\right\} \tag{1.2}$$

where ϱ_0 and $\boldsymbol{j}_0$ are the densities of the external charges and currents, and ϱ and $\boldsymbol{j}$ are the densities of the charge and current created by the plasma particles. These quantities are connected with the particle distribution functions by relations† of the following type:

$$\varrho = \sum_\alpha e_\alpha \int F^\alpha\, d^3\boldsymbol{v}, \quad \boldsymbol{j} = \sum_\alpha e_\alpha \int \boldsymbol{v} F^\alpha\, d^3\boldsymbol{v}. \tag{1.3}$$

2. *Binary Collisions*

The functionals $L^\alpha\{F^\beta\}$, which are called the collision integrals, describe binary collisions of particles. In a completely ionized plasma the collisions are caused by Coulomb interactions of the particles. Since the Coulomb forces diminish slowly with distance large collision parameters and small scattering angles play a major part. Under these conditions the collision integrals $L^\alpha\{F^\beta\}$ take the form of divergences of the particle currents in velocity space:

$$L^\alpha\{F^\beta\} = \frac{\partial}{\partial v_i} I_i^\alpha,$$

$$I_i^\alpha = \frac{2\pi e_\alpha^2}{m_\alpha} L \sum e'^2 \int d^3 v' \left(F \frac{\partial F'}{\partial p_k'} - F' \frac{\partial F}{\partial p_k} \right) \frac{w^2 \delta_{ik} - w_i w_k}{w^3}, \tag{1.4}$$

† The self-consistent field was first introduced into the kinetic equation by A. A. Vlasov [1938, 1945].

where $F \equiv F^\alpha$, $F' \equiv F^\beta$, $e' \equiv e_\beta$, $\boldsymbol{w} = \boldsymbol{v} - \boldsymbol{v}'$, $\boldsymbol{p}$, $\boldsymbol{p}'$ are the particle momenta and L is the so-called Coulomb logarithm (summation is carried out with respect to all kinds of particles including kind α).†

The quantity L is the logarithm of the ratio of the maximum collision parameter $\varrho_{\max}$ to the minimum parameter $\varrho_{\min}$, i.e. $L = \ln(\varrho_{\max}/\varrho_{\min})$. The maximum collision parameter is equal in order of magnitude to the Debye radius $a = \sqrt{T/4\pi e^2 n_0}$ (T is the temperature in energy units and n_0 the density of the particles), i.e. $\varrho_{\max} \approx a$. The minimum collision parameter corresponds to a scattering angle of the order of unity, i.e. to an interaction energy $e^2/\varrho_{\min}$ equal to the mean kinetic energy, T, of the particles; therefore $\varrho_{\min} \approx e^2/T$. This expression can be used if $e^2/T > \lambda$, where λ is the de Broglie wavelength of the plasma particles.‡ If $\lambda > e^2/T$, then $\varrho_{\min} \approx \hbar/\sqrt{mT}$.

The collision integrals become zero for the equilibrium Maxwellian distributions

$$F_0^\alpha = n_\alpha \left(\frac{m_\alpha}{2\pi T}\right)^{3/2} e^{-\frac{m_\alpha v^2}{2T}}.$$

The kinetic equation (1.1) permits us in principle to explain how the relaxation process takes place, i.e. the approach of the particle distribution functions, which are at first non-equilibrium, to Maxwellian distributions. This problem can be solved precisely only by numerical methods [MacDonald, Rosenbluth and Chuck, 1957]; however, the characteristic relaxation time can be simply estimated in order of magnitude from dimensional arguments.

Let us first estimate the mean free path of the particles. Since the charge e and the particle density n_0 are contained in the collision integral only in the combination $e^4 n_0 L$ the mean free path should be determined only by the magnitude of $e^4 n_0 L$, the temperature T and the mass of the particles m. We can make up from these quan-

† This expression was first derived by Landau [1937].

‡ We are not discussing here the conditions of applicability of the kinetic equations taking only binary collisions into account since later we shall study the oscillatory properties of a "collisionless" plasma and shall use the expression for L^α only to estimate the part played by collisions.

tities a single quantity that has the dimensions of length [Landau, 1937], viz.,

$$l \sim \frac{T^2}{e^4 n_0 L}, \tag{1.5}$$

so the mean free path should be of the order of l [Landau, 1937].

The relaxation time τ_α of particles of a kind α is in order of magnitude $\tau_\alpha \sim l/v_\alpha$, where $v_\alpha = \sqrt{2T/m_\alpha}$ is the mean thermal velocity of the particles. At low densities and high temperature the relaxation time τ_α may be very large.

Thanks to the large difference among the masses of the electrons and the ions the exchange of energy between the electrons and the exchange of energy among the ions separately proceeds far more rapidly than the exchange of energy between the electrons and ions. Therefore equilibrium distributions of electrons and ions with different temperatures which gradually approach each other are established first.

By using the expressions for the particle fluxes in velocity space we can determine the rate of change of the particle temperatures. In order of magnitude the temperature equalization time is [Landau, 1937]

$$\tau \approx \frac{mM}{e^4 n_0 L}\left(\frac{T_e}{m} + \frac{T_i}{M}\right)^{3/2}, \tag{1.6}$$

where T_e and T_i are the electron and ion temperatures, and m and M are their masses (it is assumed that there is only one kind of ion).

2. Electron Oscillations

1. Development of Initial Perturbation

No matter what the form of the initial (when $t = 0$) particle distribution F_0^α, after a time τ_α the particle distribution hardly differs at all from a Maxwell distribution. The question arises as to how particle distributions which have been subjected to a certain initial perturbation change in time intervals $t \ll \tau_\alpha$. Here the action of the self-consistent field is most important and binary collisions of particles have no important part to play. In other words we can neglect the collision integrals in the kinetic equations when $t \ll \tau_\alpha$ [Vlasov, 1938, 1945]. As we shall see later, thanks to the action of the self-consistent field the particles' distribution functions and the fields are subjected to oscillations which may be damped or undamped depending upon the form of F_α.

Let us now study these collective oscillations of a plasma. We shall start discussing the electron oscillations in an infinite and free (i.e. not acted upon by external fields) plasma, assuming the ions to be stationary. If the initial perturbation is small, then the deviation of the electron distribution function F from the initial function F_0 (which in future we shall consider to be independent of the coordinates) will also be small, so the kinetic equation (1.1) can be linearized for this deviation. Introducing the notation $f = F - F_0$ and neglecting the term $(e/m)(\boldsymbol{E} + \{1/c\}\,[\boldsymbol{v} \wedge \boldsymbol{H}] \cdot \partial f/\partial \boldsymbol{v})$, we obtain the linearized kinetic equation

$$\frac{\partial f}{\partial t} + \left(\boldsymbol{v} \cdot \frac{\partial f}{\partial \boldsymbol{r}}\right) + \frac{e}{m}\left(\left\{\boldsymbol{E} + \frac{1}{c}\,[\boldsymbol{v} \wedge \boldsymbol{H}]\right\} \cdot \frac{\partial F_0}{\partial \boldsymbol{v}}\right) = 0. \tag{2.1}$$

Let us first examine the longitudinal electron oscillations [Landau, 1946]. In this case the electric field is irrotational, i.e. $\boldsymbol{E} = -\operatorname{grad} \varphi$ (φ is the potential) and there is no magnetic field, i.e. $\boldsymbol{H} = 0$.

The potential φ satisfies the equation

$$\nabla^2 \varphi = -4\pi e \int f\, d^3\boldsymbol{v}, \tag{2.2}$$

which must be solved in combination with the equation (2.1) and the initial condition $f(\boldsymbol{v}, \boldsymbol{r}, t)_{t=0} = g(\boldsymbol{v}, \boldsymbol{r})$, where g is the initial perturbation of the electron distribution function.†

The equations (2.1) and (2.2) do not contain the coordinates explicitly so it is convenient to rewrite them for the individual Fourier space components of the distribution function and potential. Introducing the notations

$$\varphi_k(t) = \int \varphi(\boldsymbol{r}, t)\, e^{-i(\boldsymbol{k}\cdot\boldsymbol{r})}\, d^3\boldsymbol{r},$$

$$f_k(\boldsymbol{v}, t) = \int f(\boldsymbol{v}, \boldsymbol{r}, t)\, e^{-i(\boldsymbol{k}\cdot\boldsymbol{r})}\, d^3\boldsymbol{r}$$

and

$$g_k(\boldsymbol{v}) = \int g(\boldsymbol{v}, \boldsymbol{r})\, e^{-i(\boldsymbol{k}\cdot\boldsymbol{r})}\, d^3\boldsymbol{r},$$

† Here and henceforth the plasma is assumed to be quasi-neutral, i.e. it is considered that the charge and current densities in the original state are zero.

we obtain

$$\left.\begin{aligned} &\frac{\partial}{\partial t} f_k(\boldsymbol{v}, t) + i(\boldsymbol{k} \cdot \boldsymbol{v}) f_k(\boldsymbol{v}, t) - \frac{ie}{m} \varphi_k(t) \left(\boldsymbol{k} \cdot \frac{\partial F_0}{\partial \boldsymbol{v}} \right) = 0, \\ &k^2 \varphi_k(t) = 4\pi e \int f_k(\boldsymbol{v}, t)\, d^3\boldsymbol{v}. \end{aligned} \right\} \tag{2.3}$$

We apply to these equations a Laplace time transform, multiplying them by e^{-pt} and integrating with respect to t. Assuming that the real part of p is large enough for the integrals

$$\left.\begin{aligned} \varphi_{kp} &= \int_0^\infty \varphi_k(t)\, e^{-pt}\, dt, \\ f_{kp}(\boldsymbol{v}) &= \int_0^\infty f_k(\boldsymbol{v}, t)\, e^{-pt}\, dt, \end{aligned} \right\} \tag{2.3'}$$

to exist and remembering the initial condition for the distribution function, we obtain

$$\varphi_{kp} = \frac{4\pi e}{k^2} \cdot \frac{N(\boldsymbol{k}, p)}{D(\boldsymbol{k}, p)}, \tag{2.4}$$

where

$$D(\boldsymbol{k}, p) = 1 - \frac{4\pi i e^2}{mk} \int_{-\infty}^{\infty} \frac{F_0'(w)}{p + ikw}\, dw; \tag{2.4'}$$

$$N(\boldsymbol{k}, p) = \int_{-\infty}^{\infty} \frac{g_k(w)}{p + ikw}\, dw; \tag{2.4''}$$

$$w = \frac{(\boldsymbol{k} \cdot \boldsymbol{v})}{k}; \quad F_0(w) = \int F_0(\boldsymbol{v})\, d^2\boldsymbol{v}_\perp \quad \text{and}$$

$$g_k(w) = \int g_k(\boldsymbol{v})\, d^2\boldsymbol{v}_\perp$$

($\boldsymbol{v}_\perp$ is the component of the electron velocity at right angles to $\boldsymbol{k}$).

The function $f_{kp}(w) = \int f_{kp}(\boldsymbol{v})\, d^2\boldsymbol{v}_\perp$ is connected with φ_{kp} by the relation

$$f_{kp}(w) = \frac{1}{p + ikw} \left\{ g_k(w) + \frac{iek}{m} \varphi_{kp} F_0'(w) \right\}. \tag{2.5}$$

Knowing φ_{kp} and f_{kp} we can, by using an inverse Laplace transform, find $\varphi_k(t)$ and $f_k(w, t)$:

$$\left.\begin{aligned} \varphi_k(t) &= \frac{1}{2\pi i}\int_{-i\infty+\sigma}^{i\infty+\sigma} \varphi_{kp}\, e^{pt}\, dp, \\ f_k(w, t) &= \frac{1}{2\pi i}\int_{-i\infty+\sigma}^{i\infty+\sigma} f_{kp}(w)\, e^{pt}\, dp, \end{aligned}\right\} \qquad (2.6)$$

where integration is carried out along the straight line $\mathrm{Re}\, p = \sigma$ lying to the right of all the singularities of the functions φ_p and f_p.

The formulae (2.6) permit us to explain the behaviour of the potential $\varphi_k(t)$ and the deviation $f_k(w, t)$ from the initial distribution function as t increases. As is well known, the asymptotic behaviour of the functions at large values of t is determined by the nature of the singularities of their Laplace transforms (i.e. the functions φ_p and f_p in the problem under discussion). The expression (2.5) for f_p shows that the function f_p has the same singularities as the function φ_p and an additional pole at the point $p = -ikw$.

Let us therefore examine the question of the singularities of the function φ_p.

The function φ_p was defined above only for large enough values of $\mathrm{Re}\, p$. In order to study its singularities we must first of all define this function in the whole plane of the complex variable, i.e. continue analytically the definition (2.4) to smaller values of $\mathrm{Re}\, p$. The analytical continuation of φ_p can obviously be defined as before by the formula (2.4) right down to the imaginary p axis.

Since when $\mathrm{Re}\, p > 0$ the function $N(\mathbf{k}, p)$ and the integral in the expression for D have no singularities, the singularities of the function φ_p when $\mathrm{Re}\, p > 0$ can only be the zeros of the denominator of (2.4), i.e. the roots of the equation

$$D(\mathbf{k}, p) = 0.$$

For the purely imaginary values of p the denominators in the integrals defining φ_{kp} become zero when $w = ip/k$. Therefore for the analytical continuation of φ_{kp} into the region $\mathrm{Re}\, p \leq 0$ the integration path in the integrals (2.4′) and (2.4″) must be indented round the pole $w = ip/k$. This deformation of the path assumes in its turn the possibility of analytical continuation of the functions

$F_0'(w)$ and $g_k(w)$, which are initially defined only for real values of w, into the region of complex values of w.

Therefore knowledge of the analytical properties of the functions $F_0(w)$ and $g_k(w)$ is necessary in order to find out the nature of the singularities of the function φ_p (and also f_p) which determine the asymptotic nature of $\varphi_k(t)$ (and $f_k(w, t)$) for large values of t.

We shall further limit ourselves to discussing the functions $F_0(w)$ which permit analytical extension into the region of complex values of w. In this case the function $D(\boldsymbol{k}, p)$, defined when $\operatorname{Re} p > 0$ by the relation (2.4′), can be extended analytically into the region $\operatorname{Re} p \leq 0$, by defining it everywhere as

$$D(\boldsymbol{k}, p) = 1 - \frac{4\pi i e^2}{mk} \int_C \frac{F_0'(w)\, dw}{p + ikw}, \tag{2.7}$$

where integration is carried out along the real w axis, with an indentation below the pole ip/k.

We notice that if the particle distribution is characterized by the maximum velocity w_0, i.e. if $F_0(w) = 0$ when $|w| > w_0$, then a unique analytical extension of the function $D(\boldsymbol{k}, p)$ into the half-plane $\operatorname{Re} p < 0$ is impossible. When $\operatorname{Re} p = 0$ the function $D(\boldsymbol{k},p)$ is defined by the formula (2.7) in which integration should be carried out along the real w axis from $-w_0$ to $+w_0$ down past the possible pole $w_0 = ip/k$. Of course for the purely imaginary values of p, $p = -i\omega$, for which $\omega/k > w_0$, the integration in (2.7) can be carried out along the real axis. This is always so when $\omega/k \geq c$ since there are no particles whose velocity exceeds the velocity of light, and also in the case of a degenerate electron gas (at absolute zero temperature) if $\omega/k > v_F$, where v_F is the limiting, Fermi velocity of the electrons.

It is clear that for distributions with an extreme velocity the function $D(\boldsymbol{k}, -i\omega)$ is purely real when $\omega/k > w_0$.

We have determined the denominator of the expression (2.4) for φ_p, i.e. the function $D(\boldsymbol{k}, p)$ in the whole plane of the complex variable p. Let us now find the analytical properties of the numerator of this expression, i.e. of the function $N(\boldsymbol{k}, p)$. The formula (2.4″) defines it when $\operatorname{Re} p > 0$; as has already been pointed out, the function $N(\boldsymbol{k}, p)$ has no singularities in this region. The position and nature of this function's singularities when $\operatorname{Re} p \leq 0$ are determined by the properties of the function $g_k(w)$.

If the function $g_k(w)$ has singularities (integrable, of course) for real w, then the function $N(\mathbf{k}, p)$ will have singularities with purely imaginary p. This is the position in particular if the function $g_k(w)$ has a δ-type singularity or has a discontinuity or break, and also if some derivative or other of it has a break (in these cases the function $g_k(w)$ cannot be extended analytically from the real axis).

If the function $g_k(w)$ has no singularities on the real axis and can be extended analytically into the region of the complex values of w, then the function $N(\mathbf{k}, p)$ (and therefore also the function φ_p) will have no singularities on the imaginary p axis, but may have singularities when $\operatorname{Re} p < 0$, viz., at the points $p = -ikw_r$, where w_r is some singularity of the function $g_k(w)$ lying in the lower half-plane of the complex variable w.

There is particular interest in the initial perturbations $g_k(w)$ for which the function $N(\mathbf{k}, p)$ has no singularities at all for finite p, i.e. is an entire function. It is clear from what has been said above that this is so if $g_k(w)$ is also entire† (i.e. has no singularities for finite values of w) and at the same time decreases rapidly enough when $w \to \pm\infty$. For example, the function $N(\mathbf{k}, p)$ will be entire with initial perturbations of the form

$$g_k(w) = P(w)\, e^{-\alpha w^2},$$

where $P(w)$ is a polynomial of arbitrary order and α is a positive constant.

Let us examine the case of entire functions $g_k(w)$ in slightly more detail. Since in this case the numerator of the expression (2.4) for φ_p has no singularities with finite p the only singularities of φ_p will be the zeros of the denominator, i.e. the roots of the equation

$$D(\mathbf{k}, p) = 0, \tag{2.8}$$

where D is defined by the expression (2.7).

We denote the roots of this equation by $p_r \equiv -iw_r - \gamma_r$ (w_r and γ_r are real, $r = 1, 2, 3, \ldots$). Then for large t (t should, however, be small compared with the relaxation time τ since binary collisions must be taken into consideration when $t \gtrsim \tau$) the function $\varphi_k(t)$

† Strictly speaking, it is sufficient for the function $g_k(w)$ to be holomorphic only in the lower half-plane of w (including the real axis) for the function $N(\mathbf{k}, p)$ to be entire.

behaves asymptotically as

$$\varphi_k(t) \sim \sum_r \varphi_{kp_r}^{(r)}\, e^{-\gamma_r t}\, e^{-i\omega_r t}, \tag{2.9}$$

where $\varphi_{kp_r}^{(r)}$ is the residue of φ_{kp} at the point $p = p_r$.

The analogous expression for $f_k(w, t)$ is of the form

$$f_k(w, t) \sim a_k(w)\, e^{-ikwt} + \sum_r f_{kp_r}^{(r)}(w)\, e^{-\gamma_r t}\, e^{-i\omega_r t}, \tag{2.9'}$$

where a_k and $f_{kp_r}^{(r)}$ are the residues of f_{kp} at the points $p = -ikw$ and $p = p_r$. (As well as the contributions made by the poles of the function φ_{kp} this expression also contains a contribution from the pole $p = -ikw$ which the function φ_{kp} has not got.)

Therefore in the case of entire functions $g_k(w)$ the asymptotic behaviour of $\varphi_k(t)$ when $t \to \infty$ is determined only by the unperturbed particle distribution in the plasma $F_0(w)$ (which determines the roots of the equation $D(\boldsymbol{k}, p) = 0$) and does not depend on the actual form of the perturbation. It may be said, therefore, that the roots of the equation (2.8) determine the spectrum of the longitudinal electron eigen oscillations of a plasma; the imaginary parts of these roots are the oscillation frequencies, and the real parts their damping decrements (if $\gamma_r > 0$) or growth rate (if $\gamma_r < 0$). The equation (2.8) is called the dispersion equation.

If all the roots of the dispersion equation lie in the left half-plane of p ($\gamma_r > 0$), then the function $\varphi_k(t)$ approaches zero when $t \to \infty$ (it is assumed, however, that $t \ll \tau$), i.e. the field oscillations will be damped.

As for the deviation $f_k(w, t)$ of the distribution function from the initial function $F(w)$, it, as can be seen from the expression (2.9′), does not approach zero when $\gamma_r \to 0$ and is subject to undamped oscillations with an amplitude $a_k(w)$. This behaviour of $f_k(w, t)$ is connected with the fact that an equilibrium particle distribution cannot be established by the action of a self-consistent field alone, without binary collisions, since this field does not alter the system's entropy

$$S = -\sum_\alpha \int F_\alpha \ln \frac{F_\alpha}{G_\alpha}\, d^3\boldsymbol{v}\, d^3\boldsymbol{r} \tag{2.10}$$

(G_α is the density of states of the particle of kind α). In fact

$$\dot{S} = -\sum_\alpha \int \left(1 + \ln \frac{F_\alpha}{G_\alpha}\right) \frac{\partial F_\alpha}{\partial t}\, d^3\boldsymbol{v}\, d^3\boldsymbol{r}.$$

If we substitute the expression given by the kinetic equation (1.1) without the collision integral instead of $\partial F_\alpha/\partial t$ here we obtain $\dot{S} = 0$.

If even one of the roots of the equation (2.8) lies in the right half-plane of p ($\gamma_r < 0$), then the functions $\varphi_k(t)$ and $f_k(w, t)$ increase exponentially with time (it is assumed that $t \ll \tau$). In this case the initial particle distribution F_0 will be unstable.

Let us now find out the nature of the asymptotic behaviour of $\varphi_k(t)$ for functions $g_k(w)$ that are not entire. In this case to the singularities of φ_p defined by the roots of the dispersion equation $D(\mathbf{k}, p) = 0$ we add the singularities of the function $N(\mathbf{k}, p)$. The disposition of these singularities depends only upon the form of the function $g_k(w)$, i.e. on the nature of the initial perturbation, and does not depend on the properties of the plasma (the function $F_0(w)$). As has already been pointed out, an essential property of the singularities of the function N is that they can all lie only in the left half-plane of p. Therefore even if only one of the roots of the dispersion equation $D(\mathbf{k}, p) = 0$ lies in the right half-plane of p, $\gamma_r < 0$ (which corresponds to the possibility of an increase of the oscillations) the nature of the initial perturbation has no significant effect on the asymptotic behaviour of $\varphi_k(t)$ as $t \to \infty$.

If $N(\mathbf{k}, p)$ has singularities at the points $p = p'_n = -\gamma'_n - i\omega'_n$ ($n = 1, 2, 3, \ldots$), then the contribution of these singularities to the asymptotic behaviour of $\varphi_k(t)$ as $t \to \infty$ is of the form $\Sigma_n \alpha_n e^{-\gamma'_n t} e^{-i\omega'_n t}$, where the α_n are certain constants. Adding this sum to (2.9) we find the asymptotic expression for $\varphi_k(t)$ in the general case of functions $g_k(w)$ which are not entire (but which have no singularities for real w):†

$$\varphi_k(t) \sim \sum_r \varphi^{(r)}_{kp_r} e^{-\gamma_r t} e^{-i\omega_r t} + \sum_n \alpha_n e^{-\gamma'_n t} e^{-i\omega'_n t}. \qquad (2.11)$$

Therefore for large values of t (it is assumed, however, that $t \ll \tau$) the potential $\varphi_k(t)$ is a superposition of the plasma eigen oscillations whose complex frequencies $\omega_r - i\gamma_r$ are determined by the properties of the plasma (the first sum in the expression (2.11)) and of the oscillations whose complex frequencies $\omega'_n - i\gamma'_n$ are determined by the form of the initial perturbation function $g_k(w)$ (the second sum in the expression (2.11)).

† The case of a function $g_k(w)$ having a singularity on the real w axis is discussed below.

The eigen oscillations may be damped or amplified, whilst the oscillations whose frequencies are determined by the form of the function $g_k(w)$ can only be damped.

In future we shall study only the eigen oscillations of a plasma since only they can increase and only they can be intensely excited by external sources (under resonance conditions). Here we shall give two examples of oscillations whose frequencies and damping decrements are determined by the initial perturbation and do not depend on the properties of the plasma.

As the first example we shall discuss the oscillations which appear if $g_k(w)$ is of the form

$$g_k(w) = \frac{g_0 w_1}{(w - w_0)^2 + w_1^2}, \tag{2.12}$$

where g_0, w_0, w_1 are certain constants. In this case

$$N(\boldsymbol{k}, p) = \int_{-\infty}^{\infty} \frac{g_k(w)}{p + ikw}\, dw = - \frac{\pi g_0}{p + ikw_0 + kw_1}.$$

The function $N(\boldsymbol{k}, p)$ has a singularity when $p = -ikw_0 - kw_1$ which introduces the contribution

$$\varphi_k(t) \sim g_0\, e^{-kw_1 t}\, e^{-ikw_0 t}. \tag{2.12$'$}$$

into the asymptotic behaviour of $\varphi_k(t)$ when $t \to \infty$.

We see that the frequency and damping decrement of the oscillations that appear in the case of an initial perturbation of the form (2.12) are equal to kw_0 and kw_1 respectively.

If $w_1 \to \infty$ the damping disappears. We notice that in this case the function $g_k(w)$ acquires a δ-singularity on the real axis, $g_k(w) \to \pi g_0\, \delta(w - w_0)$.

As a second example we shall take the case of the oscillations that appear in the case of discontinuous functions $g_k(w)$. Let

$$g_k(w) = \begin{cases} g_0, & \text{if } -w_0 < w < w_0, \\ 0, & \text{if } |w| > w_0. \end{cases} \tag{2.13}$$

In this case the function

$$N(\boldsymbol{k}, p) = \frac{g_0}{ik} \ln \frac{p + ikw_0}{p - ikw_0}$$

has branch points on the imaginary p axis, $p = \pm ikw_0$. The contribution made by the singularities of the function $N(\mathbf{k}, p)$ to the function $\varphi_k(t)$ is of the form

$$\varphi_k(t) \sim g_0 \frac{\sin kw_0 t}{t}. \tag{2.13'}$$

Therefore the δ-singularity on the real axis of the function $g_k(w)$ leads to undamped oscillations of the potential $\varphi_k(t)$; a discontinuity in the function $g_k(w)$, i.e. a δ-singularity in its first derivative, leads to oscillations of the potential damped as $1/t$.

It is easy to show that a discontinuity of the n-th derivative of the function $g_k(w)$, i.e. a δ-singularity of its $n+1$ derivative, leads to a potential asymptotically proportional to $t^{-(n+1)}\, e^{ikw_0 t}$, where w_0 is the discontinuity point.

Returning to the study of the eigen oscillations of a plasma we shall first discuss the simplest longitudinal oscillation corresponding to $k = 0$ (uniform oscillation). In this case the dispersion equation can be rewritten in the form

$$\lim_{k\to 0} \frac{4\pi i e^2}{mkp} \int \left(1 - i\,\frac{kw}{p}\right) F_0'(w)\, dw = 1.$$

Noting that

$$\int F_0'(w)\, dw = 0, \quad \int wF_0'(w)\, dw = -n_0,$$

where n_0 is the particle density, we obtain for p the purely imaginary value $p = \pm i\Omega$, where

$$\Omega = \sqrt{\frac{4\pi e^2 n_0}{m}}. \tag{2.14}$$

Therefore undamped longitudinal electron eigen oscillations for which the wave vector is zero are possible in a plasma. The frequency of these oscillations is determined only by the particle density and does not depend on the nature of their velocity distribution. The quantity Ω is called the Langmuir frequency, and the longitudinal plasma oscillations the Langmuir oscillations.†

† Editor's Note. In this book the expressions Langmuir oscillations and Langmuir frequency (Ω) are used in place of the more common plasma oscillations and plasma frequency (ω_p).

2. *Frequency and Damping of Langmuir Oscillations*

Let us examine the longitudinal electron eigen oscillations with a non-zero wave vector in a plasma. We shall assume the plasma to be an equilibrium and non-relativistic one. In this case the velocity distribution of the electrons is Maxwellian, i.e.

$$F_0(w) = n_0 \sqrt{\frac{m}{2\pi T}}\, e^{-\frac{mw^2}{2T}} \qquad (T \ll mc^2).$$

By substituting this expression in (2.7) we obtain the dispersion equation which defines the spectrum of the longitudinal eigen oscillations of a plasma:

$$\frac{1}{a^2k^2}\left(1 - \frac{z}{\sqrt{\pi}}\int_C \frac{e^{-y^2}}{z-y}\,dy\right) + 1 = 0, \tag{2.15}$$

where

$$z = \frac{\omega - i\gamma}{kv_e} \quad (\omega - i\gamma \equiv ip), \quad v_e = \sqrt{\frac{2T}{m}}, \quad a = \sqrt{\frac{T}{4\pi e^2 n_0}}.$$

We shall assume that $\omega/k \ll c$ (i.e. Re $z \ll c/v_e$, $v_e \ll c$). In this case we must allow in (2.15) for the presence of a pole at $y = z$ and integrate along the real axis indented below the pole. (Since the pole corresponds to an electron velocity which is small compared with c it is legitimate to use a non-relativistic Maxwellian distribution.)

Introducing the function (Faddeyeva and Terent'ev, 1954)†

$$w(z) = e^{-z^2}\left(1 + \frac{2i}{\sqrt{\pi}}\int_0^z e^{t^2}\,dt\right), \tag{2.16}$$

we can put the equation (2.15) in the form

$$\frac{1}{a^2k^2}\left(1 + i\sqrt{\pi}\, zw(z)\right) + 1 = 0, \tag{2.17}$$

† For real values of z it is convenient to use the function $\varphi(z) = 2ze^{-z^2}\int_0^z e^{x^2}\,dx$, which is connected with the function $w(z)$ by the relation

$$w(z) = \frac{i}{\sqrt{\pi}\, z}\{\varphi(z) - i\sqrt{\pi}\, z\, e^{-z^2}\}.$$

where the term $i\sqrt{\pi}\, z\, e^{-z^2}$ is due to going round the pole in the integrand of (2.15).

It is easy to find the solution of the equation (2.17) in the extreme cases $ak \ll 1$ and $ak \gg 1$. The first case corresponds to $\mathrm{Re}\, z \gg 1$, $\mathrm{Im}\, z \ll 1$ (however $\mathrm{Re}\, z \ll c/v_e$) and the second to $\mathrm{Re}\, z \ll 1$, $\mathrm{Im}\, z \gg 1$. In the first case we can use the expansion

$$w(z) = \frac{i}{z\sqrt{\pi}}\left(1 + \frac{1}{2z^2} + \frac{3}{4z^4} + \cdots\right) + e^{-z^2}, \qquad (2.18)$$

substitution of which in (2.17) gives

$$\omega = \omega_L(k) \equiv \Omega\,(1 + \tfrac{3}{2}\, a^2k^2), \qquad (2.19)$$

$$\gamma = \sqrt{\frac{\pi}{8}}\,\frac{\Omega}{a^3k^3}\, e^{-\frac{3}{2}-\frac{1}{2a^2k^2}}. \qquad (2.20)$$

These formulae determine the frequency and damping decrement of the longitudinal electron eigen oscillations as a function of the wave vector. They are valid if $ak \ll 1$ and $\Omega/k \ll c$.

We can see that the longitudinal oscillations are damped even if we neglect binary collisions, but when $ak \ll 1$ their damping decrement is exponentially small, $\gamma \ll \omega$.†

The formulae (2.19) and (2.20) give the correct result when $k = 0$, but for small k ($k \lesssim \Omega/c$) they become invalid since when $\omega/k \sim c$ the pole of the integrand in (2.15) lies in the relativistic velocity region, so in this case it is not legitimate to use a non-relativistic Maxwell distribution. Relativistic effects‡ must be taken into consideration in order to establish the nature of the dispersion (i.e. the dependence of ω and γ on k) when $\omega/k \sim c$. We shall not discuss this question in greater detail here, contenting ourselves with pointing out that when $\omega/k \geq c$ the damping decrement is identically equal to zero.

Let us now examine the extreme case $ak \gg 1$. In this case $\mathrm{Re}\, z \ll 1$, $\mathrm{Im}\, z \gg 1$ and

$$w(z) \approx 2e^{-z^2}. \qquad (2.21)$$

† The dependence of the frequency ω_L on k (2.19) was found by Vlasov [1938, 1945] and the existence of damping in a "collisionless" plasma and the formula (2.20) for γ were established by Landau [1946] (the quantity γ is called the Landau damping).

‡ There is a detailed examination of the electromagnetic properties of a relativistic plasma in the monograph by Silin and Rukhadze [1961].

The substituting of (2.21) in the equation (2.17) gives [Landau, 1946]

$$\omega = \pi\Omega \frac{ak}{\xi}, \; \gamma = \Omega ak\xi, \tag{2.22}$$

where ξ is a root of the equation

$$\xi \, e^{\xi^2/2} = \frac{a^2k^2}{\sqrt{2\pi}}.$$

It is easy to see that $\gamma \gg \omega$, the ratio γ/ω increasing with k as $\ln ak$.

We notice that in a real plasma the damping when $ak \gg 1$ is determined chiefly by the ion, and not the electron, component, so when discussing the case $ak \gg 1$ we must allow for the motion of the ions. This allowance does not, however, alter the conclusion that $\gamma \gg \omega$ when $ak \gg 1$ [Gordeyev, 1954].

Therefore the only oscillations that are weakly damped are long-wave eigen oscillations whose wavelength is large compared with the Debye radius, $ak \ll 1$.

The damping of the field oscillations in a "collisionless" equilibrium plasma has a simple and obvious physical meaning. It is caused by the interaction of the electrons with the wave field and this proceeds most efficiently if the component of the electron velocity along k coincides with the wave's phase velocity, i.e. $w = \omega/k$. (This is manifested mathematically in that the integrand in (2.15) has a pole when $w = \omega/k$, the presence of which leads to damping.) It is clear that the electrons, the component of whose velocity is slightly greater than ω/k, give up their energy to the wave, and the electrons, the component of whose velocity is slightly less than the wave's phase velocity, obtain energy from the wave. For a Maxwellian distribution the number of the former electrons is less than the number of the latter, so the oscillations of the field should be damped, the magnitude of this damping being proportional to the derivative of $F_0'(w)$ at the point $w = \omega/k$. By putting $w \approx \Omega/k$ we obtain the characteristic dependence of the damping γ on k, $\gamma \sim \exp[-1/(2a^2k^2)]$. If $\omega/k > c$, then there are no electrons moving in phase with the wave, so there is no damping in this case (unless, of course, we take binary collisions into consideration).

It is easy to understand the rise in the damping as the wavelength decreases. When $k \sim 1/a$ the phase velocity of a longitudinal wave is comparable with the thermal velocity of the electrons. Therefore the number of electrons interacting effectively with the field becomes very large, thus leading to strong damping.

When defining the oscillation spectrum of a plasma we started with the kinetic equation in which we neglected the collision integral. This neglect is permissible only if $\omega \gg 1/\tau$. In this case we obtain the correct values (with an accuracy up to terms of the order of $1/\omega\tau$) for the oscillation frequencies.

If $\gamma \gg 1/\tau$, then we obtain the correct values for the damping decrements of the oscillations as well. If, however, $\gamma < 1/\tau$, then the quantity calculated with the collision integral ignored does not define the true damping of the oscillations; here we must allow for binary collisions.

We notice that the condition $\omega\tau \gg 1$ is well satisfied over a wide range of variation in the plasma density and temperature. For example, if $n_0 \sim 10^{13}$ cm^{-3}, $T \sim 10^5$ °K, then $\Omega \sim 10^{11}$ sec^{-1}, $\tau \sim 10^{-8}$ sec and $\Omega\tau \sim 10^3$.

3. Dielectric Permittivity Tensor of a Plasma

1. Dispersion Equations for Longitudinal and Transverse Oscillations

In the preceding section we discussed the simplest form of a plasma's eigen oscillations (linear longitudinal electron oscillations) and derived for them the dispersion equation that establishes the dependence of the frequency and damping decrement of the oscillations on the wave vector (these quantities are generally combined into one quantity—the complex frequency).

Other forms of eigen oscillations† may also be propagated in a plasma along with the linear longitudinal electron oscillations, each of them being characterized by a definite dependence of the complex frequency on the wave vector. There is no need to solve each time the plasma perturbation problem with its initial conditions, as was done in deriving the dispersion equation (2.8), in order to derive the dispersion equations connecting the complex frequencies of the oscillations with the wave vector. The dispersion equations can be obtained for a free plasma and for a plasma located in external constant fields if from the very beginning we

† Here and later only linear oscillations are discussed.

look for the self-consistent fields and the deviations of the particle distribution functions F^α from the initial distribution functions F_0^α in the form of plane monochromatic waves ($\sim e^{(i(\boldsymbol{k}\cdot\boldsymbol{r})-\omega t)}$) with complex frequencies ω and write the solubility condition for the linearized kinetic equations and Maxwell equations.

For this purpose it is convenient to introduce the electric displacement vector $\boldsymbol{D}(\boldsymbol{r}, t)$, which is connected with the electric field $\boldsymbol{E}(\boldsymbol{r}, t)$ by the relation

$$\frac{\partial}{\partial t}\boldsymbol{D} = \frac{\partial}{\partial t}\boldsymbol{E} + 4\pi\sum_\alpha e_\alpha \int \boldsymbol{v} f^\alpha\, d^3\boldsymbol{v}, \quad f^\alpha = F^\alpha - F_0^\alpha. \tag{3.1}$$

Since the deviation of the particle distribution from the initial distribution is assumed to be small the function f^α is linear with respect to $\boldsymbol{E}$. Therefore the equation (3.1) (remembering the equations (1.2) and (2.1)) establishes a linear connexion between the electric displacement $\boldsymbol{D}$ and the field $\boldsymbol{E}$

$$\boldsymbol{D}(\boldsymbol{r}, t) = \hat{\varepsilon}\boldsymbol{E}(\boldsymbol{r}, t), \tag{3.2}$$

where $\hat{\varepsilon}$ is a certain integral operator called the plasma dielectric permittivity operator.

Using the relations (3.1) and (3.2) and eliminating the magnetic field $\boldsymbol{H}$ from the Maxwell equations we obtain the equation for the electric field

$$\text{curl curl}\,\boldsymbol{E} + \frac{\hat{\varepsilon}}{c^2}\frac{\partial^2}{\partial t^2}\boldsymbol{E} = 0. \tag{3.3}$$

Henceforth we shall always assume that the initial distribution F_0^α is uniform. In this case the operator relation (3.2) leads to the linear algebraic relation between the Fourier components of the induction $\boldsymbol{D}_{k\omega}$ and the field $\boldsymbol{E}_{k\omega}$ (with the complex frequency ω)

$$\boldsymbol{D}_{k\omega} = \hat{\varepsilon}\,\boldsymbol{E}_{k\omega}, \tag{3.2'}$$

where $\hat{\varepsilon} \equiv \varepsilon_{ij}(\boldsymbol{k}, \omega)$ is the dielectric permittivity tensor whose components can be found if we change to the Fourier components in the equations (1.2) and (2.1).

For a free "collisionless" plasma with an isotropic initial particle distribution function $F_0^\alpha(\boldsymbol{v})$ the dielectric permittivity tensor is of the form

$$\varepsilon_{ij}(\boldsymbol{k}, \omega) = \delta_{ij} - \sum_{\alpha} \frac{4\pi e_{\alpha}^2}{m_{\alpha}\omega} \int \frac{v_i \dfrac{\partial}{\partial v_j} F_0^{\alpha}}{(\boldsymbol{k}\cdot\boldsymbol{v}) - \omega - i\,0} d^3\boldsymbol{v}$$

$$\equiv \delta_{ij} + 4\pi\varkappa_{ij}(\boldsymbol{k}, \omega), \tag{3.4}$$

where the term $-i0$ in the denominatorof the integrand defines the rule for going round the pole $(\boldsymbol{k}\cdot\boldsymbol{v}) = \omega$ (in exactly the same way as was done in the expression (2.7)). The quantity $\varkappa_{ij}$ is the tensor of the electrical susceptibility (polarizability) of the plasma and is equal to the sum of the susceptibility tensors $\varkappa_{ij}^{\alpha}$ of the individual components of the plasma

$$\varkappa_{ij}^{\alpha}(\boldsymbol{k}, \omega) = \frac{e_{\alpha}^2}{m_{\alpha}\omega} \int \frac{v_i \dfrac{\partial}{\partial v_j} F_0^{\alpha}}{\omega - (\boldsymbol{k}\cdot\boldsymbol{v}) + i\,0} d^3\boldsymbol{v}. \tag{3.4'}$$

The expressions (3.4′) and (3.4) define a certain function of the complex variable ω (for a given real $\boldsymbol{k}$).

For real ω the function $\varkappa_{ij}^{\alpha}(\boldsymbol{k}, \omega)$ can be represented in the form

$$\varkappa_{ij}^{\alpha}(\boldsymbol{k}, \omega) = \frac{e_{\alpha}^2}{m_{\alpha}\omega} \int v_i \frac{\partial F_0^{\alpha}}{\partial v_j} \left\{ P \frac{1}{\omega - (\boldsymbol{k}\cdot\boldsymbol{v})} - \pi i \delta(\omega - (\boldsymbol{k}\cdot\boldsymbol{v})) \right\} d^3\boldsymbol{v},$$

where the symbol P denotes the principal value of the integral.

The term with the δ-function here is clearly equal to

$$\varkappa_{ij}^{\alpha''}(\boldsymbol{k}, \omega) = -\frac{i\pi e_{\alpha}^2}{m_{\alpha}\omega k} \int v_i \frac{\partial F_0^{\alpha}(\boldsymbol{v})}{\partial v_j} d^2\boldsymbol{v}_{\perp} \bigg|_{v_{\|} = \frac{\omega}{k}},$$

where $v_{\|}$ and $v_{\perp}$ are the velocity components of $\boldsymbol{v}$ parallel and at right angles to $\boldsymbol{k}$. The function $\varkappa_{ij}^{\alpha''}$ is the imaginary part of the function $\varkappa_{ij}^{\alpha}$ for real values of ω.

For complex values of ω the function $\varkappa_{ij}^{\alpha}$ is obviously of the form

$$\varkappa_{ij}^{\alpha}(\boldsymbol{k}, \omega) = \frac{e_{\alpha}^2}{m_{x}\omega} \int d^2\boldsymbol{v}_{\perp} \int_C \frac{v_i \dfrac{\partial}{\partial v_j} F_0^{\alpha}}{\omega - k v_{\|}} dv_{\|},$$

where integration with respect to $v_{\|}$ is carried out along the real axis indented below the pole $v_{\|} = \omega/k$.

The function $\varepsilon_{ij}(\boldsymbol{k}, \omega)$ can be obtained in a similar way for complex ω.

Up to now it has been assumed that the initial distribution function F_0^α is isotropic. In the general case of a non-isotropic function $F_0^\alpha(\boldsymbol{v})$ not only the alternating electric field but also the alternating magnetic field must be allowed for in the kinetic equations when determining the dielectric permittivity tensor. In this case the dielectric permittivity tensor becomes

$$\varepsilon_{ij}(\boldsymbol{k}, \omega) = \delta_{ij} - \sum_\alpha \frac{4\pi e_\alpha^2}{m\omega^2} \int \frac{v_i\{(\omega - (\boldsymbol{k} \cdot \boldsymbol{v}))\, \delta_{lj} + k_l v_j\} \dfrac{\delta}{\partial v_l} F_0^\alpha}{(\boldsymbol{k} \cdot \boldsymbol{v}) - \omega - i\,0}\, d^3\boldsymbol{v}. \tag{3.5}$$

The function $\varepsilon_{ij}(\boldsymbol{k}, \omega)$ can be used to rewrite the equation (3.3) for the individual Fourier field components $\boldsymbol{E}_{k\omega}$

$$\Lambda_{ij}(\boldsymbol{k}, \omega)\, E^j_{k\omega} = 0, \tag{3.6}$$

where

$$\Lambda_{ij}(\boldsymbol{k}, \omega) = n^2(k_i k_j/k^2 - \delta_{ij}) + \varepsilon_{ij}(\boldsymbol{k}, \omega), \tag{3.6'}$$

$n = ck/\omega$ is the refractive index. From this it is easy to obtain the dispersion equation for determining the plasma's eigen oscillation spectrum as a condition of solubility of the system (3.6)

$$\Delta(\boldsymbol{k}, \omega) \equiv \det\, [n^2(k_i k_j/k^2 - \delta_{ij}) + \varepsilon_{ij}(\boldsymbol{k}, \omega)] = 0. \tag{3.7}$$

For given $\boldsymbol{k}$ this equation has a number of roots (generally speaking complex roots) which we shall denote by $\omega_r(\boldsymbol{k}) - i\gamma_r(\boldsymbol{k})$ $(r = 1, 2, \ldots)$. The real part of the r-th root $\omega_r(\boldsymbol{k})$ defines the frequency of the r-th eigen oscillation and the imaginary part $\gamma_r(\boldsymbol{k})$ its damping decrement (if $\gamma_r > 0$) or growth rate (if $\gamma_r < 0$). The various roots looked upon as functions of $\boldsymbol{k}$ correspond to different branches of the plasma's eigen oscillations.

For an isotropic plasma when there are no external fields the tensor $\varepsilon_{ij}(\boldsymbol{k}, \omega)$ can be put in the form

$$\varepsilon_{ij}(\boldsymbol{k}, \omega) = \left(\delta_{ij} - \frac{k_i k_j}{k^2}\right) \varepsilon_t(\boldsymbol{k}, \omega) + \frac{k_i k_j}{k^2}\, \varepsilon_l(\boldsymbol{k}, \omega), \tag{3.8}$$

where ε_l and ε_t are the longitudinal and transverse dielectric constants of the plasma [Gertsenshtein, 1952a; Lindhard, 1954]:

$$\left.\begin{aligned}\varepsilon_l(\boldsymbol{k},\omega) &\equiv 1 + 4\pi\varkappa_l(\boldsymbol{k},\omega)\\ &= 1 - \sum_\alpha \frac{4\pi e_\alpha^2}{m_\alpha k^2}\int \frac{\left(\boldsymbol{k}\cdot\dfrac{\partial F_0^\alpha}{\partial \boldsymbol{v}}\right)}{(\boldsymbol{k}\cdot\boldsymbol{v}) - \omega - i0}\,d^3\boldsymbol{v},\\ \varepsilon_t(\boldsymbol{k},\omega) &\equiv 1 + 4\pi\varkappa_t(\boldsymbol{k},\omega)\\ &= 1 - \sum_\alpha \frac{2\pi e_\alpha^2}{m_\alpha k^2\omega}\int \frac{\left([[\boldsymbol{k}\wedge\boldsymbol{v}]\wedge\boldsymbol{k}]\cdot\dfrac{\partial F_0^\alpha}{\partial \boldsymbol{v}}\right)}{(\boldsymbol{k}\cdot\boldsymbol{v}) - \omega - i0}\,d^3\boldsymbol{v}\end{aligned}\right\} \tag{3.9}$$

($\varkappa_l$ and $\varkappa_t$ are the longitudinal and transverse polarizabilities of the plasma).

In this case the dispersion equation (3.7) degenerates into the two equations

$$\left.\begin{aligned}\varepsilon_l(\boldsymbol{k},\omega) &= 0,\\ \varepsilon_t(\boldsymbol{k},\omega) - \frac{c^2k^2}{\omega^2} &= 0,\end{aligned}\right\} \tag{3.10}$$

which define the longitudinal and transverse oscillations respectively in the plasma.

By using (2.15) and (2.17) we can show that for a two-temperature plasma with Maxwellian distributions of the electrons and ions characterized by the different temperatures T_e and T_i the longitudinal dielectric constant is of the following form:

$$\varepsilon_l(\boldsymbol{k},\omega) = 1 + \frac{1}{a_e^2k^2}\left\{1 + i\sqrt{\pi}\, z_e w(z_e)\right\} + \frac{1}{a_i^2k^2}\left\{1 + i\sqrt{\pi}\, z_i w(z_i)\right\}, \tag{3.11}$$

where

$$a_\alpha = \sqrt{\frac{T_\alpha}{4\pi e_\alpha^2 n_\alpha}},\quad z_\alpha = \frac{\omega}{kv_\alpha},\quad v_\alpha = \sqrt{\frac{2T_\alpha}{m_\alpha}}$$

and the function $w(z)$ is defined by the expression (2.16). This formula is valid when $\omega/k \ll c$, i.e. $z_\alpha \ll c/v_\alpha$, $v_\alpha \ll c$.

The transverse dielectric permittivity of the plasma is defined by the analogous formula

$$\varepsilon_t(\boldsymbol{k}, \omega) = 1 + i\sqrt{\pi}\,\frac{\Omega_e^2}{\omega^2}\,z_e w(z_e) + i\sqrt{\pi}\,\frac{\Omega_i^2}{\omega^2}\,z_i w(z_i), \tag{3.12}$$

where $\Omega_\alpha = \sqrt{4\pi e_\alpha^2 n_\alpha/m_\alpha}$. This formula, in the same way as the formula (3.11), is valid when $\omega/k \ll c$.

If $\omega/k \gg c$, then the quantity ε_t will be purely real since the integrand in (3.9) has no pole in this case. Neglecting terms of the order of m/M and v_e^2/c^2 we obtain the following expression for ε_t:

$$\varepsilon_t = 1 - \frac{\Omega_e^2}{\omega^2}, \quad \frac{\omega}{k} \gg c. \tag{3.13}$$

By substituting (3.12) and (3.13) in the second of the formulae (3.10) we can find the dependence of ω on k for transverse waves. When $\omega/k \ll c$ these waves will be strongly damped. When $\omega/k > c$ the dependence of the frequency on the wave vector will be

$$\omega = \sqrt{k^2c^2 + \Omega_e^2}. \tag{3.14}$$

This dependence is similar to the dependence of energy on momentum for a relativistic particle whose mass is $\hbar\Omega_e/c^2$.

We should point out that the transverse waves in a plasma whose phase velocity is greater than c are not damped (unless binary collisions of particles are taken into consideration).

2. *Low-Frequency Longitudinal Oscillations of a Non-Isothermal Plasma*†

In the preceding section the ions were considered to be stationary when discussing the natural longitudinal oscillations of a plasma. Let us now examine the effect of the motion of the ions on the eigen oscillation spectrum of a plasma. We shall assume that the

† Editor's Note. In this book, problems in which there is a spatial variation in temperature are not considered. An isothermal plasma means one in which the electron and ion temperatures are equal.

electrons and ions are characterized by Maxwellian distributions with the different temperatures T_e and T_i. In order to determine the longitudinal oscillation spectrum of such a plasma it is necessary to make its longitudinal dielectric permittivity $\varepsilon_l(\boldsymbol{k}, \omega)$ defined by the formula (3.11) equal to zero, i.e.

$$1 + \frac{1}{a_e^2 k^2}\left(1 + i\sqrt{\pi}\, z_e w(z_e)\right) + \frac{1}{a_i^2 k^2}\left(1 + i\sqrt{\pi}\, z_i w(z_i)\right) = 0, \tag{3.15}$$

where $z_\alpha = (\omega - i\gamma)/kv_\alpha$ (ω and γ are the frequency and damping decrement of the oscillations).

In the high frequency and large phase velocity region $\omega/k \gg v_e$ (to be more precise $\operatorname{Re} z_\alpha \gg 1$, $\operatorname{Im} z_\alpha \ll 1$) this equation has only one solution corresponding to weakly damped oscillations. These oscillations are in essence electronic and their frequency and damping decrement are defined by the earlier formulae (2.19) and (2.20), but m must be taken as the reduced mass of an electron and an ion, $mM/(m + M)$.

The equation (3.15) has yet another solution, however, corresponding to weakly damped oscillations in the low frequency and low phase velocity range

$$v_i \ll \frac{\omega}{k} \ll v_e, \quad \gamma \ll \omega. \tag{3.16}$$

In order to confirm this we put $\operatorname{Re} z_i \gg 1$, $\operatorname{Im} z_i \ll 1$, $|z_e| \ll 1$ in (3.15). Using the expansion (2.18) and noting that $w(z_e) \approx 1$ we can put the dispersion equation (3.15) in the form

$$1 + \frac{1}{a_e^2 k^2}\left(1 - \frac{m}{2M}\frac{1}{z_e^2} + i\sqrt{\pi}\, z_e\right) = 0. \tag{3.17}$$

Solving the equation we find the frequency and damping decrement of the oscillations [Tonks and Langmuir, 1929a, b; Gordeyev, 1954a]

$$\omega = \frac{V_s k}{\sqrt{1 + a_e^2 k^2}}, \quad \gamma = \sqrt{\frac{\pi}{8}\frac{m}{M}}\,\frac{V_s k}{(1 + a_e^2 k^2)^2}, \tag{3.18}$$

where

$$V_s = \sqrt{\frac{T_e}{M}}. \tag{3.18'}$$

Let us find out when this solution is valid, i.e. under what conditions the inequalities (3.16) are satisfied. We can see that the ratio of the damping decrement to the frequency is small (it is proportional to $\sqrt{m/M}$), whilst the inequalities (3.16) for the phase velocity ω/k are satisfied if

$$\frac{T_e}{T_i} \gg 1 + a_e^2 k^2. \tag{3.19}$$

Therefore a plasma should be strongly non-isothermal, with hot electrons and cold ions, for the longitudinal oscillations in question to be propagated in it. These oscillations are obviously low-frequency ones since their frequency is in inverse proportion to $\sqrt{M}$ and not to $\sqrt{m}$ as in the case of high-frequency electron oscillations.

It is easy to understand the physical reason for the small amount of damping of low-frequency longitudinal waves. It is connected with the smallness of the number of particles interacting effectively with the waves. As was explained in section 2, sub-section 2, the damping is determined by the magnitude of $F_0'(\omega/k)$. For the ions this quantity is proportional to $e^{-(\omega/kv_i)^2}$, i.e. is exponentially small ($\omega/k \gg v_i$). Since $\omega/k \ll v_e$, for the electrons $F_0'(\omega/k) \sim \omega/kv_e$. Substituting here instead of ω the value given by the first of the formulae (3.18) we obtain the characteristic small factor $\sqrt{m/M}$ in the damping decrement.

The damping of the low-frequency longitudinal oscillations is basically caused by the plasma's electron component. A characteristic feature of low-frequency longitudinal oscillations is that in the long-wave range ($a_e k \ll 1$) their frequency is proportional to the wave vector, i.e.

$$\omega \approx V_s k. \tag{3.20}$$

Therefore the long-wave low-frequency oscillations of a plasma may be called sonic. Their velocity is determined by the temperature of the electrons and the mass of the ions.

If we move into the short-wave region to satisfy the conditions $a_i k \ll 1 \ll a_e k$ (these conditions are compatible with the condition (3.19)), then the frequency of the oscillations, as can be seen from (3.18), ceases to depend on the wave vector and becomes equal to the ion Langmuir frequency

$$\left.\begin{aligned} \Omega_i &= \sqrt{\frac{4\pi e^2 n_0}{M}} \\ \omega &\approx \Omega_i \qquad (a_i k \ll 1 \ll a_e k). \end{aligned}\right\} \tag{3.21}$$

These short-wave low-frequency plasma oscillations can therefore be called ion Langmuir oscillations.

Lastly, in the $a_i k \gtrsim 1$ range low-frequency longitudinal oscillations are subject to strong damping caused by their absorption by the plasma's ions.

Up to now it has been assumed that the ions in the plasma have a unit charge. If the ion charge is Z, then the frequency and damping decrement of the low-frequency oscillations is as before defined by the formulae (3.18), where V_s is the velocity of non-isothermal sound, equal in this case to

$$V_s = \sqrt{\frac{ZT_e}{M}}. \tag{3.20'}$$

Therefore the velocity of non-isothermal sound is determined by the ion mass of a unit of its charge.

CHAPTER II

Spectra of Plasma Oscillations in a Magnetic Field

4. Dielectric Permittivity Tensor of a Plasma in a Magnetic Field

1. Components of Dielectric Permittivity Tensor

Let us now discuss the oscillation spectra of a plasma located in an external constant uniform magnetic field $\boldsymbol{H}_0$.†

It has been shown in section 3 that the oscillation spectra of a plasma are determined by its dielectric permittivity tensor

$$\varepsilon_{ij}(\boldsymbol{k}, \omega) = \delta_{ij} + 4\pi \sum_{\alpha} \varkappa_{ij}^{\alpha}(\boldsymbol{k}, \omega) \tag{4.1}$$

($\varkappa_{ij}^{\alpha}$ is the polarizability tensor of particles of a kind α), which in its turn is determined by the distribution functions of the plasma particles. We shall assume as before that the conditions $\omega\tau \gg 1$, $\gamma\tau \gg 1$ (ω is the frequency, τ is the relaxation time) are satisfied and that the oscillations are small. Under these conditions we can start with the linearized kinetic equations for the distribution functions without the collision integral. These equations for the Fourier components of the deviations of the distribution functions f^{α} from the initial distribution functions $F_0^{\alpha}(\boldsymbol{v})$ (which are considered to be

† There is a discussion of a number of the questions relating to the oscillations of a plasma in a magnetic field in the works by Ginzburg [1960], Silin and Rukhadze [1961] and Shafranov [1963].

homogeneous) are of the following form:

$$i\,((\boldsymbol{k}\cdot\boldsymbol{v})-\omega)\,f^{\alpha}-\varepsilon_{\alpha}\omega_{\alpha}\frac{\partial f^{\alpha}}{\partial\varphi}+\frac{e_{\alpha}}{m_{\alpha}}\left(\left\{\boldsymbol{E}+\frac{1}{c}\,[\boldsymbol{v}\wedge\boldsymbol{H}]\right\}\cdot\frac{\partial F_0^{\alpha}}{\partial\boldsymbol{v}}\right)=0, \qquad (4.2)$$

where $\omega_{\alpha}=|e_{\alpha}|\,H_0/m_{\alpha}c$ is the gyro-frequency of particles of a kind α; $\varepsilon_{i,e}=\pm 1$ and φ is the polar angle in the velocity space with the polar axis z along the external magnetic field $\boldsymbol{H}_0$. The alternating fields $\boldsymbol{E}$ and $\boldsymbol{H}$ are connected with each other by the relation

$$\boldsymbol{H}=\frac{c}{\omega}\,[\boldsymbol{k}\wedge\boldsymbol{E}].$$

Integrating the equation (4.2) we obtain

$$f^{\alpha}=\frac{\varepsilon_{\alpha}e_{\alpha}}{m_{\alpha}\omega_{\alpha}}\,e^{i\psi(\varphi)}\times$$

$$\times\left\{\int_0^{\varphi}e^{-i\psi(\varphi')}\left[\left(1-\frac{(\boldsymbol{k}\cdot\boldsymbol{v})}{\omega}\right)\delta_{lj}+\frac{k_l v_j}{\omega}\right]\frac{\partial F_0^{\alpha}}{\partial v_l}\,d\varphi'+C_j\right\}E_j,$$

where

$$\psi(\varphi)=\frac{k_{\parallel}v_{\parallel}-\omega}{\varepsilon_{\alpha}\omega_{\alpha}}\,\varphi+\frac{k_{\perp}v_{\perp}}{\varepsilon_{\alpha}\omega_{\alpha}}\sin\varphi,$$

$k_{\parallel}=k\cos\theta$ and $k_{\perp}=k\sin\theta$ are the longitudinal and transverse components of the vector $\boldsymbol{k}$ (relative to the field $\boldsymbol{H}_0$), θ is the angle between the vectors $\boldsymbol{k}$ and $\boldsymbol{H}_0$ and $v_{\parallel}$ and $v_{\perp}$ are the longitudinal and transverse components of the particle velocity. The constants C_j are determined from the periodicity condition of the function $f^{\alpha}(v_{\perp}, v_{\parallel}, \varphi)$ with respect to φ:

$$f^{\alpha}(v_{\perp}, v_{\parallel}, \varphi+2\pi)=f^{\alpha}(v_{\perp}, v_{\parallel}, \varphi),$$

from which

$$C_j=\int_0^{2\pi}e^{-i\psi(\varphi)}\left[\left(1-\frac{(\boldsymbol{k}\cdot\boldsymbol{v})}{\omega}\right)\delta_{lj}+\frac{k_l v_j}{\omega}\right]\times$$

$$\times\frac{\partial F_0^{\alpha}}{\partial v_l}\,d\varphi\,(e^{-i\psi(2\pi)}-1)^{-1}.$$

Having found f^{α} it is easy to determine the current density due to particles of a kind α

$$j_i^{\alpha}=e_{\alpha}\int v_i f^{\alpha}\,d^3v=\sigma_{ij}^{\alpha}E_j,$$

where

$$\sigma_{ij}^{\alpha} = \frac{\varepsilon_\alpha e_\alpha^2}{m_\alpha \omega_\alpha} \int d^3 v \, v_i \, e^{i\psi(\varphi)} \times$$

$$\times \left\{ \int_0^{\varphi} e^{-i\psi(\varphi')} \left[\left(1 - \frac{(\boldsymbol{k} \cdot \boldsymbol{v})}{\omega} \right) \delta_{lj} + \frac{k_l v_j}{\omega} \right] \frac{\partial F_0^\alpha}{\partial v_l} \, d\varphi' + C_j \right\}.$$

We shall assume that F_0^α depends only upon the longitudinal and transverse components of the particle velocity and does not depend on φ. By using the relations

$$e^{ia\sin\varphi} = \sum_{l=-\infty}^{\infty} J_l(a) \, e^{il\varphi},$$

$$\int_0^{2\pi} e^{i(l\varphi - a\sin\varphi)} \, d\varphi = 2\pi J_l(a),$$

where $J_l(a)$ is a Bessel function, we obtain the following expressions for the components $\varkappa_{ij}^{\alpha} = (i/\omega)\, \sigma_{ij}^{\alpha}$ of the polarizability tensor of the particles of a kind α of a plasma located in a magnetic field:

$$\left.\begin{aligned}
\varkappa_{11}^{\alpha} &= -\frac{\Omega_\alpha^2}{2\omega\omega_\alpha} \sum_{l=-\infty}^{\infty} \int \frac{R_\alpha l^2 J_l^2}{a^2(l+b)} v_\perp^2 \, dv_\perp \, dv_\parallel ; \\
\varkappa_{22}^{\alpha} &= -\frac{\Omega_\alpha^2}{2\omega\omega_\alpha} \sum_{l=-\infty}^{\infty} \int \frac{R_\alpha J_l'^2}{l+b} v_\perp^2 \, dv_\perp \, dv_\parallel ; \\
\varkappa_{33}^{\alpha} &= -\frac{\Omega_\alpha^2}{2\omega\omega_\alpha} \sum_{l=-\infty}^{\infty} \int \frac{R_\alpha J_l^2}{l+b} v_\parallel^2 \, dv_\perp \, dv_\parallel \\
&\quad - \frac{\Omega_\alpha^2}{2\omega^2} \left(\frac{1}{2\pi} + \frac{1}{n_\alpha} \int \frac{\partial F_0^\alpha}{\partial v_\perp} v_\parallel^2 \, dv_\perp \, dv_\parallel \right) ; \\
\varkappa_{12}^{\alpha} &= -\varkappa_{21}^{\alpha} = -\frac{i\varepsilon_\alpha \Omega_\alpha^2}{2\omega\omega_\alpha} \sum_{l=-\infty}^{\infty} \int \frac{R_\alpha l J_l J_l'}{a(l+b)} v_\perp^2 \, dv_\perp \, dv_\parallel ; \\
\varkappa_{13}^{\alpha} &= \varkappa_{31}^{\alpha} = -\frac{\Omega_\alpha^2}{2\omega\omega_\alpha} \sum_{l=-\infty}^{\infty} \int \frac{R_\alpha l J_l^2}{a(l+b)} v_\perp v_\parallel \, dv_\perp \, dv_\parallel ; \\
\varkappa_{23}^{\alpha} &= -\varkappa_{32}^{\alpha} = \frac{i\varepsilon_\alpha \Omega_\alpha^2}{2\omega\omega_\alpha} \sum_{l=-\infty}^{\infty} \frac{R_\alpha J_l J_l'}{l+b} v_\perp v_\parallel \, dv_\perp \, dv_\parallel .
\end{aligned}\right\} \quad (4.3)$$

Here

$$R_\alpha = \frac{1}{\omega n_\alpha} \left[(\omega - k_\parallel v_\parallel) \frac{\partial F_0^\alpha}{\partial v_\perp} + k_\parallel v_\perp \frac{\partial F_0^\alpha}{\partial v_\parallel} \right];$$

and

$$a = \frac{k_\perp v_\perp}{\omega_\alpha}; \qquad b = \frac{k_\parallel v_\parallel - \omega}{\omega_\alpha},$$

$\Omega_\alpha = (4\pi e_\alpha^2 n_\alpha / m_\alpha)^{1/2}$ is the Langmuir frequency of the particles of a kind α; n_α is their equilibrium density; $J_l \equiv J_l(a)$, $J_l' \equiv dJ_l/da$. The $\varkappa_{ij}^\alpha$ components are written in a system of coordinates in which the z axis is parallel to $\boldsymbol{H}_0$ and the x axis lies in the plane of the vectors $\boldsymbol{k}$ and $\boldsymbol{H}_0$ ($k_x = k_\perp$, $k_y = 0$, $k_z = k_\parallel$).

Integration with respect to $v_\perp$ in the equation (4.3) is carried out from 0 to ∞ and integration with respect to $v_\parallel$ along the real axis from $-\infty$ to $+\infty$ (if $\operatorname{Im}\omega > 0$) and along the contour C running from $-\infty$ to $+\infty$ down past the singular points $v_\parallel = (\omega - l\omega_\alpha)/k_\parallel$ when $k_\parallel > 0$ and up past them when $k_\parallel < 0$ (if $\operatorname{Im}\omega \leq 0$).

For Maxwellian distributions of the form

$$F_0^\alpha = \frac{n_\alpha}{(\pi)^{3/2} v_\alpha^3} \exp\left[-\frac{(v_\parallel - u_\alpha)^2 + v_\perp^2}{v_\alpha^2}\right],$$

where u_α is the mean directional velocity of particles of a kind α (it is assumed that it is parallel to $\boldsymbol{H}_0$), and $v_\alpha = (2T_\alpha/m_\alpha)^{1/2}$ is their thermal velocity (T_α is the temperature), the tensor $\varkappa_{ij}^\alpha$ is of the form [Sitenko and Stepanov, 1955]:

$$\left.\begin{aligned}
\varkappa_{11}^\alpha &= \frac{i\Omega_\alpha^2 z_0}{4\sqrt{\pi}\,\omega^2 \mu} e^{-\mu} \sum_{l=-\infty}^{\infty} l^2 I_l w(z_l);\\
\varkappa_{22}^\alpha &= \frac{i\Omega_\alpha^2 z_0}{4\sqrt{\pi}\,\omega^2} e^{-\mu} \sum_{l=-\infty}^{\infty} \left[\left(\frac{l^2}{\mu} + 2\mu\right) I_l - 2\mu I_l'\right) w(z_l);\\
\varkappa_{33}^\alpha &= \frac{\Omega_\alpha^2}{2\pi\omega^2}\left[y_0^2 + i\sqrt{\pi}\, z_0\, e^{-\mu} \sum_{l=-\infty}^{\infty} y_l^2 I_l w(z_l)\right];\\
\varkappa_{12}^\alpha &= \frac{\varepsilon_\alpha \Omega_\alpha^2 z_0}{4\sqrt{\pi}\,\omega^2} e^{-\mu} \sum_{l=-\infty}^{\infty} l(I_l - I_l')\, w(z_l);\\
\varkappa_{13}^\alpha &= \frac{i\Omega_\alpha^2 z_0}{\sqrt{8\pi\mu}\,\omega^2} e^{-\mu} \sum_{l=-\infty}^{\infty} l\, I_l y_l w(z_l);\\
\varkappa_{23}^\alpha &= \frac{\varepsilon_\alpha \Omega_\alpha^2 z_0 \sqrt{\mu}}{\sqrt{8\pi}\,\omega^2} e^{-\mu} \sum_{l=-\infty}^{\infty} (I_l' - I_l)\, y_l w(z_l).
\end{aligned}\right\} \quad (4.4)$$

Here $I_l \equiv I_l(\mu)$ is a modified Bessel function;

$$\mu = \frac{1}{2}\left(\frac{k_\perp v_\alpha}{\omega_\alpha}\right)^2; \quad y_l = \frac{\omega - l\omega_\alpha}{k_\parallel v_\alpha};$$

$$z_l = \frac{\omega - l\omega_\alpha - k_\parallel u_\alpha}{k_\parallel v_\alpha}$$

and $w(z)$ is the probability integral of complex argument

$$w(z) = e^{-z^2}\left(\pm 1 + \frac{2i}{\sqrt{\pi}}\int_0^z e^{t^2}\,dt\right)$$

(in this expression the top sign is taken when $k_\parallel > 0$, the bottom one when $k_\parallel < 0$).

The dielectric permittivity tensor of a plasma is not Hermitian. Its anti-Hermitian part is connected with the damping of (or amplification of) the oscillations which arises because of the interaction of the particles with the wave field. This interaction proceeds particularly effectively when one of the resonance conditions

$$\omega = k_\parallel v_\parallel + l\omega_\alpha \quad (l = 0, \pm 1, \pm 2, \ldots) \tag{4.5}$$

is satisfied.

If $l = 0$ this condition coincides with the well-known Cherenkov emission condition. Therefore the anti-Hermitian components with $l = 0$ in the expressions (4.3) and (4.4) define the Cherenkov damping or amplification of the waves.

When $l = \pm 1, \pm 2, \ldots$ the condition (4.5) coincides with the resonance condition for oscillators with the natural frequency $|l|\omega_\alpha$ moving along $\boldsymbol{H}_0$ at the velocity $v_\parallel$ (in this case in the system of coordinates in which the oscillator is at rest the wave frequency ω is equal to the frequency of the oscillator $|l|\omega_\alpha$).

The term $k_\parallel v_\parallel$ in (4.5) allows for the Doppler frequency shift. If $l > 0$, then the Doppler effect is called normal (in this case the phase velocity of the wave is greater than $v_\parallel$). If $l < 0$ the Doppler effect is called anomalous (in this case the wave's phase velocity is less than $v_\parallel$).

The interaction of the particles with the wave field when the resonance condition (4.5) is satisfied with $l \neq 0$ is connected with cyclotron (magnetic bremsstrahlung) emission and absorption of waves. Therefore the anti-Hermitian terms with $l \neq 0$ define the cyclotron (magnetic bremsstrahlung) damping or increase of the waves under conditions of normal ($l > 0$) or anomalous ($l < 0$) Doppler effect.

Using the expressions for the components of the dielectric permittivity tensor we can, in accordance with the expression (3.5), write the dispersion equation for the oscillations of a plasma located in an external magnetic field:

$$\Delta = \det\left(n^2\left(\frac{k_i k_j}{k^2} - \delta_{ij}\right) + \varepsilon_{ij}\right)$$
$$= An^4 + Bn^2 + C = 0, \qquad (4.6)$$

where $n = kc/\omega$ is the refractive index and

$$\left.\begin{aligned} A &= \varepsilon_{11}\sin^2\theta + 2\varepsilon_{13}\sin\theta\cos\theta + \varepsilon_{33}\cos^2\theta; \\ B &= -\varepsilon_{11}\varepsilon_{33} - (\varepsilon_{22}\varepsilon_{33} + \varepsilon_{23}^2)\cos^2\theta + \varepsilon_{13}^2 \\ &\quad - (\varepsilon_{11}\varepsilon_{22} + \varepsilon_{12}^2)\sin^2\theta \\ &\quad + 2(\varepsilon_{12}\varepsilon_{23} - \varepsilon_{13}\varepsilon_{22})\cos\theta\sin\theta; \\ C &= \det(\varepsilon_{ij}) = \varepsilon_{33}(\varepsilon_{11}\varepsilon_{22} + \varepsilon_{12}^2) + \varepsilon_{11}\varepsilon_{23}^2 \\ &\quad + 2\varepsilon_{12}\varepsilon_{13}\varepsilon_{23} - \varepsilon_{22}\varepsilon_{13}^2. \end{aligned}\right\} \qquad (4.7)$$

We should point out that the oscillations of a plasma cannot, generally speaking, be divided into longitudinal and transverse oscillations. However, if $A \to 0$, then the longitudinal component of the electrical field $\boldsymbol{E}_{\parallel} = \boldsymbol{k}(\boldsymbol{E}\cdot\boldsymbol{k})/k^2$ will be considerably greater than the transverse component $\boldsymbol{E}_{\perp} = [\boldsymbol{k} \wedge [\boldsymbol{E} \wedge \boldsymbol{k}]]/k^2$. In fact by multiplying the equation (3.6) by k_i we obtain

$$E_{\parallel} = -\frac{k_i \varepsilon_{ij} E_{\perp j}}{kA},$$

where

$$A = \frac{k_i \varepsilon_{ij} k_j}{k^2} = \varepsilon_{11}\sin^2\theta + 2\varepsilon_{13}\sin\theta\cos\theta + \varepsilon_{33}\cos^2\theta.$$

It can be seen from this that the two equations $\Delta = 0$ and $A = 0$ must be satisfied for purely longitudinal oscillations ($E_{\perp} = 0$). In the general case with arbitrary θ these equations are not satisfied simultaneously. The only exception is the case of $\theta = 0$ when the propagation of purely longitudinal oscillations is possible. If, however, $\theta \neq 0$ the equations $\Delta = 0$ and $A = 0$ can be simultaneously satisfied only approximately. In other words, when $\theta \neq 0$ the oscillations of the plasma can be almost longitudinal, i.e. $E_{\parallel} \gg E_{\perp}$ if $A \approx 0$.

2. Dielectric Permittivity Tensor of a Cold Plasma

The dielectric permittivity tensor has its simplest form for a cold plasma if charged particle fluxes are not passing across it. In this case there is no spatial dispersion and the tensor ε_{ij} depends only on the frequency:

$$\left.\begin{aligned} &\varepsilon_{11} = \varepsilon_{22} \equiv \varepsilon_1 = 1 - \sum_\alpha \frac{\Omega_\alpha^2}{\omega^2 - \omega_\alpha^2};\\ &\varepsilon_{33} \equiv \varepsilon_3 = 1 - \sum_\alpha \frac{\Omega_\alpha^2}{\omega^2};\\ &\varepsilon_{12} \equiv i\varepsilon_2 = -\sum_\alpha \frac{i e_\alpha \Omega_\alpha^2 \omega_\alpha}{\omega(\omega^2 - \omega_\alpha^2)};\\ &\varepsilon_{13} = \varepsilon_{23} = 0. \end{aligned}\right\} \tag{4.8}$$

The quantities A, B, C for a cold plasma take the form:

$$\left.\begin{aligned} &A = \varepsilon_1 \sin^2\theta + \varepsilon_3 \cos^2\theta;\\ &B = -\varepsilon_1\varepsilon_3(1 + \cos^2\theta) - (\varepsilon_1^2 - \varepsilon_2^2)\sin^2\theta;\\ &C = \varepsilon_3(\varepsilon_1^2 - \varepsilon_2^2). \end{aligned}\right\} \tag{4.9}$$

By using (4.6) we can find the refractive indices of the waves as functions of the frequency ω and the angle θ

$$n_\pm^2 = \frac{-B \pm \sqrt{B^2 - 4AC}}{2A}. \tag{4.10}$$

Therefore with given ω and θ two waves with different wave vector values, i.e. with different propagation velocities, can be propagated in a cold plasma. These waves are characterized by elliptical polarization.

We notice that in a hot plasma the quantities A, B and C are themselves functions of the wave vector, so in the case of a hot plasma the expressions (4.10) do not define the refractive indices in an explicit form.

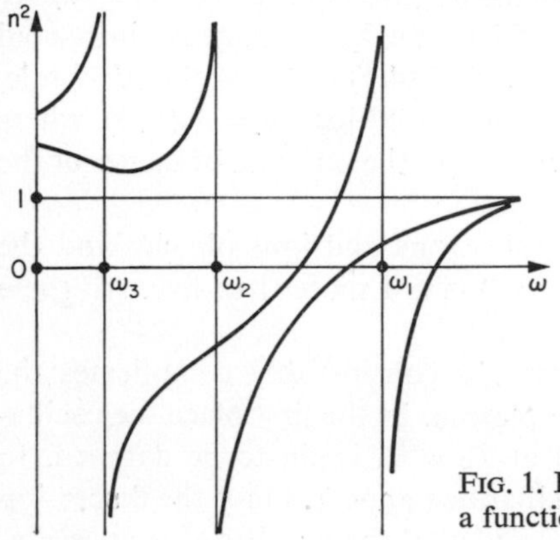

FIG. 1. Refractive indices $n_{\pm}$ as a function of frequency.

In Fig. 1 we have plotted diagrammatically the squares of the refractive indices as a function of the frequency when $\theta \neq 0, \pi/2$ [Shafranov, 1963].

The formulae (4.8)–(4.10) are derived for $T_\alpha = 0$ but they can also be used when $T_\alpha \neq 0$, provided that the temperature is low enough, so that

$$\mu = \frac{1}{2}\left(\frac{k_\perp v_\alpha}{\omega_\alpha}\right)^2 \ll 1, \qquad |z_l| = \left|\frac{\omega - l\omega_\alpha}{k_\parallel v_\alpha}\right| \gg 1$$

$$(l = 0, \pm 1, \pm 2). \qquad (4.11)$$

Let us examine the meaning of these conditions in greater detail. The first of them means that the wavelength in the direction at right angles to the field $\boldsymbol{H}_0$ should be far greater than the Larmor radius of particles with a velocity $v_\perp$ of the order of the thermal velocity ($v_\perp \sim v_\alpha$).

The condition $|z_0| \gg 1$ means that the distance travelled by a particle with a velocity $v_\parallel$ of the order of the mean thermal velocity in a period of the field oscillations should be far less than the wavelength in the direction parallel to $\boldsymbol{H}_0$.

Lastly, the conditions $|z_1| \gg 1$, $|z_2| \gg 1$ require (when the condition $|z_0| \gg 1$ is satisfied) that the wave frequency should not be too close to ω_α or $2\omega_\alpha$. It should be pointed out that the expressions (4.8)–(4.10) can also be used if $\omega \approx 2\omega_\alpha$, when $|z_2| \lesssim 1$, with the exception of special cases (see below).

Let us now pause to examine the question of the number of waves with a given wave vector $\boldsymbol{k}$ which can be propagated in a cold plasma. Since the dispersion equation (4.6) for $T_\alpha = 0$ is algebraic, for a given $\boldsymbol{k}$ it has a finite number of solutions $\omega = \omega_j(k, \theta)$, where the suffix $j = 1, 2, \ldots$ is used to denote the separate branches of the oscillations.

For a plasma consisting of electrons and ions of one kind the number of branches when $T_\alpha = 0$ is not more than five. All these oscillations are undamped.

Thermal motion of the particles considerably complicates the picture of the oscillations in a plasma. In the first place the oscillations, which were undamped at $T_\alpha = 0$, begin to be damped. In addition, new branches of oscillations appear. Since the dispersion equation when $T_\alpha \neq 0$ is transcendental the number of new oscillation branches, generally speaking, is infinitely great. As a rule, however, the damping decrements of the new oscillations that appear when $T_\alpha \neq 0$ are large (of the order of the frequency) and the wavelengths small (of the order of the Larmor radius of the ions or electrons or of the Debye radius). Only in certain special cases does thermal motion lead to the appearance of large-scale weakly damped oscillations (the sonic oscillations in a strongly non-isothermal plasma without a magnetic field discussed above are oscillations of this type).

Moving on to the study of the oscillations of a plasma in a magnetic field we first note that oscillations with a large refractive index and oscillations whose frequency is close to $l\omega_\alpha$ ($l = 1, 2, \ldots$) are of greatest interest.

Waves with a large refractive index have a small phase velocity and so interact effectively with the plasma particles. This interaction leads to a number of specific effects—a rise in the damping of the waves, an increase in the level of the fluctuations, the appearance of instabilities when fluxes of charged particles pass through the plasma, etc.

If the frequency is close to $l\omega_\alpha$ (cyclotron resonance) the wave is subject to strong damping when $T_\alpha \neq 0$. This allows us to use cyclotron resonance for "pumping" electromagnetic energy into a plasma. As a result of binary collisions and the interaction between the waves this energy is transferred to the thermal energy of the plasma. This question is not discussed here.

5. Longitudinal Oscillations of a Plasma in a Magnetic Field

1. Frequencies of Plasma Resonances

Let us first examine waves in a cold plasma with an infinitely great refractive index. In accordance with (4.10) the refractive index $n \to \infty$ if $A \to 0$. In this case

$$n_-^2 = -\frac{B}{A}, \quad n_+^2 = -\frac{C}{B}. \tag{5.1}$$

Since $B \neq 0$ the refractive index approaches infinity when $A \to 0$ for only one of the waves.

As has been shown in section 4, the equation $A = 0$ is the condition for the oscillations to be longitudinal so that in a cold plasma the waves with an infinitely great refractive index are longitudinal.

By making $A = 0$ we can obtain the equation for determining the frequencies of the longitudinal oscillations when $T_\alpha = 0$. If the plasma consists of electrons and ions of one kind the equation $A = 0$ becomes

$$1 - \frac{\Omega_e^2 \cos^2\theta}{\omega^2} - \frac{\Omega_e^2 \sin^2\theta}{\omega^2 - \omega_e^2} - \frac{\Omega_i^2 \cos^2\theta}{\omega^2} - \frac{\Omega_i^2 \sin^2\theta}{\omega^2 - \omega_i^2} = 0. \tag{5.2}$$

It defines the frequencies $\omega = \omega_j(\theta)$ of the three longitudinal eigen oscillations of a cold plasma in a magnetic field as a function of the angle θ between the direction of propagation and the magnetic field.

Since the oscillations with frequencies $\omega = \omega_j(\theta)$ are longitudinal they can be considered as analogues of the Langmuir oscillations when there is no magnetic field. The frequencies $\omega_j(\theta)$ are called the plasma resonance frequencies (they are also called hybrid frequencies since they depend both on the Langmuir and cyclotron frequencies of plasma particles).

Neglecting the contribution of the ions in the equation (5.2) we obtain the following expressions for the two resonance frequencies

$\omega_1(\theta)$ and $\omega_2(\theta)$ [Akhiezer and Pargamanik, 1948]:

$$\omega_1^2(\theta) = \tfrac{1}{2}(\Omega_e^2 + \omega_e^2) + \tfrac{1}{2}\sqrt{(\Omega_e^2 + \omega_e^2)^2 - 4\Omega_e^2\omega_e^2\cos^2\theta}; \qquad (5.3)$$

$$\omega_2^2(\theta) = \tfrac{1}{2}(\Omega_e^2 + \omega_e^2) - \tfrac{1}{2}\sqrt{(\Omega_e^2 + \omega_e^2)^2 - 4\Omega_e^2\omega_e^2\cos^2\theta}. \qquad (5.4)$$

As can be seen from the equation (5.2), the ions have to be allowed for when $\omega \approx \omega_i$. In this frequency range lies the third resonance frequency

$$\omega_3(\theta) = \omega_i\left(1 - \frac{1}{2}\frac{m_e}{m_i}\tan^2\theta\right). \qquad (5.5)$$

The frequency $\omega_1(\theta)$ rises when the angle θ increases from $\omega_1 = \max(\Omega_e, \omega_e)$ for $\theta = 0$ to the value $\omega_1 = \sqrt{\Omega_e^2 + \omega_e^2}$ for $\theta = \pi/2$ [Gross, 1951].

The frequency $\omega_2(\theta)$ drops when the angle θ increases from $\omega_2 = \min(\Omega_e, \omega_e)$ for $\theta = 0$ and approaches zero for $\theta \to \pi/2$:

$$\omega_2(\theta) = \frac{\Omega_e\omega_e\cos\theta}{\sqrt{\Omega_e^2 + \omega_e^2}}. \qquad (5.6)$$

The expression (5.3) can be used with an accuracy up to terms of the order of m_e/m_i for any angles θ, but the expressions (5.4) and (5.5) for $\omega_2(\theta)$ and $\omega_3(\theta)$ only when $|(\pi/2) - \theta|^2 \gg m_e/m_i$.

If the angle θ is close to $\pi/2$, then the resonant frequencies $\omega_2(\theta)$ and $\omega_3(\theta)$ are defined by the formulae [Stepanov, 1958d):

$$\omega_{2,3}^2(\theta) = \frac{1}{2(1+q)}\{\Omega_e^2\cos^2\theta + \Omega_i^2 + \omega_i^2$$

$$\pm\sqrt{(\Omega_e^2\cos^2\theta + \Omega_i^2 + \omega_i^2)^2 - 4(1+q)\,\omega_i^2\Omega_e^2\cos^2\theta}\}, \qquad (5.7)$$

where

$$q = \frac{\Omega_e^2}{\omega_e^2}.$$

When $\theta \to \pi/2$ [Körper, 1957]

$$\omega_2 = \omega_k \equiv \sqrt{\frac{\omega_i^2 + \Omega_i^2}{1+q}} \quad \left(\cos^2\theta \ll \frac{m_e}{m_i}\right). \qquad (5.8)$$

When $\theta \to \pi/2$ the frequency $\omega_3(\theta)$ approaches zero:

$$\omega_3(\theta) = \frac{\Omega_e \omega_i \cos\theta}{\sqrt{\Omega_i^2 + \omega_i^2}} \quad \left(\cos^2\theta \ll \frac{m_e}{m_i}\right). \tag{5.9}$$

The behaviour of the resonance frequencies as a function of the angle θ is shown diagrammatically in Fig. 2.

The formulae (5.1)–(5.9) are derived for a cold plasma but they can also be used when $T_\alpha \neq 0$ provided the conditions (4.11) are satisfied. In this case when the frequencies $\omega_j(\theta)$ are not close to ω_e or ω_i it is necessary for the wavelength to be considerably greater than the Larmor radius of the electrons and ions and the Debye radius. If $\theta \to 0$, then one of the frequencies $\omega_{1,2}$ approaches ω_e. The expressions (5.3) or (5.4) can be used in this case if $k^2 v_e^2/\omega_e^2 \ll q\theta^2/4|1-q| \ll 1$.

The expression (5.5) for $\cos\theta \sim 1$ can be used if the inequality $8\pi n_0 T_i/H_0^2 \ll (\theta^2 m_e/m_i)^3 \lesssim 10^{-9}$ is satisfied. If $8\pi n_0 T_i/H_0^2$

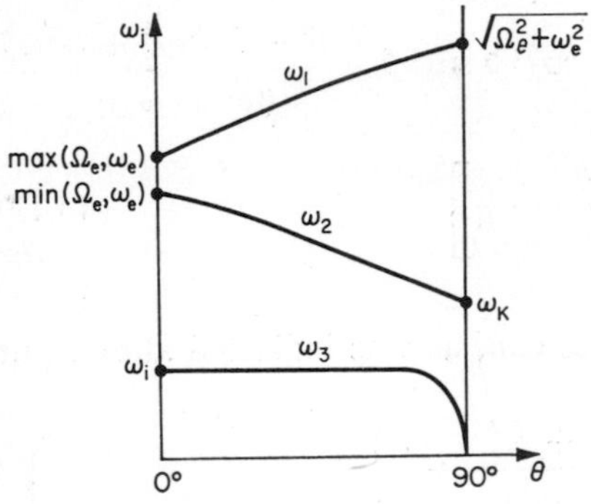

FIG. 2. Resonance frequencies $\omega = \omega_j(\theta)$ ($j = 1, 2, 3$) as functions of angle θ.

$\gtrsim (\theta^2 m_e/m_i)^3$, then the oscillations with the frequency $\omega_3(\theta)$ are strongly damped because of cyclotron absorption by the plasma ions. Therefore when $\cos\theta \sim 1$, longitudinal oscillations with a frequency $\omega_3(\theta)$ can be propagated only in a low-density, low-temperature plasma.

2. *Effect of Thermal Motion of Electrons on High-Frequency Resonances*

Let us investigate how the thermal motion of the plasma particles affects the behaviour of the refractive index near the resonance frequencies $\omega_j(\theta)$. We shall first discuss the high-frequency resonance when $\omega \approx \omega_2(\theta)$ ($\cos^2\theta \gg m_e/m_i$) or $\omega \approx \omega_1(\theta)$. It is chiefly electrons that take part in these oscillations so we take only their thermal motion into consideration. Since the quantity A becomes zero when $T_\alpha = 0$ and $\omega = \omega_j(\theta)$, and B and C are non-zero quantities, it is sufficient to find the corrections connected with the thermal motion for the quantity A.

Expanding A into a series for powers of T_e and taking the first two terms into consideration we obtain

$$A = A_0 - A_1\beta_e^2 n^2, \tag{5.10}$$

where

$$A_0 = \frac{(\omega^2 - \omega_1^2)(\omega^2 - \omega_2^2)}{\omega^2(\omega^2 - \omega_e^2)}, \tag{5.11}$$

$$A_1 = \frac{\Omega_e^2}{2\omega^2}\left[3\cos^4\theta + \cos^2\theta\sin^2\theta\,\frac{6\omega^6 - 3\omega^4\omega_e^2 + \omega^2\omega_e^4}{(\omega^2 - \omega_e^2)^3} + \frac{3\omega^4\sin^4\theta}{(\omega^2 - \omega_e^2)(\omega^2 - 4\omega_e^2)}\right] \tag{5.12}$$

and $\beta_e = v_e/c$.

In the quantities B and C we can, as was indicated above, put $T_e = 0$:

$$\left.\begin{aligned} B &= \frac{(\omega^2 - \Omega_e^2)(2\Omega_e^2 + \omega_e^2 - \omega^2)}{\omega^2(\omega^2 - \omega_e^2)}, \\ C &= \left(1 - \frac{\Omega_e^2}{\omega^2}\right)\left[1 - \frac{\Omega_e^2}{\omega(\omega + \omega_e)}\right]\left[1 - \frac{\Omega_e^2}{\omega(\omega - \omega_e)}\right]. \end{aligned}\right\} \tag{5.13}$$

Taking the expansion (5.10) into account the dispersion equation (4.6) becomes [Gershman, 1953]

$$(A_0 - A_1\beta_e^2 n^2)\, n^4 + Bn^2 + C = 0. \tag{5.14}$$

This equation contains n^2 cubed unlike the dispersion equation for a cold plasma which was quadratic in n^2. Therefore in a hot plasma in the region of the plasma resonances, $\omega \approx \omega_1(\theta)$ and $\omega \approx \omega_2(\theta)$, three waves with different refractive indices can be propagated† (unlike a cold plasma in which only two waves with the refractive indices $n = n_\pm$ can be propagated at a given frequency).

Electron thermal motion has little effect on a refractive index with no singularities in the plasma resonance region. It need not be taken into consideration, therefore, and we can use the previous expression $n_+^2 \equiv n_1^2 = -B/C$ for the refractive index of this wave.

The refractive indices of the other two waves are far greater than unity. In order to determine them we can neglect the quantity C in the equation (5.14). As a result we obtain [Sitenko and Stepanov, 1955]

$$n_j^2 = \sqrt{\frac{B}{\beta_e^2\,|A_1|}}\,\varphi_\pm(x) \quad (j = 2, 3), \tag{5.15}$$

where

$$\varphi_\pm(x) = \alpha\left(x \pm \sqrt{x^2 + \alpha}\right),$$

$$x = \frac{A_0}{2\beta_e\sqrt{B\,|A_1|}}, \qquad \alpha = \operatorname{sign} A_1 \tag{5.16}$$

and A_1 and B are the values of the functions A_1 and B when $\omega \approx \omega_j(\theta)$ ($j = 2, 3$ depending on the sign in front of the radical in (5.15)).

A wave with the refractive index $n_3^2 \sim \varphi_-$ is generally called a plasma wave and a wave with a refractive index $n_2^2 \sim \varphi_+$ is called extraordinary if $\omega \approx \omega_1$, and ordinary if $\omega \approx \omega_2$. A wave with a refractive index $n_1^2 = n_+^2$ is called ordinary if $\omega \approx \omega_1$, and extraordinary if $\omega \approx \omega_2$.

Figure 3 shows graphs of the functions $y = \varphi_\pm(x)$ when $\alpha = 1$ (Fig. 3a) and when $\alpha = -1$ (Fig. 3b).‡

We can see that when $\alpha = 1$ only one wave with a refractive index $n_2^2 \sim \varphi_+$ can be propagated. The propagation of a wave with a refractive index $n_3^2 \sim \varphi_-$ when $\alpha = 1$ is impossible since $n_3^2 < 0$.

† The conclusion that there is a third wave present was drawn by Pargamanik [1948].

‡ The qualitative picture of the behaviour of the refractive indices of the waves when $\omega \approx \omega_{1,2}$ and $T_e \neq 0$ has been discussed by Gershman [1955, 1956].

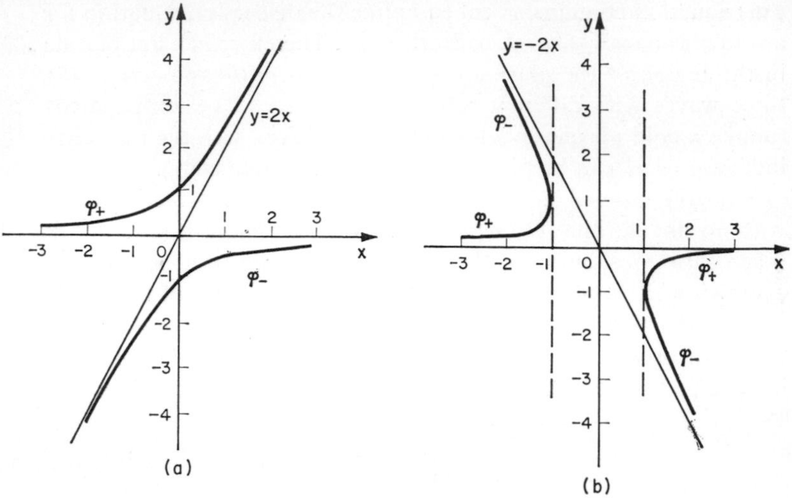

FIG. 3. Graphs of functions $y = \varphi_{\pm}(x)$: (a) for $\alpha = 1$; (b) for $\alpha = -1$.

This wave is completely internally reflected and it penetrates into the plasma to a depth of $c/\omega|n_3|$.

If $|x| \gg 1$, then from (5.15) we obtain for one of the refractive indices the hydrodynamic expression

$$n_j^2 = -\frac{B}{A_0}$$

($j = 2$ when $x < 0$ and $j = 3$ when $x > 0$) and for the other the expression [Gershman, 1953]

$$n_j^2 = \frac{A_0}{\beta_e^2 A_1}, \tag{5.17}$$

where $j = 3$ when $x < 0$ and $j = 2$ when $x > 0$.

We notice an interesting feature of a plasma wave when $\alpha = -1$. Here the angle ψ between the direction of the group velocity (i.e. the direction of the time-averaged energy flux) [Gertsenshtein, 1954; Ginzburg and Gershman, 1963] and the direction of the phase velocity is greater than $\pi/2$.† When $\cos^2 \theta \to 0$

† For a wave with the refractive index (5.17) this result was obtained in the paper by Gershman [1960a], and in the general case in the paper by Kitsenko and Stepanov [1963].

the angle ψ approaches π, i.e. the phase and group velocities are in opposite directions. For a wave with a refractive index $n^2 \sim \varphi_\pm$ we have the angle $\psi < \pi/2$ with $\psi \approx \pi/2$ if $\cos^2\theta \sim 1$ and $\psi \to 0$ if $\theta \to \pi/2$.

By using the dispersion equation (5.14) we can find the corrections to the frequencies ω_1 and ω_2 caused by electron thermal motion. Putting

$$\omega = \omega_j(\theta)(1 + \xi) \tag{5.18}$$

and considering that $|\xi| \ll 1$, we obtain

$$\xi = \frac{\omega_j^2\left(\beta_e^2 n^2 A_1 - \dfrac{B}{n^2}\right)(\omega_j^2 - \omega_i^2)^2}{2\Omega_e^2[\cos^2\theta\,(\omega_j^2 - \omega_i^2)^2 + \sin^2\theta\,\omega_j^4]}, \tag{5.19}$$

where

$$n = \frac{kc}{\omega_j(\theta)}; \quad A_1 = A_1(\omega, \theta)|_{\omega=\omega_j}; \quad B = B(\omega, \theta)|_{\omega=\omega_j}.$$

The behaviour of the frequencies (5.18) as a function of the wave vector is clear from Fig. 3 (we should mention that if $\omega \approx \omega_j(\theta)$, then $x \sim \omega - \omega_j(\theta)$ and $y \sim k^2$).

3. *Effect of Thermal Motion of Particles on Low-Frequency Resonances*

We have just discussed the effect of electron thermal motion on the behaviour of the refractive index near the high-frequency plasma resonances ($\omega \approx \omega_2(\theta)$ when $\cos^2\theta \gg m_e/m_i$ and $\omega \approx \omega_1(\theta)$).

Let us now examine the effect of thermal motion of the particles on the behaviour of the refractive index near the low-frequency plasma resonances. These resonances correspond to the frequencies $\omega = \omega_2(\theta)$ and $\omega = \omega_3(\theta)$ at angles $\theta \approx \pi/2$ (we shall not discuss the resonance $\omega = \omega_3(\theta)$ when $\cos\theta \sim 1$ since it can occur only in a very rarefied plasma).

When investigating the behaviour of the refractive index near the resonance frequencies ω_2 and ω_3 for $\theta \approx \pi/2$ we must allow for both electron and ion thermal motion. Taking into consideration in the dispersion equation (4.6) the term $\sim\beta_e^2 n^6$ and $\beta_i^2 n^6$, where $\beta_i = v_i/c$, we obtain the following expressions for the refractive indices that have singularities when $\omega \approx \omega_2$ and $\omega \approx \omega_3$ [Kitsenko and Stepanov, 1963]:

$$n_j^2 = \frac{2\Omega_e^2\zeta}{(1+q)\,|\beta|\,\omega^2\sqrt{\Delta}}\,\varphi_\pm(x) \qquad (j = 2, 3), \tag{5.20}$$

where

$$x = \frac{(\omega^2-\omega_2^2)(\omega^2-\omega_3^2)}{|\beta|\sqrt{\Delta}\,\omega^4};$$

$$\Delta = \frac{6\Omega_e^2\Omega_i^2|\zeta|}{|\omega^2-4\omega_i^2|\,(1+q)\,\omega^2};$$

$$\zeta = (1+q)\left(1-\frac{\omega_i^2}{\omega^2}\right)-\frac{\Omega_i^2}{\omega^2}+\frac{m_e}{m_i}\,\frac{\omega^2\Omega_i^2}{\omega_i^2(\omega^2-\omega_i^2)};$$

$$\beta^2 = \beta_i^2+\frac{m_i}{m_e}\,\beta_e^2\left(1-\frac{4\omega_i^2}{\omega^2}\right)\left(1-\frac{\omega_i^2}{\omega^2}\right)\times$$

$$\times\left(\cos^4\theta-\frac{1}{3}\,\frac{\omega^2}{\omega_e^2}\cos^2\theta+\frac{\omega^4}{4\omega_e^4}\right).$$

The functions $\varphi_+(x)$ are defined by the previous formula (5.16) in which we must put $\alpha = \operatorname{sign}\zeta\beta^2(1-2\omega_i/\omega)$.

Therefore three waves with different refractive indices can be propagated in a hot plasma in the low-frequency plasma resonance region (just as in the high-frequency plasma resonance region).

Let us now examine the nature of the longitudinal oscillations of a plasma consisting of ions of several kinds. In this case the dispersion equation $A = 0$ when $T_\alpha = 0$ has $2+\nu$ solutions†, where ν is the number of ions of different kinds. If the angle θ is not close to $\pi/2$, then the additional resonance frequencies $\omega_j(\theta)$ that appear are close to the ion gyro-frequencies

$$\omega_j(\theta) = \omega_\alpha\left[1+O\left(\frac{m_e}{m_\alpha}\right)\right] \quad (j = 3, 4, \ldots, \nu).$$

When $|(\pi/2)-\theta|^2 \lesssim m_e/m_i$ the frequencies $\omega_j(\theta)$ differ noticeably from the gyro-frequencies ω_α (if the concentrations of the different kinds of ions are not too low).

† Plasma resonances in a multi-component plasma when $T_\alpha = 0$ and $\theta = \pi/2$ are investigated in Buchsbaum's paper [1960].

Thanks to electron and ion thermal motion the refractive index becomes finite when $\omega = \omega_j(\theta)$ $(j = 1, 2, \ldots, \nu)$ and, just as in the case of a two-component plasma, the propagation of three waves with different refractive indices becomes possible in the region of each of the resonance frequencies $\omega = \omega_j(\theta)$ $(j = 1, 2, \ldots, \nu)$.

6. Cyclotron and Cherenkov Damping of Electron Oscillations

1. Cyclotron Damping at Electron Gyro-Resonance

We shall now discuss the damping of high-frequency electron oscillations caused by electron thermal motion. For long-wave oscillations ($kv_e \ll \omega_e$) it is significant in two cases: when the frequency is close to a multiple frequency of the electron gyro-resonance ($\omega \approx l\omega_e$, where $l = 1, 2, \ldots$) or when the wave's phase velocity is less than or of the order of the thermal velocity of the electrons. In the first of these cases $|z_l| = |(l_\omega - \omega_e)/k_{\|}v_e| \lesssim 1$ $(l = 1, 2, \ldots)$, and in the second $|z_0| = |\omega/k_{\|}v_e| \lesssim 1$. (If $|z_l| \gg 1$, $l = 0, 1, \ldots$, then the anti-Hermitian parts of the dielectric permittivity tensor, which define the Cherenkov and cyclotron dampings, are exponentially small $[\sim e^{-z_l^2}]$. Under these conditions the Cherenkov and cyclotron dampings are as a rule less than the damping caused by binary collisions.)

Let us first examine the cyclotron damping of waves propagated along the magnetic field. In this case the dispersion equation (4.6) degenerates into three equations:

$$\varepsilon_{33} = 0; \tag{6.1}$$

$$n^2 - \varepsilon_{11} \pm i\varepsilon_{12} = 0. \tag{6.2}$$

The equation (6.1) is the same as the equation (2.15) for longitudinal oscillations of a plasma when $\boldsymbol{H}_0 = 0$ (obviously the magnetic field does not affect longitudinal oscillations propagated along the field).

The equations (6.2) define the refractive indices of two transverse electromagnetic waves with circular polarization for which the direction of rotation of the electric field is either opposite to ($n = n_+$) or in the same direction ($n = n_-$) as the direction of rotation of the electrons in the magnetic field $\boldsymbol{H}_0$. By using the formulae (4.4) and (4.2), when $\theta = 0$ the equation (6.2) can be given as

$$n_{\pm}^2 = 1 + \frac{i\sqrt{\pi}\,\Omega_e^2}{\omega^2\beta_e n_{\pm}} w(z_{\pm}), \tag{6.3}$$

where

$$z_{\pm} = \frac{\omega \pm \omega_e}{\omega\beta_e n_{\pm}}.$$

If $|z_{\pm}| \gg 1$, then the refractive indices become

$$n_{\pm}^2 = 1 - \frac{\Omega_e^2}{\omega(\omega \pm \omega_e)}. \tag{6.4}$$

We see that $n_+ < 1$, i.e. the wave's phase velocity is greater than c. Therefore waves with a refractive index n_+ are not damped (unless, of course, binary collisions are taken into consideration).

Cyclotron damping of a wave with a refractive index n_- is exponentially small when $|z_-| \gg 1$. When the frequency ω approaches ω_e the damping increases and becomes very considerable when $|z_-| \lesssim 1$. If $|z_-| \ll 1$, then [Silin, 1955]

$$n_- = \frac{\sqrt{3} + i}{2}\left(\frac{\sqrt{\pi}\,c\Omega_e^2}{v_e\omega_e^2}\right)^{1/3}. \tag{6.5}$$

In this case the field penetrates into the plasma to a depth

$$\delta_e \approx \left(\frac{c^2 v_e}{\sqrt{\pi}\Omega_e^2\omega}\right)^{1/3} \tag{6.6}$$

(the case of anomalous skin effect).

We notice that the condition $|z_-| \ll 1$ is satisfied if

$$\left|1 - \frac{\omega_e}{\omega}\right| \ll \left(\frac{\Omega_e v_e}{\omega_e c}\right)^{2/3}.$$

In order of magnitude the refractive index n_- is defined by the expression (6.5) even when $|z_-| \lesssim 1$, and also when the direction of propagation subtends a small angle θ with the direction of the magnetic field ($\theta^3 \lesssim \beta_e[\Omega_e^2/\omega_e^2]$).

When the angle θ increases the imaginary part of the refractive index n_- decreases and when $\theta^3 \gg \beta_e(\Omega_e^2/\omega_e^2)$ this wave becomes weakly damped ($\operatorname{Im} n_- \ll \operatorname{Re} n_-$) even if $|z_-| \lesssim 1$. A wave with a refractive index n_+, for which there is no damping when $\theta = 0$, also remains weakly damped when $\theta \sim 1$.

If $\Omega_e^2 \, |w(z_\pm)|/\omega_e^2 \beta_e n_\pm \gg 1$, then the real parts of the refractive indices of the two waves when $\theta \neq 0$ are given by the expressions [Sitenko and Stepanov, 1955]

$$n_\pm^2 = \frac{1}{\sin^2\theta}\left[1 + \frac{1}{2}\sin^2\theta - q \mp \sqrt{\left(1 + \frac{1}{2}\sin^2\theta - q\right)^2 - \sin^2\theta(1-q)(2-q)}\right], \quad (6.7)$$

where

$$q = \frac{\Omega_e^2}{\omega_e^2}.$$

Wave propagation is therefore possible only when $q < 2$. If $q > 2$, then $n_\pm^2 < 0$ and the electromagnetic waves are subject to total internal reflexion.

It follows from the expressions (6.7) that when $\theta \sim 1$ both the refractive indices are of the order of unity. In other words, when $\theta \sim 1$ (as opposed to the case of $\theta^3 \lesssim \beta_e[\Omega_e^2/\omega_e^2]$) the refractive index n_- has no singularity when $\omega \approx \omega_e$.

The imaginary parts of the refractive indices $\varkappa_\pm$ of the two waves can be defined by the formula [Stepanov and Pakhomov, 1960]

$$\varkappa_\pm = \frac{\beta_e \, |\cos\theta| \, Q}{\sqrt{\pi}(2\sin^2\theta \, n_\pm^2 + 2q - 2 - \sin^2\theta)\, q} f(z_\pm), \quad (6.8)$$

where

$$Q = n_\pm^4 \left(1 - q + \tfrac{7}{4} q \sin^2\theta\right) + n_\pm^2\left[(1+q)\left(\tfrac{1}{2}q - 1\right)\sin^2\theta + \tfrac{1}{4} q^2 \tan^2\theta(1 + \cos^2\theta) - (1-q)\left(1 - \tfrac{1}{4}q\right)(1 + \cos^2\theta)\right] + (1-q)\left(1 - \tfrac{1}{2}q\right) + \tfrac{1}{4}(q-2)\, q^2 \tan^2\theta,$$

and

$$f(z_\pm) = \frac{e^{-z_\pm^2}}{|w(z_\pm)|^2}; \quad z_\pm = \frac{\omega - \omega_e}{\omega \beta_e n_\pm \cos\theta}. \tag{6.9}$$

A graph of the function $f(z)$ which defines the contour of the absorption line is shown in Fig. 4. As z increases the function $f(z)$ steadily decreases from the value $f(0) = 1$ and approaches $f(z) = \pi z^2 e^{-z^2}$ when $|z| \gg 1$.†

If $|z_\pm| \lesssim 1$ and $\Omega_e \sim \omega_e$, then $n_\pm \sim 1$ and $\varkappa_\pm \sim \beta_e$.

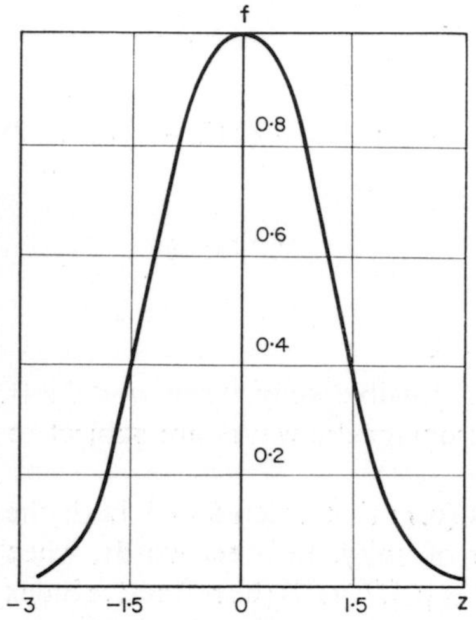

FIG. 4. Graph of function $f(z) = e^{-z^2}/|w(z)|^2$.

2. Cyclotron Damping at Multiple Electron Gyro-Resonance

Let us move on to examining cyclotron damping in the case of multiple electron gyro-resonance.

Assuming that $kv_e \ll \omega_e$ from the dispersion equation (4.6) we obtain for the refractive indices the previous expressions (4.10) which are valid for a cold plasma. The damping coefficients (the imaginary parts of the refractive indices) are defined by the formula [Stepanov and Pakhomov, 1960]‡

$$\varkappa_\pm = \beta_e^{2l-3} \sigma \frac{Q_2}{Q_1} e^{-z_\pm^2}; \quad z_\pm = \frac{\omega - l\omega_e}{\omega \beta_e n_\pm \cos\theta}, \tag{6.10}$$

† The equation (6.8) in the case $|z_\pm| \ll 1$ was derived in Gershman's paper [1960b].

‡ The expression (6.10) for $\omega \approx 2\omega_e$ and $\omega \approx 3\omega_e$ was also derived in Gershman's paper [1960b].

where

$$\sigma = \frac{\sqrt{\pi}\,(ln_\pm \sin\theta)^{2l-2}\Omega_e^2}{2^{2l}l!\,|\cos\theta|\,\omega_e^2}; \quad Q_1 = 2C + Bn_\pm^2,$$

$$Q_2 = n_\pm^4 \sin^2\theta - n_\pm^2\left(1 - \frac{\Omega_e^2}{\omega^2}\right)(1 + \cos^2\theta)$$

$$+ 2\left(1 - \frac{\Omega_e^2}{\omega^2 - \omega_e^2} + \frac{\Omega_e^2\omega_e}{\omega(\omega^2 - \omega_e^2)}\right)\left(1 - \frac{\Omega_e^2}{\omega^2} - n_\pm^2 \sin^2\theta\right)$$

(the quantities B and C are defined by the formulae (4.9)).

The shape of the absorption line is determined by the function $e^{-z_\pm^2}$.

If $\theta \sim 1$ and $\Omega_e \sim \omega_e$, then $n_\pm \sim 1$ and $\varkappa_\pm \sim \beta_e^{2l-3}$, in particular $\varkappa_\pm \sim \beta_e$ when $\omega = 2\omega_e$, i.e. the cyclotron damping at the frequencies $\omega = \omega_e$ and $\omega = 2\omega_e$ is of the same order of magnitude if the angle θ is not small.

The strong cyclotron damping when $\omega \approx l\omega_e$ may considerably exceed in the case of a rarefied high-temperature plasma the damping caused by binary collisions. For example if $n_0 \sim 10^{13}$ cm^{-3}, $H_0 \sim 10^4$ oe, $\omega_e \sim \Omega_e \sim 10^{11}$ sec^{-1} and $T_e \sim 100$ eV, then with $\omega = \omega_e$ and $\omega = 2\omega_e$ ($\lambda \sim 0{\cdot}1$ cm) the cyclotron damping is $\varkappa \sim \beta_e \sim 10^{-2}$ and in order of magnitude the damping length is $\delta \sim \lambda/\beta_e \sim 10$ cm. The collision frequency under these conditions is $\nu \sim 10^6$ sec^{-1} and the damping length due to the collisions is $\delta \sim c/\nu \sim 10^5$ cm.

Knowing the imaginary part of the refractive index $\varkappa$ we can find the damping decrement

$$\gamma = \frac{\varkappa\omega}{c}\frac{d\omega}{dk},$$

where $\omega = \omega(k, \theta)$ is the solution of the dispersion equation (4.6) for $T_e = 0$.†

† The expressions for the damping decrement when $\omega \approx l\omega_e$ ($l = 2, 3, \ldots$) were derived in the paper by Stepanov [1958c].

3. Cyclotron Damping at Double Resonance

The refractive index of an extraordinary wave n_- and its damping coefficient $\varkappa_-$ become very large in the case of double resonance when $\omega \approx l\omega_e \approx \omega_1(\theta)$, where $\omega_1(\theta)$ is the frequency of the longitudinal oscillations of a plasma in a magnetic field defined by the formula (5.3). In this case we obtain from (4.10) and (6.10)

$$n_-^2 = -\frac{B}{A_0}; \quad \varkappa_- = \beta_e^{2l-3}\,\frac{\sigma n_-^2 \sin^2\theta}{B}\,e^{-z_-^2}, \tag{6.11}$$

where $A_0 \to 0$ when $\omega \to \omega_1(\theta)$, and the quantities A_0 and B are defined by the formulae (5.11) and (5.13). The expressions (6.11) can no longer be used, however, if $|1 - [\omega_1(\theta)/\omega]| \lesssim \beta_e$. In this case the behaviour of the refractive index of a extraordinary wave is essentially determined by the thermal motion of the electrons in the plasma. In addition, as follows from section 5, a plasma wave may appear when $\omega \approx \omega_1(\theta)$.

The refractive indices of an extraordinary wave ($n_- = n_2$) and a plasma wave ($n = n_3$) are defined by the formulae (5.15) and (5.16). Under the double resonance conditions $\omega \approx \omega_1(\theta) \approx l\omega_e$ ($l = 3, 4, \ldots$) the damping coefficient of an extraordinary wave is of the form [Stepanov, 1960]

$$\varkappa_2 = \frac{\beta_e^{2l-3}\sigma n_2^2 \sin^2\theta}{A_0 n_2^2 + 2B}\,e^{-z^2}, \tag{6.12}$$

where

$$\sigma = \frac{\sqrt{\pi}\,(l n_2 \sin\theta)^{2l-2}\Omega_e^2}{2^{2l} l!\,|\cos\theta|\,\omega_e^2}; \quad z = \frac{\omega - l\omega_e}{\omega\beta_e n_2 \cos\theta};$$

the quantities A_0 and B are defined by the formulae (5.11) and (5.13).

We notice that when $|1 - (\omega_1/\omega)| \gg \beta_e$ and $\omega < \omega_1$ the formula (6.12) turns into the expression (6.11) for $\varkappa_-$.

Let us estimate the damping coefficient $\varkappa_2$ when $|1 - (\omega_1/\omega)| \sim \beta_e$ and $|1 - (l\omega_e/\omega)| \sim \beta_e n_2$. In this case $n_2 \sim \beta_e^{-1/2}$ and $\varkappa_2 \sim \beta_e^{l-5/2}\,n_2$, i.e. the damping coefficient is small compared with the refractive index, in particular when $l = 3$ $\varkappa_2/n_2 \sim \beta_e^{1/2}$ and the damping length is of the order of $\delta \sim c/\omega$.

We should mention that if $\omega \approx l\omega_e$ but ω is not close to $\omega_1(\theta)$ ($|1 - \omega_1/\omega| \sim 1$), then in order of magnitude the damping coefficient is equal to $\varkappa \sim \beta_e^{2l-3}$. Under conditions of double resonance, therefore, the damping coefficient of an extraordinary wave $\varkappa_- = \varkappa_2$ is increased by a factor of β_e^{-l} ($l = 3, 4, \ldots$).

We notice that when $\omega \approx l\omega_e \approx \omega_1(\theta)$, where $l = 3, 4, \ldots$, the propagation of a plasma wave is impossible ($n_3^2 < 0$).

Cyclotron damping of extraordinary and plasma waves is particularly great when $\omega \approx 2\omega_e \approx \omega_1(\theta)$. In this case the formula (6.12) becomes unusable when $|z| \lesssim 1$ since it is derived on the assumption that $\varkappa_2 \ll n_2$. The refractive indices of these waves should be determined in accordance with (4.6) by the equation

$$[A_0 + iA_2\beta_e w(z)\, n]\, n^2 + B = 0, \qquad (6.13)$$

where

$$A_2 = \frac{\sqrt{\pi}\sin^4\theta\, \Omega_e^2}{4\cos\theta\, \omega_e^2}; \quad z = \frac{\omega - 2\omega_e}{\omega\beta_e n\cos\theta};$$

the quantities A_0 and B are defined by the formulae (5.11) and (5.13).

It follows from this equation that when $|A_0|^3 \sim |1 - \omega_1/\omega|^3 \sim \beta_e^l$ and $|1 - 2\omega_e/\omega| \lesssim \beta_e^{3/2}$ extraordinary and plasma waves are strongly damped ($\mathrm{Re}\, n \sim \mathrm{Im}\, n$). In order of magnitude the refractive indices are determined by the formula

$$\mathrm{Re}\, n_{2,3} \sim \mathrm{Im}\, n_{2,3} \sim \beta_e^{-1/3}. \qquad (6.14)$$

4. Cherenkov Damping of Low-Frequency Electron Oscillations

In the preceding sub-sections we have discussed the propagation of waves whose phase velocity is far greater than the electron thermal velocity. In this case the Cherenkov damping of the waves is exponentially small (it is proportional to e^{-z^2}, where $z = \omega/k_{\|}v_e \gg 1$). If $z \lesssim 1$ the propagation of oscillations in which only the plasma electrons take part becomes impossible because of strong Cherenkov damping.

The weakly damped low-frequency electron oscillations which can be propagated in a high-density plasma when $\Omega_e^2 \gg \omega\omega_e$ are the exception. The frequencies of these oscillations lie in the range

$\omega_i \ll \omega \ll \omega_e$, whilst the angle between the direction of propagation and the external magnetic field is not close to $\pi/2$.† Remembering that when these inequalities are satisfied $|\varepsilon_{33}| \gg |\varepsilon_{12}|$ and $|\varepsilon_{12}| \gg |\varepsilon_{11}|, |\varepsilon_{22}|, |\varepsilon_{23}|, |\varepsilon_{13}|$ and assuming that $kv_e \ll \omega_e$ we obtain from the dispersion equation (4.6) the following expressions for the frequencies and refractive indices of these oscillations:

$$\omega = \omega_e |\cos\theta| \frac{k^2 c^2}{\Omega_e^2}; \quad n = \frac{\Omega_e}{\sqrt{\omega\omega_e |\cos\theta|}}. \tag{6.15}$$

The damping coefficient of these oscillations caused by Cherenkov absorption by the plasma electrons is determined by the formula [Stepanov, 1963]

$$\frac{\varkappa}{n} = \frac{\sqrt{\pi}}{4} \frac{\sin^2\theta}{|\cos\theta|} \frac{\omega}{\omega_e} \varphi(z), \tag{6.16}$$

where

$$z = (\beta_e n \cos\theta)^{-1},$$

$$\varphi(z) = \frac{1}{2z}\left[1 + \frac{1}{|1 + i\sqrt{\pi}\, z w(z)|^2}\right] e^{-z^2}. \tag{6.17}$$

If $z \gg 1$, then $\varphi(z) \approx 2z^3 e^{-z^2}$ and the damping in this case is exponentially small.‡ When the phase velocity decreases, i.e. when z increases, the damping increases.

If $z \lesssim 1$, then $\varphi(z) \sim 1/z$ and $\varkappa/n \sim kv_e/\omega_e$. A graph of the function $\varphi(z)$ is shown in Fig. 5.

7. Ion-Cyclotron and Magnetohydrodynamic Waves

1. Low-Frequency Oscillations of a Plasma at Low Pressure

Let us pass on to an investigation of the oscillation spectra of a plasma in the range of frequencies less than or of the order of the ion-cyclotron frequency. We shall first determine the spectra of the low-frequency oscillations in the hydrodynamic approximation ($T_\alpha = 0$).

† These waves are sometimes called whistling atmospherics or simply whistlers, and also helicons.

‡ The expressions for $\varkappa$ when $z \gg 1$ are derived in papers by Shafranov [1958c] and Gershman [1958b].

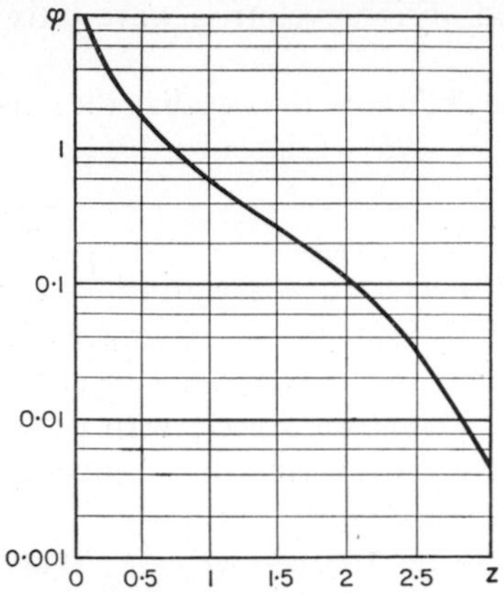

FIG. 5. Graph of function $\varphi(z)$.

Remembering that in the low-frequency range (for values of θ not close to $\pi/2$) $\cos^2\theta\,|\varepsilon_3| \gg |\varepsilon_1|, |\varepsilon_2|$, we obtain from the dispersion equation (4.6) the following expressions for the squares of the eigen frequencies of the plasma oscillations [Shafranov, 1958b]

$$\omega_j^2(k,\theta) = \tfrac{1}{2}k^2V_A^2[1+\cos^2\theta + r\cos^2\theta \pm \sqrt{(1+\cos^2\theta + r\cos^2\theta)^2 - 4\cos^2\theta}] \quad (j = 1, 2), \tag{7.1}$$

where $r = k^2c^2/\Omega_i^2$ and V_A is the Alfvén velocity

$$V_A = c\,\frac{\omega_i}{\Omega_i} = \frac{H_0}{\sqrt{4\pi n_0 m_i}} \tag{7.2}$$

(when deriving these expressions it was assumed that $V_A \ll c$).

The expressions (7.1) can be considerably simplified in special cases. If $r \gg 1$, then from (7.1) follows the expression (6.15) for the frequency of the low-frequency electron oscillations

$$\omega_2(k,\theta) = \omega_i\cos\theta\,\frac{k^2c^2}{\Omega_i^2} = \omega_e\cos\theta\,\frac{k^2c^2}{\Omega_e^2}. \tag{7.3}$$

When $r \gg 1$ the frequency ω is close to the ion-cyclotron frequency

$$\omega_1(k,\theta) = \omega_i\left(1 - \frac{1+\cos^2\theta}{2\cos^2\theta}\,\frac{\Omega_i^2}{k^2c^2}\right). \tag{7.4}$$

A wave with this frequency is called an ion-cyclotron wave [Stix, 1957].

When $r \ll 1$ the two frequencies $\omega_j(k, \theta)$ are far less than the ion-cyclotron frequency ω_i [Aström, 1950, 1951; Ginzburg, 1951]:

$$\omega_1 = kV_A \cos\theta; \quad \omega_2 = kV_A. \tag{7.5}$$

These expressions are the same as the well-known expressions for the frequencies of the Alfvén and fast magnetosonic waves in magnetohydrodynamics (provided that the Alfvén velocity is far greater than the velocity of sound). Therefore a wave with a frequency ω_1 is also called an Alfvén wave and a wave with a frequency ω_2 a fast magnetosonic wave.

The refractive indices of waves with the frequencies $\omega_j(k, \theta)$ are determined by the formulae [Shafranov, 1958 b]

$$n_j^2 = \frac{1}{2\cos^2\theta}\Big[\varepsilon_1(1 + \cos^2\theta) \pm \sqrt{\varepsilon_1^2(1 + \cos^2\theta)^2 - 4(\varepsilon_1^2 - \varepsilon_2^2)\cos^2\theta}\Big], \tag{7.6}$$

where

$$\varepsilon_1 = 1 - \frac{\Omega_i^2}{\omega^2 - \omega_i^2}; \quad \varepsilon_2 = -\frac{\Omega_i^2 \omega}{\omega_i(\omega^2 - \omega_i^2)}.$$

If $\omega \gg \omega_i$ the expression (6.14) follows from the formula (7.6). When $\omega \approx \omega_i$ and $V_A \ll c$

$$n_1^2 = \frac{n_A^2}{\dfrac{\omega_i}{\omega} - 1} \frac{1 + \cos^2\theta}{2\cos^2\theta}, \tag{7.7}$$

$$n_2^2 = \frac{n_A^2}{1 + \cos^2\theta}, \tag{7.8}$$

where

$$n_A = \frac{c}{V_A} \gg 1.$$

The refractive index n_1 of an ion-cyclotron wave approaches ∞ as $\omega \to \omega_i$. This wave can be propagated only if $\omega < \omega_i$. It should be pointed out that when deriving the formula (7.6) we neglected quantities of the order of $|\varepsilon_1/\varepsilon_3| \sim (m_e/m_i)\,\omega/(\omega_i - \omega)$ compared with unity, so in the expression (7.7) the difference $(\omega_i/\omega) - 1$ should be large compared with m_e/m_i.

If $V_A \ll c$ and $\omega \lesssim \omega_i$, then in order of magnitude $|\varepsilon_1| \sim |\varepsilon_2| \sim n_A^2$ and $n_j \sim n_A$. Therefore in order of magnitude the phase velocities of the waves with the frequencies $\omega_j(k,\theta)$ are the same as the Alfvén velocity.

The expressions (7.1)–(7.8) are derived for a "cold" plasma, i.e. when the inequalities (4.11) are satisfied. It follows in particular from these inequalities that the phase velocity of waves with the frequencies $\omega_j(k, \theta)$ should be far greater than the thermal velocity of the electrons, i.e. $V_A \gg v_e$. In actual fact the expressions (7.1)–(7.8) can also be used in the more general case (provided $\omega_j(k, \theta)$ as not close to ω_i), viz. when the inequalities

$$n_0(T_e + T_i) \ll \frac{H_0^2}{8\pi}$$

are satisfied. In this case the phase velocities of waves with frequencies $\omega_j(k, \theta)$ will be far greater than the thermal velocity of the ions but may be of the order of or less than the thermal velocity of the electrons.

The expressions (7.4) and (7.7) can be used only when $|(\omega - \omega_i)/k_\parallel v_i| \gg 1$, i.e. when $|1 - \omega_i/\omega|^{3/2} \gg v_i/V_A$. In this case the ion-cyclotron damping is exponentially small.

2. Cherenkov Damping of Low-Frequency Oscillations

Let us estimate the damping coefficients $\varkappa_j$ of waves with the frequencies $\omega_j(k, \theta)$ caused by Cherenkov absorption by the plasma's electrons. Using the equalities (4.4) and (4.6) we can show that [Stepanov, 1960]

$$\varkappa_j = \frac{\sqrt{\pi}}{4}\,\frac{m_e}{m_i}\,\beta_e\,\frac{p_1}{p_2}\,e^{-z^2}, \tag{7.9}$$

where

$$z = (\beta_e n_j \cos\theta)^{-1};$$

$$p_1 = n_A^2 \tan^2\theta\,(\varepsilon_1 - n_j^2\cos^2\theta) + \frac{\omega^2 n_j^2 \sin^2\theta\,(\varepsilon_1^2 - \varepsilon_2^2 - \varepsilon_1 n_j^2)}{\omega_i^2 n_A^2 |1 + i\sqrt{\pi}\,z w(z)|^2};$$

and

$$p_2 = \varepsilon_1 \frac{1 + \cos^2 \theta}{|\cos \theta|} - 2 |\cos \theta| n_j^2 .$$

If $\omega \sim \omega_i$, $n \sim n_A$, $V_A \lesssim v_e$, then $\varkappa \sim (m_e/m_i)(v_e/V_A) n_A$.

When $\omega \ll \omega_i$ the formulae (7.9) define the damping coefficients of Alfvén and fast magnetosonic waves [see also Stepanov, 1958b; Braginskii and Kazantsev, 1958; Gershman, 1958a]

$$\frac{\varkappa_1}{n_1} = \frac{\sqrt{\pi}}{4} \frac{m_e}{m_i} \frac{v_e}{V_A} \frac{\omega^2}{\omega_i^2} \times$$

$$\times \left[\cot^2 \theta + \frac{\tan^2 \theta}{|1 + i\sqrt{\pi}\, z w(z)|^2}\right] e^{-z^2}, \tag{7.10}$$

$$\frac{\varkappa_2}{n_2} = \frac{\sqrt{\pi}}{4} \frac{m_e}{m_i} \frac{v_e}{V_A} \frac{\sin^2 \theta}{|\cos \theta|} e^{-z^2}, \tag{7.11}$$

where $n_1 = n_A/|\cos \theta|$ and $n_2 = n_A$ are the refractive indices of the Alfvén and fast magnetosonic waves.

It can be seen from (7.10) and (7.11) that the Cherenkov damping of an Alfvén wave is much less than the Cherenkov damping of a magnetosonic wave ($\varkappa_1/\varkappa_2 \sim \omega^2/\omega_i^2 \ll 1$ when $z < 1$). The damping of an Alfvén wave is slight even when $V_A \sim v_i$, when the propagation of a fast magnetosonic wave and waves with frequencies of the order of ω_i become generally impossible because of strong Cherenkov absorption in the ion gas ($\varkappa_j \sim n_j$).

The formula (7.10) determines the Alfvén wave damping caused by Cherenkov absorption in the plasma's electron component only. This formula can be used when $V_A \gg v_i$. In a plasma with a low magnetic pressure ($V_A \lesssim v_i$) the Alfvén waves are chiefly absorbed by the plasma's ions. If we take into consideration Cherenkov absorption by both the electrons and the ions of the plasma, then we obtain for the Alfvén wave damping coefficient the expression

$$\frac{\varkappa_1}{n_1} = \frac{\omega^2}{\omega_i^2} \operatorname{Im} q, \tag{7.12}$$

where

$$q = \frac{a(a\cot^2\theta\, f_3 + 2\beta_i^2 n_A^2 f_1)}{2f_3 - 2\beta_i^2 n_A^2(2f_2 f_3 - f_1^2)} - \frac{\beta_i^2 n_A^2 \tan^2\theta}{f_3 - \beta_i^2 n_A^2(2f_2 f_3 - f_1^2)};$$

$$f_1 = i\sqrt{\pi}\,[z_i w(z_i) - z_e w(z_e)];$$

$$f_2 = i\sqrt{\pi}\left[z_i w(z_i) + \frac{T_e}{T_i}\, z_e w(z_e)\right];$$

$$f_3 = 1 + \frac{T_i}{T_e} + i\sqrt{\pi}\left[z_i w(z_i) + \frac{T_i}{T_e}\, z_e w(z_e)\right];$$

$$a = 1 + \frac{v_i^2}{2V_A^2}\left(1 - \frac{3}{2}\tan^2\theta\right);$$

$$z_\alpha = (\beta_\alpha n_A)^{-1} = \frac{V_A}{v_\alpha}; \quad \beta_\alpha = \frac{v_\alpha}{c}.$$

When $v_i \ll V_A$ the Cherenkov damping caused by the ions is exponentially small and it may be ignored. In this case the formula (7.12) is the same as the formula (7.10).

If $v_i \sim V_A$, then in order of magnitude $\varkappa_1/n_A \sim \omega^2/\omega_i^2 \ll 1$. In this case the Cherenkov absorption takes place chiefly in the plasma's ion component: in order of magnitude absorption by the ions is $[(m_i/m_e)(T_e/T_i)]^{1/2}$ times greater than absorption by the electrons.

If $v_i \ll V_A$, then

$$\frac{\varkappa_1}{n_1} = \frac{1}{32\pi^{1/2}}\left(\frac{\omega}{\omega_i}\right)^2\left(\frac{v_i}{V_A}\right)^3 (2\cot\theta - 3\tan\theta)^2. \quad (7.13)$$

This formula shows that the Alfvén wave damping is great ($\varkappa_1 \sim n_1$) only in a plasma with a low magnetic pressure, when $V_A \lesssim v_i(\omega/\omega_i)^{2/3}$.

We notice that the expressions (7.10)–(7.13) for the damping coefficients of fast magnetosonic and Alfvén waves become unusable for small angles θ (the expressions for $\varkappa_1$ and $\varkappa_2$ when $\theta \ll 1$ are given in a paper by Stepanov [1958b].

3. Cyclotron Damping of Low-Frequency Oscillations

Let us examine the absorption of waves with a frequency ω close to the ion-cyclotron frequency ω_i.

If the frequency ω approaches ω_i the cyclotron damping of a wave with the refractive index (7.4) rises and in the $|1 - (\omega_i/\omega)|^{3/2} \lesssim v_i/V_A$ frequency range this wave becomes strongly damped. In this case the real and imaginary parts of the refractive index are the same in order of magnitude:

$$\operatorname{Re} n_1 \sim \operatorname{Im} n_1 \sim \left(\frac{c^3}{V_A^2 v_i}\right)^{1/3}. \tag{7.14}$$

If

$$\left|1 - \frac{\omega_i}{\omega}\right|^{3/2} \ll \frac{v_i}{V_A},$$

we have

$$n_1 = \frac{\sqrt{3} + i}{2}\left(\frac{\sqrt{\pi}\,(1 + \cos^2\theta)}{2\,|\cos^3\theta|}\,\frac{c^3}{V_A^2 v_i}\right)^{1/3}. \tag{7.15}$$

Under these conditions a wave penetrates the plasma to a depth of the order of

$$\delta_i = \left(\frac{V_A^2 v_i}{\sqrt{\pi}\,\omega_i^3}\right)^{1/3} \tag{7.16}$$

(the case of anomalous skin effect).

For example, if $n_0 \sim 10^{13}$ cm^{-3}, $T_i \sim 100$ eV, $H_0 \sim 10^4$ oe, then $\omega_i \sim 10^8$ sec^{-1}, $V_A \sim 10^9$ cm/sec, $v_i \sim 10^7$ cm/sec and the depth of penetration is $\delta_i \sim 3$ cm.

A wave with the refractive index n_2 defined by the formula (7.8) is subject to little damping:

$$\frac{\varkappa_2}{n_2} = \frac{|\cos\theta|\sin^4\theta}{4\sqrt{\pi}\,(1 + \cos^2\theta)^{5/2}}\,\frac{v_i}{V_A}\,f(z), \tag{7.17}$$

where

$$f(z) = \frac{e^{-z^2}}{|w(z)|^2}, \quad z = \left(1 - \frac{\omega_i}{\omega}\right)\left(1 + \frac{1}{\cos^2\theta}\right)^{1/2}\frac{V_A}{v_i}.$$

When $|z| \gg 1$ the quantity $\varkappa_2$ is exponentially small.†

† The expressions for the damping coefficients of the two waves were derived in Shafranov's paper [1958b] when $|(\omega - \omega_i)/k_{||} v_i| \gg 1$.

If $|z| \lesssim 1$, then $\varkappa_2/n_2 \sim v_i/V_A \ll 1$. For the example discussed above the wavelength of a weakly damped wave in the plasma is $\lambda \sim V_A/\omega_i \sim 10$ cm and the damping length for $|z| \lesssim 1$ is

$$\delta \sim \lambda \frac{V_A}{v_i} \sim 100\lambda \sim 10^3 \text{ cm}.$$

4. Cyclotron Damping at Multiple Ion Gyro-Resonance

In the case of the multiple ion gyro-resonances $\omega \approx l\omega_i$ $(l = 2, 3, \ldots)$ the damping coefficient of waves with the refractive indices n_1 and n_2 determined by the formula (7.6) is of the form [Stepanov, 1960]

$$\frac{\varkappa_j}{n_j} = \sigma \frac{n_A^2[(1 + \cos^2\theta)\, n_j^2 - 2\varepsilon_1 + 2\varepsilon_2]}{2\cos^2\theta\, n_j^4 - \varepsilon_1(1 + \cos^2\theta)\, n_j^2}, \tag{7.18}$$

where

$$\sigma = \frac{\sqrt{\pi}\, l^{2l-2} (\sin\theta)^{2l-2}}{2^{2l} l!\, |\cos\theta|} (\beta_i n_j)^{2l-3} e^{-z^2}$$

and

$$z = \frac{\omega - l\omega_i}{\omega\beta_i n_j \cos\theta}.$$

If $n_A \gg 1$, then when $\omega > \omega_i$ only one wave with a refractive index $n_2 \sim n_A$ can be propagated; in this case in order of magnitude

$$\frac{\varkappa_2}{n_2} \sim \left(\frac{v_i}{V_A}\right)^{2l-3}, \quad \left(\left|1 - \frac{l\omega_i}{\omega}\right| \lesssim \frac{v_i}{V_A}\right).$$

In particular if $\omega = 2\omega_i$, then $\varkappa_2/n_2 \sim v_i/V_A$, i.e. the damping of this wave is the same as when $\omega = \omega_i$.

The cyclotron damping increases when the plasma density increases. For example when $n_0 \sim 10^{15}$ cm^{-3}, $T_i \sim 100$ eV, $H_0 \sim 10^4$ oe the penetration depth of a strongly damped wave when $\omega = \omega_i$ is $\delta \sim 1$ cm, and the penetration depth of weakly damped wave when $\omega = l\omega_i$ $(l = 1, 2)$ is $\delta \sim 10$ cm.

It can be seen from this that high-frequency heating of a high-density plasma under conditions of cyclotron resonance by means of a strongly damped wave becomes ineffective because of the low penetration of the high-frequency field into the plasma. In this case the high-frequency energy is absorbed by the ions located in a narrow layer $\sim\delta_i$ thick on the periphery of the plasma.

Resonance at a frequency $\omega = \omega_i$ or $\omega = 2\omega_i$ using a weakly damped wave may prove more efficient for heating a high-temperature, high-density plasma. Although this wave is far more weakly absorbed than a strongly damped one when $\omega = \omega_i$ its absorption occurs over a large volume of the plasma and the total amount of energy absorbed may be greater than during a resonance $\omega = \omega_i$ using a strongly damped wave.

8. Low-frequency Oscillations of a Non-Isothermal Plasma in a Magnetic Field

1. Longitudinal Oscillations of a Non-Isothermal Plasma at Low Pressure

As has been shown in section 3, in a strongly non-isothermal plasma with hot electrons and cold ions low-frequency longitudinal weakly damped oscillations may be propagated with a frequency and damping decrement

$$\omega = \omega_s(k) = \frac{kV_s}{(1 + k^2a^2)^{1/2}},$$

$$\gamma = \gamma_s = \sqrt{\frac{\pi m_e}{8m_i}}\,\frac{kV_s}{(1 + k^2a^2)^2}, \tag{8.1}$$

where $V_s = \sqrt{T_e/m_i}$ (the conditions $v_i \ll \omega/k \ll v_e$ are satisfied for these oscillations).

Low-frequency longitudinal oscillations (to be more precise, almost longitudinal oscillations) can also be propagated in a strongly non-isothermal plasma located in an external magnetic field [Stepanov, 1958d]. The dispersion equation for these oscillations is of the form

$$A = \varepsilon_{11}\sin^2\theta + 2\varepsilon_{13}\sin\theta\cos\theta + \varepsilon_{33}\cos^2\theta = 0. \tag{8.2}$$

It is obvious that the dispersion law (8.1) does not change in the case of weak magnetic fields when both the electrons and the ions of the plasma may be considered non-magnetized, i.e. when the wavelength is far less than the Larmor radii of the ions and the electrons, $kv_\alpha \gg \omega_\alpha$.

For stronger magnetic fields the electrons may be considered to be magnetized ($kv_e \ll \omega_e$) and the ions to be non-magnetized ($kv_i \gg \omega_i$). Assuming that $v_i \ll \omega/k \ll v_e \cos\theta$, we obtain from the dispersion equation (8.2) the following expressions for the frequency and damping decrement:

$$\omega = \omega_s(k), \quad \gamma = \frac{\gamma_s}{|\cos\theta|}. \tag{8.3}$$

The damping of these oscillations is caused by Cherenkov absorption by the plasma electrons.

For still stronger magnetic fields the ions are also magnetized ($kv_i \ll \omega_i$). Assuming that

$$v_i \ll \frac{\omega}{k\cos\theta} \ll v_e, \quad \frac{|\omega - \omega_i|}{kv_i\cos\theta} \gg 1,$$

we obtain from the dispersion equation (8.2) the following expressions for the frequencies of the longitudinal oscillations of a plasma in a strong magnetic field

$$\omega_j^2(k,\theta) = \tfrac{1}{2}(\omega_s^2 + \omega_i^2) \pm \tfrac{1}{2}\sqrt{(\omega_s^2 + \omega_i^2)^2 - 4\omega_s^2\omega_i^2\cos^2\theta}, \tag{8.4}$$

where $j = 1, 2$ depending on the sign in front of the radical.

When the angle θ changes from 0 to $\pi/2$ the frequency $\omega_1(k,\theta)$ increases from $\omega_1 = \max(\omega_s, \omega_i)$ to $\omega_1 = \sqrt{\omega_s^2 + \omega_i^2}$ and the frequency $\omega_2(k,\theta)$ decreases from $\omega_2 = \min(\omega_s, \omega_i)$ when $\theta = 0$ to zero when $\theta = \pi/2$.

We should point out that one of the expressions (8.4) approaches ω_i when $\theta \to 0$: $\omega_j = \omega_i[1 + \omega_s^2\theta^2/2(\omega^2 - \omega_s^2)]$. However, this expression can be used only when $\theta^2 \gg (2kv_i/\omega_i)(|\omega_i^2 - \omega_s^2|/\omega_s^2)$.

In the extreme case of $\omega_i \gg kV_s$ and $ka \ll 1$ the formulae (8.4) become simpler

$$\omega_1 = \omega_i\left(1 + \frac{k^2V_s^2\sin^2\theta}{2\omega_i^2}\right), \tag{8.5}$$

$$\omega_2 = kV_s|\cos\theta|. \tag{8.6}$$

The expression (8.6) determines the frequency of a slow magnetosonic wave [Bernstein, 1958; Stepanov, 1958d].

The frequencies $\omega_j(k, \theta)$ are shown as a function of the wave vector k for $ka \ll 1$ in Fig. 6.

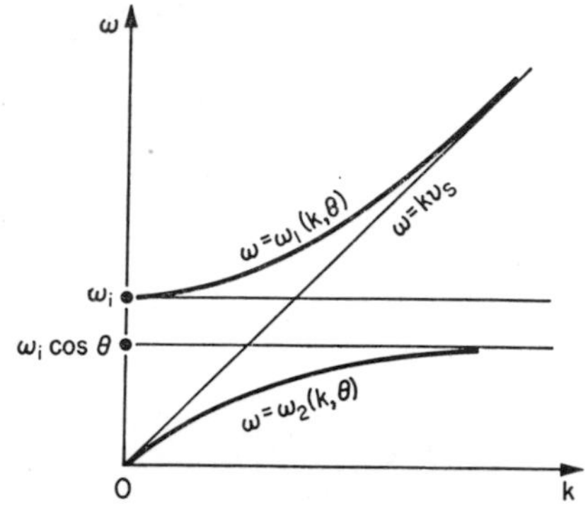

FIG. 6. Frequencies $\omega = \omega_j(k, \theta)$ as functions of wave vector k.

The refractive index of waves with the frequencies $\omega_j(k, \theta)$ when $ka \ll 1$ is determined by the expression

$$n^2 = \frac{c^2}{V_s^2} \frac{\omega^2 - \omega_i^2}{\omega^2 - \omega_i^2 \cos^2 \theta}. \tag{8.7}$$

The damping of longitudinal low-frequency oscillations of a plasma in a magnetic field is caused chiefly by their Cherenkov absorption by the electrons. The damping decrement is

$$\gamma_e = \sqrt{\frac{\pi m_e}{8 m_i}} \frac{\omega_j^4 (\omega_j^2 - \omega_i^2)^2}{k^3 V_s^3 |\cos \theta| [\cos^2 \theta (\omega_j^2 - \omega_i^2)^2 + \sin^2 \theta \, \omega_j^4]}. \tag{8.8}$$

When $\omega_j \sim kV_s \sim \omega_i$, γ_e is of order of magnitude $\omega_i \sqrt{m_e/m_i}$. If $\omega_i \gg kV_s$ and $ka \ll 1$, then for the damping decrement of a slow magnetosonic wave we obtain the expression

$$\gamma_e = \sqrt{\frac{\pi m_e}{8 m_i}} \, k V_s |\cos \theta| . \tag{8.9}$$

We notice that if the frequency $\omega_1(k, \theta)$ is close to $l\omega_i$ ($l = 2, 3, \ldots$), then we must make allowance for cyclotron absorption of the oscillations in question by the plasma ions. The damping decrement caused by this absorption is determined by the formula

$$\gamma_i = \frac{\sqrt{\pi}\, l^4(l^2-1)^2 (\sin\theta)^{2l} k v_i}{2^{2l}\, |\cos\theta|^3\, [(l^2-1)^2 + \tan^2\theta\, l^4]} \left(\frac{k v_i}{\omega_i}\right)^{2l-4} e^{-z^2},$$

where (8.10)

$$z = \frac{\omega_2(k,\theta) - l\omega_i}{k v_i \cos\theta} \quad (l = 2, 3, \ldots).$$

If $\omega_2 \sim \omega_i \sim kV_s$ and $|z| \lesssim 1$, then $\gamma_i \sim (T_i/T_e)^{l-3/2}\omega_i$.

The Cherenkov absorption of the oscillations in question by the plasma ions and the cyclotron absorption by the ions at the basic harmonic are exponentially small when the conditions $|\omega/kv_i \cos\theta| \gg 1$ and $|(\omega - \omega_i)/kv_i \cos\theta| \gg 1$ are satisfied.

Let us glance at the conditions of applicability of the formulae (8.4). When deriving them it was assumed that $\omega \ll k_{\parallel} v_i$ and $kv_i \ll \omega_i$. Putting $\omega_j \sim kV_s \sim \omega_i$ we find that these inequalities are satisfied if $T_e \gg T_i$.

In addition, it must be borne in mind that the longitudinal oscillations can be isolated if the individual terms in the expression (8.2) are far greater than $|B|/n^2$ and $|C|/n^4$, where B and C are defined by the expressions (4.7). When $\omega_j \sim kV_s \sim \omega_i$ and $\cos\theta \sim 1$ these conditions are satisfied if $H_0^2/8\pi \gg n_0 T_e$, that is the magnetic pressure should be considerably higher than the gas kinetic pressure of the electron gas.

We notice that in an isothermal plasma the longitudinal low-frequency oscillations with a phase velocity considerably less than the thermal velocity of the ions are, generally speaking, strongly damped. Only when $\theta \approx \pi/2$ is it possible to propagate weakly damped longitudinal waves with a frequency ω close to the ion cyclotron frequency and a wavelength of the order of the Larmor radius of the ions ($kv_i \sim \omega_i$); the phase velocity of these waves along the direction of the external magnetic field is considerably less than the thermal velocity of the electrons [Drummond and Rosenbluth, 1962].

2. Magnetosonic Waves in a Non-Isothermal Plasma

Above we have discussed the low-frequency weakly damped magnetohydrodynamic waves which can be propagated in a plasma at low pressure, when the Alfvén velocity is far greater than the thermal velocity of the ions and the velocity of sound V_s. As the pressure rises the damping of these waves increases and when the magnetic pressure is comparable with the gas kinetic pressure of the plasma the propagation of magnetosonic waves becomes impossible if $T_e \lesssim T_i$. (At the same time the Alfvén wave remains weakly damped.)

The propagation conditions of low-frequency ($\omega \ll \omega_i$) waves are quite different in a strongly non-isothermal plasma with hot electrons and cold ions when $T_e \gg T_i$ [Stepanov, 1959a]. In this case the propagation of weakly damped magnetosonic waves in a plasma is possible if the inequality $V_A \gg v_i$ is satisfied.

The frequencies of these waves are determined by the formulae

$$\omega = kV_j \quad (j = 2, 3), \tag{8.11}$$

where

$$V_j^2 = \tfrac{1}{2}(V_A^2 + V_s^2) \pm \tfrac{1}{2}\sqrt{(V_A^2 + V_s^2)^2 - 4V_A^2 V_s^2 \cos^2\theta}. \tag{8.12}$$

(V_2 is the phase velocity of a fast and V_3 of a slow magnetosonic wave.)

The Alfvén wave frequency is defined by the previous formula

$$\omega_1 = kV_A|\cos\theta|. \tag{8.13}$$

The damping decrement of magnetosonic waves caused by Cherenkov absorption by the plasma electrons is determined by the formula

$$\gamma_j = \sqrt{\frac{\pi m_e}{8m_i}} \cdot \frac{kV_s \sin^2\theta}{|\cos\theta|} \times \\ \times \frac{V_j^4 + 2\cos^2\theta V_s^2(V_s^2\cos^2\theta - V_j^2)}{(V_j^2 - V_s^2\cos^2\theta)(2V_j^2 - V_A^2 - V_s^2)} \tag{8.14}$$

(the damping decrement of the Alfvén wave is determined by the formula (7.10) or (7.12)).

If $V_A \gg V_s$, then from the formulae (8.11) and (8.14) we obtain the expressions (7.5), (7.11) for ω_2 and γ_2 and the expressions (8.6), (8.9) for ω_3 and γ_3.

9. Excitation of Oscillations in a Plasma by External Currents

1. Excitation Intensity

In the preceding sections we have been studying the eigen oscillations of a plasma. They can be excited by external currents and beams of charged particles passing through the plasma.† Let us start by examining the first method of exciting oscillations [Aleksin and Stepanov, 1964; Glazov, Dubovoi and Rutkevich, 1962; Kondratenko, 1963].‡

The Fourier components of an electric field $\boldsymbol{E}(\boldsymbol{k}, \omega)$ in a plasma (which is assumed to be infinite) are connected with the Fourier components of the electric current density $\boldsymbol{j}(\boldsymbol{k}, \omega)$ by the relation

$$\Lambda_{ij}E_j = -\frac{4\pi i}{\omega} j_i, \tag{9.1}$$

where the tensor $\hat{\Lambda}$ is defined by the formula (3.6′). Hence

$$E_i = -\frac{4\pi i}{\omega\Delta} \lambda_{ik} j_k. \tag{9.2}$$

Here $\Delta = \det(\Lambda_{ij})$ and $\hat{\lambda} = \hat{\Lambda}^{-1}\Delta$ ($\hat{\Lambda}^{-1}$ is the inverse tensor to the tensor $\hat{\Lambda}$). The Fourier components of the magnetic field $\boldsymbol{H}(\boldsymbol{k}, \omega)$ are obviously

$$\boldsymbol{H} = \frac{c}{\omega} [\boldsymbol{k} \wedge \boldsymbol{E}].$$

By introducing the Green function (to be more precise, the Green tensor) of the equation (9.1)

$$G_{ij}(\boldsymbol{r}, t) = -\frac{i}{4\pi^3} \int\int \frac{\lambda_{ij}}{\omega\Delta} e^{i[(\boldsymbol{k}\cdot\boldsymbol{r}) - \omega t]} d^3\boldsymbol{k}\, d\omega, \tag{9.3}$$

we can determine the electric field as a function of the coordinates and time

$$E_i(\boldsymbol{r}, t) = \int\int G_{ij}(\boldsymbol{r} - \boldsymbol{r}', t - t') j_j(\boldsymbol{r}', t')\, d^3\boldsymbol{r}'\, dt'. \tag{9.4}$$

† We note that modulated beams of charged particles can be looked upon as external currents at the initial stage of passage of the beams through the plasma when the inverse action of the plasma oscillations on the beam are still insignificant.

‡ The second method will be considered in Chapter III.

Finally, by using this formula we can find the radiation intensity of waves excited by the external currents, i.e. the increase in plasma energy in unit time

$$P = -\int (\boldsymbol{j}\cdot\boldsymbol{E})\, d^3\boldsymbol{r}$$

$$= 8\pi^2 i \int \frac{\lambda_{ij}(\boldsymbol{k},\omega)}{\omega\Delta(\boldsymbol{k},\omega)} j_i(\boldsymbol{k},\omega)\, j_j^*(\boldsymbol{k},\omega')\, e^{i(\omega-\omega')t}\, d^3\boldsymbol{k}\, d\omega\, d\omega'. \tag{9.5}$$

2. *Excitation of Oscillations by Modulated Azimuthal Currents*

Let us start with the examination of the case when the excitation of the oscillations is achieved by modulated azimuthal currents flowing in the plasma along the surface of a cylinder of radius a with a density

$$j_\varphi = j_0 \cos(k_\parallel z - \omega t)\, \delta(r - a). \tag{9.6}$$

The plasma oscillations caused by this kind of current clearly have a frequency ω and a longitudinal wave vector component $k_\parallel$. Knowing ω and $k_\parallel$ in the dispersion equation (4.6) we can find the transverse component $k_\perp$ of the wave vector of the oscillations excited in the plasma.

In the case of a cold plasma the dispersion equation leads to the following expressions for the transverse refractive index $n_\perp = k_\perp c/\omega$:

$$n_{\perp j}^2 = \frac{1}{2\varepsilon_1}\Big\{(\varepsilon_1 + \varepsilon_3)(\varepsilon_1 - n_\parallel^2) - \varepsilon_2^2$$

$$\pm \sqrt{[(\varepsilon_1 + \varepsilon_3)(\varepsilon_1 - n_\parallel^2) - \varepsilon_2^2]^2 - 4\varepsilon_1\varepsilon_3[(n_\parallel^2 - \varepsilon_1)^2 - \varepsilon_2^2]}\Big\}, \tag{9.7}$$

where $n_\parallel = k_\parallel c/\omega$ and the $\pm$ signs correspond to the values $j = 1, 2$.

The radiation intensity of oscillations with the transverse refractive index $n_{\perp j}$ per unit length of the cylinder is determined by the formula [Aleksin and Stepanov, 1964]

$$P^{(j)} = \frac{2\pi^3 j_0^2 a^2}{c^2} \frac{\omega(-1)^j[\varepsilon_3(\varepsilon_1 - n_\parallel^2) - \varepsilon_1 n_j^2]}{\varepsilon_1(n_1^2 - n_2^2)} J_1^2(\alpha n_j), \tag{9.8}$$

where $\alpha = a\omega/c$ and $n_j \equiv n_{\perp j}$. Radiation clearly occurs only if $n_j^2 > 0$. For negative and complex values of n_j^2 the radiation intensity in a cold plasma in the absence of collisions is zero.

The expressions (9.7) and (9.8) are derived for a "cold" plasma but they can also be used when $T_\alpha \neq 0$ provided that the conditions (4.11) are satisfied.

If the frequency is close to the electron gyro-frequency ω_e we must allow for electron thermal motion. By using the formula (9.5) we can show that when $n_0 T_e \ll H_0^2/8\pi$ the radiation intensity is

$$P = \frac{2\pi^3 j_0^2 a^2 \omega \varepsilon_3}{c^2 n_\parallel^2} \operatorname{Im} J_1(\alpha n_\perp)\, H_1^{(1)}(\alpha n_\perp), \qquad (9.9)$$

where

$$\varepsilon_3 = 1 - \frac{\Omega_e^2}{\omega^2}, \quad n_\perp^2 = 2\varepsilon_3 \left[1 + i\,\frac{(k_\parallel \delta_e)^3}{w(z)}\right];$$

$$\delta_e = \left(\frac{c^2 v_e}{\sqrt{\pi}\,\Omega_e^2 \omega_e}\right)^{1/3}; \quad z = \frac{\omega - \omega_e}{k_\parallel v_e}.$$

We also give the formulae for the radiation intensity in the case of ion-cyclotron resonance, i.e. when $\omega \approx \omega_i$:

$$P = \frac{2\pi^3 j_0^2 a^2 \omega}{c^2} \operatorname{Re} J_1(\alpha n_\perp)\, H_1^{(1)}(\alpha n_\perp), \qquad (9.10)$$

where

$$n_\perp^2 = \frac{(\varepsilon_1 - n_\parallel^2)^2 - \varepsilon_2^2}{\varepsilon_1 - n_\parallel^2}, \quad \varepsilon_1 = i\sigma - \frac{1}{4} n_A^2;$$

$$\varepsilon_2 = i\sigma - \frac{3}{4} n_A^2; \quad \sigma = \frac{\sqrt{\pi}\, n_A^2 \omega w(z)}{2k_\parallel v_i};$$

$$z = \frac{\omega - \omega_i}{k_\parallel v_i}.$$

3. Excitation of Oscillations by Modulated Axial Currents

Let us now examine the excitation of oscillations in a plasma by a modulated current flowing along the magnetic field with a density

$$\left.\begin{aligned} j_z &= \frac{j_0}{\pi a^2}\cos(k_\parallel z - \omega t) \quad (r < a) \\ j_z &= 0 \qquad\qquad\qquad\qquad\quad (r > a) \end{aligned}\right\}, \tag{9.11}$$

where j_0 is the total intensity of the current.

In the case of a cold plasma the mean radiation power of waves with a transverse refractive index n_j determined by the formula (9.7) is

$$P^{(j)} = \frac{2\pi j_0^2\omega(-1)^j[(n_\parallel^2 - \varepsilon_1)\,n_j^2 + (n_\parallel^2 - \varepsilon_1)^2 - \varepsilon_2^2]}{c^2\varepsilon_1(n_1^2 - n_2^2)} \cdot \frac{J_1^2(\alpha n_j)}{\alpha^2 n_j^2},$$

where (9.12)

$$\alpha = \frac{a\omega}{c}, \quad j = 1, 2.$$

If the frequency approaches $\sqrt{\Omega_e^2 + \omega_e^2}$ (the quantity $\sqrt{\Omega_e^2 + \omega_e^2}$ is the frequency of the plasma's longitudinal oscillations when $\theta = \pi/2$), then one of the transverse refractive indices (9.7) approaches infinity:

$$n_2^2 = -\frac{(1 + n_\parallel^2)\,\omega_e^2}{\omega^2\varepsilon_1} \to \infty \tag{9.13}$$

(since $\varepsilon_1 = (\omega^2 - \Omega_e^2 - \omega_e^2)/(\omega^2 - \omega_e^2) \to 0$). In this case the expression for the radiation intensity $P^{(2)}$ simplifies to

$$P^{(2)} = -\frac{2\pi j_0^2\omega n_\parallel^2}{c^2\varepsilon_1}\,\frac{J_1^2(\alpha n_2)}{\alpha^2 n_2^2}, \tag{9.14}$$

i.e. the intensity of radiation by a linear current ($a \to 0$) rises as ω approaches $\sqrt{\Omega_e^2 + \omega_e^2}$ [Kondratenko, 1963].

The expression (9.13) derived for a cold plasma can, however, be used only for frequencies which are not very close to the resonance frequency. In the range of frequencies close to $\sqrt{\Omega_e^2 + \omega_e^2}$ the behaviour of the refractive index n_2 is essentially determined by the thermal motion of the plasma's electrons. In addition, when $\omega \approx \sqrt{\Omega_e^2 + \omega_e^2}$ the propagation of a plasma wave becomes possible (see section 5). The transverse refractive index of an extraordinary wave n_2 and the transverse refractive index of a plasma wave n_3 when thermal motion of the plasma electrons is taken into consideration are determined by the formulae

$$n_j^2 = \frac{2\Omega_e^2\omega_e^2(1 + n_\parallel^2)}{\omega^4\sqrt{\varkappa}}\varphi_\pm(x) \quad (j = 2, 3), \tag{9.15}$$

where

$$x = \frac{\omega^2 - \Omega_e^2 - \omega_e^2}{\omega^2\sqrt{\varkappa}}, \quad \varkappa = \frac{6\beta_e^2\Omega_e^4\omega_e^2(1 + n_\parallel^2)}{\omega^4\,|\omega^2 - 4\omega_e^2|}$$

(the function $\varphi_\pm(x)$ is defined by the formula (5.16) in which we must take $\alpha = \text{sign}\,(1 - 2\omega_e/\omega)$).

The radiation intensity of these waves is determined by the expressions [Aleksin and Stepanov, 1964]

$$P^{(j)} = \frac{4\pi j_0^2 n_\parallel^2\,|\omega^2 - 4\omega_e^2|\,J_1^2(\alpha n_j)}{3\beta_e^2c^2\omega(n_1^2 - n_2^2)\,\alpha^2 n_j^2} \quad (j = 2, 3). \tag{9.16}$$

When $|x| \gg 1$ the expression for $P^{(2)}$ becomes the expression (9.14).

CHAPTER III

Stable and Unstable Particle Distributions in a Plasma

10. Interaction of a Flux of Charged Particles with Oscillations of a Free Plasma

1. Dispersion Equations for a Plasma-Beam System

Up to now we have been studying the oscillation spectra of an equilibrium or quasi-equilibrium (two-temperature) plasma. An important feature of theirs is that all the waves (whose phase velocity does not exceed the velocity of light in a vacuum) are damped even if binary collisions are neglected. The damping of the oscillations is caused by resonance interaction of particles with the waves and is connected with the fact that particles moving in phase with the wave obtain more energy from the field than they give up. This is connected in its turn with the nature of the equilibrium distribution function of the particles which decreases as their energy increases. Therefore the damping is connected with the fine structure of the equilibrium distribution function of the plasma particles which decreases steadily with energy.

Let us now imagine that the particle distribution function of the plasma is not in equilibrium. It has already been pointed out in section 1 that as the temperature rises the mean free path of the plasma particles increases and the time taken to establish equilibrium rises. Therefore for a hot enough and not too dense plasma the particle distribution may for long periods of time differ considerably from the equilibrium distribution. If this quasi-equilibrium distribution is not characterized by a steady decrease in the number of particles with energy, then the plasma oscillations caused by the self-consistent fields should not have to be damped since in these conditions the energy which the wave gives up to the particles does not necessarily exceed the energy received by the wave from the particles. It is clear that there may be particle distributions in which the waves receive more energy from the particles than they give up to the particles. In this case the oscillations will obviously be undamped and the particle distribution unstable.

The question therefore arises of the establishment of general criteria which have to be satisfied for the plasma oscillations to be damped or increasing. The present chapter is devoted to a study of the nature of the oscillations in non-equilibrium (but uniform in space) plasmas and to finding the criteria for the stability and instability of the particle distributions.

The simplest non-equilibrium system, which we shall start by studying, is a free plasma through which a neutralized beam of charged particles is passing. Let us first examine the high-frequency oscillations in which only the plasma and beam electrons take part. We shall assume that the electrons of the plasma and the beam are separately characterized by the Maxwellian distributions F_0 and F_0' with the different temperatures T and T':

$$F_0 = n_0 \left(\frac{m}{2\pi T}\right)^{3/2} \exp\left\{-\frac{mv^2}{2T}\right\};$$

$$F_0' = n_0' \left(\frac{m}{2\pi T'}\right)^{3/2} \exp\left\{-\frac{m(\boldsymbol{v}-\boldsymbol{u})^2}{2T'}\right\},$$

where n_0 and n_0' are densities of the electrons in the plasma and the beam and $\boldsymbol{u}$ is the mean directional velocity of the beam which is assumed to be small when compared with the velocity of light.

As has been shown in section 3, the oscillatory properties of a plasma are determined by the dielectric permittivity tensor. Using the general formula (3.5) and substituting in it the sum $F_0 + F_0'$ for the distribution function we can find the electron part of the dielectric permittivity tensor of a plasma-beam system [Silin and Rukhadze, 1961]:

$$\varepsilon_{ij} = \delta_{ij} + 4\pi(\varkappa_{ij} + \tilde{\varkappa}_{ij}), \tag{10.1}$$

where

$$\tilde{\varkappa}_{ij} = \varkappa_{ij}' + \varkappa_l'\omega^{-2}\{\omega'(u_i k_j + u_j k_i) + k^2 u_i u_j\};$$

$\varkappa_{ij} = \varkappa_{ij}(\boldsymbol{k}, \omega; n_0, T)$ is the electron polarizability of the plasma and $\varkappa'_{ij} = \varkappa_{ij}(\boldsymbol{k}, \omega'; n', T')$ is the electron polarizability of the beam for a frequency $\omega' = \omega - (\boldsymbol{k} \cdot \boldsymbol{u})$ which is the frequency of a wave in the displaced frame of reference connected with the beam ($\varkappa'_l$ is the longitudinal part of the tensor $\varkappa'_{ij}$).

Let us now turn our attention to the fact that it is not simply the quantity $\varkappa'$ that is contained in the dielectric permittivity tensor of a plasma-beam system (the quantity can be called the eigen polarizability of the beam since it relates to the frequency ω') but also additional terms containing beam velocity components.

Having the expression for ε_{ij} we can, in accordance with (3.7) obtain the dispersion equation of the oscillations. This equation degenerates into the two equations [Silin and Rukhadze, 1961]

$$(ck/\omega)^2 = 1 + 4\pi\varkappa_t + 4\pi(\omega'/\omega)^2\,\varkappa'_t, \tag{10.2}$$

$$[(ck/\omega)^2 - 1 - 4\pi(\varkappa_t + \varkappa'_t\omega'^2/\omega^2)]\,[(1 + 4\pi(\varkappa_l + \varkappa'_l)]$$
$$- 16\pi^2\,\frac{[\boldsymbol{k} \wedge \boldsymbol{u}]^2}{\omega^2}\left[\varkappa'_l + \left(\frac{\omega'}{ck}\right)^2(\varkappa'_t - \varkappa'_l)\right] \times$$
$$\times \left[\varkappa_l + \left(\frac{\omega}{ck}\right)^2(\varkappa_t - \varkappa_l)\right] = 0, \tag{10.3}$$

where $\varkappa_t$ and $\varkappa'_t$ are the transverse polarizabilities of the plasma and the beam.

The first of these equations defines the frequency of the transverse oscillations ($(\boldsymbol{k} \cdot \boldsymbol{E}) = 0$) and the second that of the longitudinal-transverse oscillations ($(\boldsymbol{k} \cdot \boldsymbol{E}) \neq 0$, $[\boldsymbol{k} \wedge \boldsymbol{E}] \neq 0$). The transverse oscillations turn out to be decreasing so we shall not discuss them any further. The longitudinal-transverse oscillations may be growing ($\operatorname{Im}\omega > 0$) and may therefore lead to instability of the plasma-beam system. Their study is therefore of great interest.

If $\varkappa u \ll c$, where $\varkappa$ is a quantity of the order of the polarizability of the plasma or the beam, then terms that are quadratic in u can be neglected in the equation (10.3). This term also becomes zero when the wave is propagated along the beam. In both cases the equation (10.3) degenerates into two, one of which is the same as the equation (10.2) and describes the transverse oscillations, whilst the second

$$1 + 4\pi(\varkappa_l + \varkappa'_l) = 0 \tag{10.4}$$

describes the longitudinal oscillations.

Therefore the dispersion equation for the longitudinal oscillations when $\varkappa u \ll c$ can be obtained if we make equal to zero the quantity $\varepsilon_l = 1 + 4\pi(\varkappa_l + \varkappa_l')$, which can be looked upon as the longitudinal dielectric permittivity of the plasma-beam system.

If there is not one beam passing through the plasma, as was assumed when deriving the equation (10.4), but several beams whose particles are characterized by Maxwellian distributions with different temperatures T_α and different directional velocities u_α, then the longitudinal oscillations in this kind of system of plasmas moving relative to each other are described by the dispersion equation

$$\varepsilon_l(\boldsymbol{k}, \omega) \equiv 1 + 4\pi \sum_\alpha \varkappa_l^\alpha(\boldsymbol{k}, \omega - (\boldsymbol{k} \cdot \boldsymbol{u}_\alpha)) = 0, \qquad (10.5)$$

where $\varkappa_l^\alpha$ is the longitudinal polarizability of the α-th plasma and summation is carried out for all plasmas. We would stress that this equation, just like equation (10.4), is valid if $\varkappa u_\alpha \ll c$.

2. *Growing Langmuir and Low-Frequency Oscillations*

Let us move on to studying the longitudinal oscillations of a plasma through which a low-density beam is passing [Akhiezer and Fainberg, 1949, 1951; Bohm and Gross, 1949]. In this case there are two possible cases depending upon the beam temperature: the general case of a not too cold beam ($kv' \gtrsim |\omega - (\boldsymbol{k} \cdot \boldsymbol{u})|$; $v' = (2T'/m)^{1/2}$) and the special case of a cold beam, when $kv' \ll |\omega - (\boldsymbol{k} \cdot \boldsymbol{u})|$.

Let us first discuss a beam which is not too cold. Here the solution can be found for the dispersion equation $\varepsilon_l = 0$ in the form of a series in powers of n_0'/n_0. In the zero approximation with respect to this parameter we obtain the dispersion law for weakly damped longitudinal oscillations of a free plasma $\omega = \omega^0 - i\gamma^0$, where for the high-frequency branch the quantities ω^0, γ^0 are defined by the formulae (2.19) and (2.20), and for the low-frequency branch (which appears in a strongly non-isothermal plasma) by the formulae (3.18).

In the first approximation with respect to n_0'/n_0 we obtain for the complex frequencies of the oscillations

$$\omega - i\gamma = \omega^0 - i\gamma^0 - 4\pi\varkappa_l'(k, \omega^0 - (\boldsymbol{k}\cdot\boldsymbol{u})) \times$$
$$\times \left(\frac{\partial}{\partial\omega}\,\varepsilon_l^0(k, \omega)\right)^{-1}_{\omega=\omega^0 - i\gamma^0}, \tag{10.6}$$

where ε_l^0 is the longitudinal dielectric constant of the plasma when there is no beam and $\varkappa' = \varkappa(k, \omega; n_0', T')$.

We see that the oscillation frequency ω differs from the oscillation frequency in a free plasma ω^0 only by a small term proportional to the beam density. When we come to the decrement γ, although the difference between γ and γ^0 is also proportional to n_0'/n_0, nevertheless the contribution of the beam to the decrement may be significant because of the smallness of γ^0. We therefore give the explicit expression for the decrement which follows from the equation (10.6)

$$\frac{\gamma}{\omega} = \frac{2\pi e^2}{k^3}\sqrt{\frac{\pi m}{2}}\left(\frac{\omega}{\Omega_\alpha}\right)^2 \left\{n_0 \frac{\omega}{T^{3/2}} \exp\left(-\frac{m\omega^2}{2Tk^2}\right)\right.$$
$$\left. + n_0' \frac{\omega - (\boldsymbol{k}\cdot\boldsymbol{u})}{T'^{3/2}} \exp\left(\frac{-m[\omega - (\boldsymbol{k}\cdot\boldsymbol{u})]^2}{2T'k^2}\right)\right\}, \tag{10.7}$$

where $\Omega_\alpha = \Omega_e$ for the high-frequency branch and $\Omega_\alpha = \Omega_i$ for the low-frequency branch of the oscillations (we have made allowance for the fact that the plasma ions make a small relative contribution to the damping of both the Langmuir and the low-frequency oscillations).

It is easy to see that if the beam velocity is small enough (in particular always when $u_\parallel < \omega/k$, where $u_\parallel = k^{-1}(\boldsymbol{u}\cdot\boldsymbol{k})$ is the projection of the beam velocity onto the direction of the wave vector), then $\gamma > 0$, so the oscillations with the wave vector $\boldsymbol{k}$ are damped.

At a certain critical velocity $u_\parallel = u_c(k)$ the decrement γ becomes zero and becomes negative upon a further increase in the beam velocity. Thus when $u_\parallel > u_c(k)$ the longitudinal oscillations with the wave vector $\boldsymbol{k}$ are not damped but increase.

In the simplest case of a beam which is not too cold we have for the critical velocity

$$u_c(k) = \frac{\omega}{k}\left[1 + \frac{n^0}{n_0'}(T'/T)^{3/2} \exp\left\{-\frac{m\omega^2}{2Tk^2}\right\}\right]. \quad (10.8)$$

By substituting $\omega = \omega_L$ ($\omega_L = \Omega + 3\Omega a_e^2 k^2/2$) in this it is easy to check that the growth in the Langmuir oscillations starts at beam velocities $u \sim v_e$ ($v_\alpha^2 = 2T_\alpha/m_\alpha$).

By substituting $\omega = V_s k(1 + a_e^2 k^2)^{-1/2}$ as the frequency in the formula (10.8) we can estimate the critical velocity $u \sim v_i$ at which the low-frequency oscillations start to grow.

By using the expression (10.7) we can show that the relative growth rate $|\gamma/\omega|$ of the low-frequency oscillations when $a_i^{-1} \gg k \gg a_e^{-1}$ (the ion Langmuir oscillations) is in order of magnitude $(T_e/T_i)^{3/2}$ times less than the relative growth rate in the sonic range ($a_e k \ll 1$).

It should be borne in mind that the expression (10.8) for the critical velocity, just as the expressions for the oscillation growth rate given in the present chapter, relate to a collisionless plasma. In actual fact allowance must be made for collisions between particles which prevent the oscillations from increasing. The oscillations will increase, generally speaking, if the increment of their increase exceeds a certain minimum value equal to the effective frequency of the collisions.

It is easy to see that the second term in (10.7), which leads to an increase in the oscillations when $u_\parallel > u_c(k)$, is proportional to the number of resonant particles in the beam, i.e. particles whose velocity is the same as the wave's phase velocity and which can therefore give up energy to the wave. We can say that in the present case of a beam which is not too cold each of the resonant particles excites oscillations independently. It will be shown later that if the velocity scatter of the beam's particles is very small a situation is possible when the beam's particles excite oscillations coherently [Akhiezer and Fainberg, 1949, 1951]; in this case the growth rate is proportional to the beam density to a power less than the first.

3. Excitation of Longitudinal Oscillations by a Cold Beam

When there is little scatter in the velocities of the beam particles ($v' \ll k^{-1}|\omega - (\boldsymbol{k}\cdot\boldsymbol{u})|$) the dispersion equation (10.5) becomes

$$\varepsilon_l^0(k,\omega) - \left(\frac{\Omega'}{\omega - (\boldsymbol{k}\cdot\boldsymbol{u})}\right)^2 + 4i\sqrt{\pi}\,\eta\left(\frac{\omega}{kv'}\right) \times$$
$$\times\ \frac{\Omega'^2(\omega - (\boldsymbol{k}\cdot\boldsymbol{u}))}{(kv')^3}\exp\left\{-\left(\frac{\omega - (\boldsymbol{k}\cdot\boldsymbol{u})}{kv'}\right)^2\right\} = 0, \quad (10.9)$$

where $\Omega'^2 = 4\pi e^2 n_0'/m$ and

$$\eta\left(\frac{\omega}{kv'}\right) = \begin{cases} 0 & \operatorname{Im}\omega/kv' \to +\infty, \\ \frac{1}{2} & \operatorname{Im}\omega/kv' \to 0, \\ 1 & \operatorname{Im}\omega/kv' \to -\infty. \end{cases}$$

(The third term in this equation appears because of going round the pole $\omega = (\boldsymbol{k}\cdot\boldsymbol{v})$ in the expression (3.5) for the electrical susceptibility.)

If the quantity $|(\boldsymbol{k}\cdot\boldsymbol{u})|$ is not close to the frequency ω^0 of some branch of the plasma's longitudinal oscillations, then the equation (10.9) has a solution corresponding to specific longitudinal oscillations of the plasma-beam system which are absent in the case of a free plasma

$$\omega = (\boldsymbol{k}\cdot\boldsymbol{u}) - \frac{\Omega'}{\sqrt{\varepsilon_l^0(k,(\boldsymbol{k}\cdot\boldsymbol{u}))}} \quad \left(\operatorname{Im}\sqrt{\varepsilon_l^0(k,(\boldsymbol{k}\cdot\boldsymbol{u}))} > 0\right). \quad (10.10)$$

It is easy to see that these oscillations increase, the growth rate being proportional to $(n_0'/n_0)^{1/2}$ (i.e. far greater than the growth rate in the oscillations in the case of a beam which is not cold, which, as was shown above, is proportional to n_0'/n_0). The phase velocity of these oscillations differs from the velocity $u_\parallel$ by a small quantity proportional to $(n_0'/n_0)^{1/2}$.

If $u_\parallel \ll v_i$ the growth rate is, in accordance with the expressions (10.10) and (3.11) [Gordeyev, 1954b],

$$|\gamma| = \frac{1}{2}\sqrt{\pi}\,\Omega'\,\frac{|u_\parallel|}{v_i}\,\frac{\bar{a}k}{(1+\bar{a}^2k^2)^{3/2}}\left(1 + \frac{T_i}{T_e}\right)^{-1}, \quad (10.11)$$

where $\bar{a} = a_e a_i (a_e^2 + a_i^2)^{-1/2}$ is the screening radius.

Therefore in the case of a cold beam the oscillations increase no matter how small the velocities u (when $u \to 0$ the growth rate approaches zero).

When $v_e \ll u_\parallel < \Omega/k$ the growth rate is

$$|\gamma| = \Omega' \, |(\boldsymbol{k} \cdot \boldsymbol{u})| \, (\Omega^2 - (\boldsymbol{k} \cdot \boldsymbol{u})^2)^{-1/2}. \tag{10.11'}$$

When $u_\parallel > \Omega/k$ the growth rate is exponentially small and decreases as $u_\parallel$ increases.

Let us now pause to examine the case $|(\boldsymbol{k} \cdot \boldsymbol{u})| \approx \omega^0$, where ω^0 is the frequency of the longitudinal oscillations of a plasma when there is no beam (the Langmuir or low-frequency oscillations). Being interested only in the solutions of the equation (10.9) with $\operatorname{Im} \omega > 0$ corresponding to increasing oscillations we can put this equation for $|(\boldsymbol{k} \cdot \boldsymbol{u})| \approx \omega^0$ in the form

$$(\omega - \omega^0)(\omega - (\boldsymbol{k} \cdot \boldsymbol{u}))^2 - \Omega'^2 \left(\frac{\partial \varepsilon^0(k, \omega)}{\partial \omega} \right)^{-1}_{\omega = \omega^0} = 0. \tag{10.12}$$

It follows from this equation that when $|(\boldsymbol{k} \cdot \boldsymbol{u})| \approx \omega^0$ in the plasma-beam system oscillations are possible which increase with a growth rate proportional to $(n_0'/n_0)^{1/3}$, the frequencies of these oscillations differing from the frequencies of the eigen oscillations of a free plasma by small terms proportional to $(n_0'/n_0)^{1/3}$ [Akhiezer and Fainberg, 1949, 1951].

In the case of resonance at the Langmuir oscillations ($|(\boldsymbol{k} \cdot \boldsymbol{u})| \approx \omega_L$) the frequency and growth rate of the increasing oscillations are

$$\left.\begin{aligned} \omega &= (\boldsymbol{k} \cdot \boldsymbol{u}) - \Omega(\Omega'/4\Omega)^{2/3} \\ |\gamma| &= \Omega \sqrt{3} \, (\Omega'/4\Omega)^{2/3} \end{aligned}\right\}. \tag{10.13}$$

In the case of resonance at the low-frequency oscillations of a non-isothermal plasma ($|(\boldsymbol{k} \cdot \boldsymbol{u})| \approx kV_s(1 + a_e^2 k^2)^{-1/2}$) the frequency and growth rate of the increasing oscillations are

$$\left.\begin{aligned} \omega &= (\boldsymbol{k} \cdot \boldsymbol{u}) - \frac{kV_s}{\sqrt{1 + a_e^2 k^2}} \left(\frac{\Omega'}{4\Omega_i} \right)^{2/3} \\ |\gamma| &= \frac{\sqrt{3} \, kV_s}{\sqrt{1 + a_e^2 k^2}} \left(\frac{\Omega'}{4\Omega_i} \right)^{2/3} \end{aligned}\right\}, \tag{10.14}$$

where

$$\Omega_i^2 = 4\pi e^2 n_0 / M.$$

Let us see how the nature of the oscillations in a plasma is altered by an increase in the velocity of a cold beam of electrons which is passing through it. We shall assume that the temperature of the plasma electrons does not differ too much from the temperature of the ions so that the propagation of weakly damped low-frequency oscillations is impossible.

If $u_{\parallel} \lesssim v_e$ and $|(\boldsymbol{k} \cdot \boldsymbol{u})| \ll \Omega$, then oscillations with a frequency $\omega \approx |(\boldsymbol{k} \cdot \boldsymbol{u})|$ and a growth defined by the formula (10.10) and proportional to $(n_0'/n_0)^{1/2}$ will be pumped in the plasma.

If the velocity of the beam becomes considerably greater than the thermal velocity of the plasma electrons, then oscillations will be pumped with a frequency close to the Langmuir frequency, whose growth rate is defined by the formula (10.13) and is proportional to $(n_0'/n_0)^{1/3}$. Resonance oscillations of this kind are propagated at a certain angle $\cos\theta \approx \Omega/ku$ to the direction of the beam. The oscillations propagated in other directions are characterized as before by the dispersion law $\omega \approx (\boldsymbol{k} \cdot \boldsymbol{u})$; their growth rate is very small and is proportional to $(n_0'/n_0)^{1/2} \exp\{-u_{\parallel}^2/v_e^2\}$.

Let us now stress the fact that the growth rates do not depend on the amplitude of the oscillations. This is obviously connected with the nature of the linear approximation we are using. If we take the non-linear effects into consideration the growth rates may decrease as the amplitude of the oscillations increases. The dependence of the growth rates on the amplitude, and thus also the finite states of a plasma-beam system, can be studied only by means of a non-linear theory and will not be discussed here.

4. Instability of a Plasma whose Electrons are Moving Relative to the Ions

Let us examine the longitudinal oscillations of a plasma consisting of hot electrons moving relative to cold ions [Gordeyev, 1954a]. The dielectric constant of such a plasma will be, in accordance with the formula (10.5)

$$\varepsilon_l(\boldsymbol{k}, \omega) = 1 + 4\pi\varkappa_l^e(k, \omega - (\boldsymbol{k} \cdot \boldsymbol{u})) + 4\pi\varkappa_l^i(k, \omega). \quad (10.15)$$

We shall consider the directional velocity of the electrons to be small by comparison with their thermal velocities; we need not then allow for the dependence of the real part of ε on the velocity $\boldsymbol{u}$. It can easily be seen that low-frequency oscillations are possible in this kind of plasma whose dispersion law differs but little from the dispersion law of the low-frequency oscillations in a plasma with stationary electrons $\omega = V_s k(1 + a_e^2 k^2)^{-1/2}$. The damping decrement of these oscillations depends essentially on the directional velocity of the electrons. In accordance with the equations (10.15) and (3.4′) the decrement is of the form

$$\gamma = \sqrt{\frac{\pi m}{8M}} \left[\frac{kV_s}{(1 + a_e^2 k^2)^2} - \frac{(\boldsymbol{k} \cdot \boldsymbol{u})}{(1 + a_e^2 k^2)^{3/2}} + \frac{kV_s}{(1 + a_e^2 k^2)^2} \sqrt{\frac{M}{m}} \left(\frac{T_e}{T_i}\right)^{3/2} \exp\left\{\frac{-MV_s^2}{2T_i(1 + a_e^2 k^2)}\right\}\right]. \tag{10.16}$$

We see that when $u_\parallel = u_c(k)$, where

$$u_c(k) = \frac{V_s}{\sqrt{1 + a_e^2 k^2}} \times \left[1 + \sqrt{\frac{M}{m}} \left(\frac{T_e}{T_i}\right)^{3/2} \exp\left\{\frac{-MV_s^2}{2T_i(1 + a_e^2 k^2)}\right\}\right], \tag{10.17}$$

the damping decrement of the oscillations with the wave vector k becomes zero; when $u_\parallel > u_c(k)$ these oscillations increase.

As the directional velocity of the electrons increases the first thing that happens is a growth in the ion Langmuir oscillations with very large k ($a_i k \sim 1$); for these oscillations, according to the equation (10.17), the critical velocity u_c is equal in order of magnitude to v_i. Upon a further increase in $u_\parallel$ the longer-wave oscillations start to increase. Finally, at a value of $u_\parallel$ slightly greater than the velocity of two-temperature sound V_s the sonic oscillations start to increase.

In this case there is an increase in the sonic oscillations propagated inside a cone the angle at whose apex is slightly less than the Cherenkov angle $\theta_c = \arccos V_s/u$.

We notice that the relative increment $|\gamma/\omega|$ of the sonic oscillations is in order of magnitude $(T_e/T_i)^{3/2}$ times greater than the relative increment of the ion Langmuir oscillations.

Let us conclude this sub-section by examining the solutions of the equation (10.3) which are not contained in the equation (10.5) for the longitudinal oscillations. It can be shown that for $(\boldsymbol{k}_\perp \cdot \boldsymbol{u})$ the dispersion equation (10.3) has a solution with $\gamma \equiv -\operatorname{Im}\omega < 0$ corresponding to growing longitudinal-transverse oscillations.

In the case of a cold plasma and a cold beam the growth rate of these oscillations is† [Rukhadze, 1958]

$$|\gamma| = ku\Omega\Omega'\{(\Omega^2 + \Omega'^2)(c^2k^2 + \Omega^2 + \Omega'^2)\}^{-1/2}. \quad (10.18)$$

In order of magnitude it is c/u times less than the growth rate of the longitudinal oscillations.

11. Interaction of a Flux of Charged Particles with Oscillations of a Plasma in a Magnetic Field

1. Excitation of Longitudinal Oscillations of a Plasma in a Magnetic Field by a Beam of Electrons

Let us move on to a study of the interaction of a beam of charged particles with a plasma when there is an external constant and uniform magnetic field $\boldsymbol{H}_0$. As before we shall assume that the density of the particles in the beam is small by comparison with the density of the particles in the plasma and that the velocity of the beam $\boldsymbol{u}$ is directed along $\boldsymbol{H}_0$.

Let us first examine the longitudinal high-frequency oscillations in a plasma-beam system [Stepanov, 1958a; Rappoport, 1960; Kovner, 1960; Stepanov and Kitsenko, 1961]. In order to find the complex frequencies of the longitudinal oscillations (to be more precise, almost longitudinal oscillations with $E_\parallel \gg E_\perp$) we must make the quantity A defined by the formula (4.7) equal to zero. Since we are discussing high-frequency oscillations we need not take into consideration the contribution of the ion component of the plasma and beam to ε_{ij} when calculating A.

Assuming that the distributions of the electrons in the plasma and the beam are Maxwellian distributions with the temperatures T_e and T'_e and using the expressions (4.4) for the components of the tensor ε_{ij}, we can put the dispersion equation $A = 0$ in the form

$$1 + \frac{2\Omega_e^2}{k^2 v_e^2}\left[1 + i\sqrt{\pi}\, z_0\, e^{-\mu} \sum_{l=-\infty}^{\infty} I_l(\mu)\, w(z_l)\right] + \frac{2\Omega_e'^2}{k^2 v_e'^2}\left[1 + i\sqrt{\pi}\, z'_0 \sum_{l=-\infty}^{\infty} e^{-\mu'} I_l(\mu')\, w(z'_l)\right] = 0, \quad (11.1)$$

† This expression was derived in Fried's paper [1959] for $n'_0 = n_0$.

where

$$z_l = \frac{\omega - l\omega_e}{k_\parallel v_e}; \qquad \mu = \frac{1}{2}\left(\frac{k_\perp v_e}{\omega_e}\right)^2;$$

$$z_l' = \frac{\omega - l\omega_e - k_\parallel u}{k_\parallel v_e'}; \qquad \mu' = \frac{1}{2}\left(\frac{k_\perp v_e'}{\omega_e}\right)^2$$

(the quantities with the prime relate to the beam).

We shall assume that the plasma is cold. In this case, as we saw in section 5, when there is no beam, oscillations are propagated in the plasma with the frequencies $\omega_j(\theta)$ defined by the formulae (5.3) and (5.4). Therefore when a low-density beam passes through the plasma the solution of the equation (11.1) should be found in the form

$$\omega = \omega_j(\theta) + \delta\omega_j - i\gamma_j, \quad (j = 1, 2)$$

where $\delta\omega_j$ is the frequency shift caused by the beam and γ_j is the damping decrement or growth rate of the oscillations.

Since we are not interested in the small frequency shift $\delta\omega_j$ we shall give only the formula for the imaginary part of the frequency derived from the equation (11.1) on the assumption that $|\gamma_j| \ll k_\parallel v_e'$:

$$\frac{\gamma_j}{\omega_j} = \frac{\sqrt{\pi}\,\Omega'^2}{k^2 v_e'^2} z_0\, e^{-\mu'} \sum_{n=-\infty}^{\infty} I_n(\mu')\, e^{-z_n^2} \left[\frac{\Omega_e^2 \cos^2\theta}{\omega_j^2} + \frac{\Omega_e^2 \omega_j^2 \sin^2\theta}{(\omega_j^2 - \omega_e^2)^2}\right]^{-1}, \tag{11.2}$$

where

$$z_n = \frac{\omega_j - n\omega_e - k_\parallel u}{k_\parallel v_e'}.$$

Therefore the quantity γ_j will be negative, i.e. the oscillations will increase, if the beam's velocity is greater than the phase velocity of the oscillations

$$u > \frac{\omega_j(\theta)}{k_\parallel}. \tag{11.3}$$

If $u < \omega_j/k_\parallel$ the presence of a beam will lead to additional damping of the oscillations.

The formula (11.2) is derived on the assumption that $|\gamma_j| \ll k_{\|}v'_e$, i.e. for beams whose velocities have a large thermal scatter (and which are of low density). In this case the increment of the oscillations is proportional to n'_0 (just as when there is no magnetic field).

If $kv'_e \ll \omega_e$, then only one term corresponding to the minimum z_n^2 need be kept in the sum (11.2). We shall denote this minimum value of z_n^2 by z_l^2. Remembering that $\mu' \ll 1$ and $I_n(\mu') \approx (\mu')^{|n|}/2^{|n|}|n|!$, we obtain

$$\frac{\gamma_j}{\omega_j} = \frac{\sqrt{\pi}\,\Omega_e'^2}{k^2 v_e'^2}\frac{(\mu')^{|l|}}{2^{|l|}|l|!} \times$$

$$\times \left[\frac{\Omega_e^2 \cos^2\theta}{\omega_j^2} + \frac{\Omega_e^2\omega_j^2 \sin^2\theta}{(\omega_j^2 - \omega_i^2)^2}\right]^{-1} z_0\, e^{-z_l^2}. \tag{11.4}$$

The quantity $|\gamma_j|$ will be particularly great if the frequency ω_j is close to $k_{\|}u + l\omega_e$, where $l = 0, \pm 1, \pm 2, \ldots$,

$$\omega_j(\theta) \approx k_{\|}u + l\omega_e \quad (l = 0, \pm 1, \pm 2, \ldots,). \tag{11.5}$$

If this condition is satisfied for $l = 0$ and at the same time $\gamma_j < 0$, then we speak of Cherenkov excitation of the oscillations. If the condition (11.5) is satisfied when $l = -1, -2, \ldots$ the excitation of the oscillations is called cyclotron excitation.

The formulae (11.2) and (11.4) define the growth rate in a cold plasma-hot beam system. Let us now examine the excitation of oscillations in a plasma by a cold beam (the plasma may be either cold or hot). The dispersion equation (11.1) in this case becomes

$$1 + \frac{2\Omega_e^2}{k^2 v_e^2}\left[1 + i\sqrt{\pi}\,z_0\, e^{-\mu}\sum_{l=-\infty}^{\infty} I_l(\mu)\, w(z_l)\right]$$

$$- \frac{\Omega_e'^2 \cos^2\theta}{(\omega - k_{\|}u)^2} - \frac{\Omega_e'^2 \sin^2\theta}{(\omega - k_{\|}u)^2 - \omega_e^2} = 0. \tag{11.6}$$

This equation shows that the effect of the beam on the plasma oscillations will be particularly great if one of the resonance conditions $\omega \approx k_{\|}u$ or $\omega \approx k_{\|}u \pm \omega_e$ is satisfied.

Let us first examine the case when $\omega \approx k_{\|}u$. Putting $\omega = k_{\|}u + \eta$, where $|\eta| \ll k_{\|}u$, we obtain

$$\eta = \frac{\Omega_e' \cos\theta}{\left\{1 + \dfrac{2\Omega_e^2}{k^2 v_e^2}\left[1 + i\sqrt{\pi}\, z_0\, e^{-\mu} \sum_{l=-\infty}^{\infty} I_l(\mu)\, w(z_l)\right]\right\}^{1/2}}$$

$$(\operatorname{Im} \eta > 0), \qquad (11.7)$$

where $z_l = (k_{\|}u - l\omega_e)/k_{\|}v_e$. Since there is a complex number under the sign of the radical in the expression (11.7) oscillations will always be excited.

If the plasma is cold (just as the beam is) the growth rate (11.7) is

$$\gamma = -\Omega_e' |\cos\theta| \left\{\frac{k_{\|}^2 u^2(\omega_e^2 - k_e^2 u^2)}{(\omega_1^2 - k_{\|}^2 u^2)(\omega_2^2 - k_{\|}^2 u^2)}\right\}^{1/2}, \qquad (11.8)$$

where ω_1 and ω_2 are the frequencies of the longitudinal oscillations of a plasma in a magnetic field defined by the formulae (5.3) and (5.4).

Therefore there is an increase in the oscillations if $\omega_e < k_{\|}u < \omega_1$ or if $k_{\|}u < \omega_2$ (it is assumed that $u \gg v_e, v_e'$); then the increment is proportional to $(n_0')^{1/2}$ just as in the analogous case for a free plasma.

The formula (11.8) becomes inapplicable if $\omega = k_{\|}u = \omega_j(\theta)$. In this case, which can be looked upon as resonance between the oscillations of the plasma and the oscillations of the beam, the growth rate of the oscillations is defined by the formula

$$\frac{\gamma_j}{\omega_j} = -\frac{\sqrt{3}}{2^{4/3}} \left\{\frac{n_0'}{n_0} \frac{(\omega_j^2 - \omega_e^2)^2 \cos^2\theta}{[(\omega_j^2 - \omega_e^2)^2 \cos^2\theta + \omega_j^4 \sin^2\theta]}\right\}^{1/3}. \qquad (11.9)$$

It is proportional to $(n_0')^{1/3}$ just as in the analogous case of the excitation of Langmuir oscillations in a free plasma by a cold beam (see section 10).

Let us now examine the oscillations in a cold plasma–cold beam system when the condition $\omega = \omega_j(\theta) = k_{\|}u - \omega_e$ is satisfied (this condition means that the frequencies of the longitudinal eigen oscillations of the plasma in the system connected with the beam are the same as the cyclotron frequency of the electrons). In this case the growth rate of the oscillations is

$$\frac{\gamma_j}{\omega_j} = -\frac{\Omega'_e \sin\theta}{2\Omega_e}\left\{\frac{\omega_j(\omega_j^2 - \omega_e^2)^2}{\omega_e[(\omega_j^2 - \omega_e^2)^2 \cos^2\theta + \omega_j^4 \sin^2\theta]}\right\}^{1/2}. \tag{11.10}$$

It is proportional to $(n'_0)^{1/2}$ and not to $(n'_0)^{1/3}$ unlike the case of the resonance $\omega_j(\theta) = k_{\parallel}u$.

The formulae (11.8)–(11.10) are valid when the condition $|\gamma_j| \gg k_{\parallel}v'_e$ is satisfied, i.e. for beams whose velocities have little thermal spread (and not very low density).

2. Excitation of Low-Frequency Electron Oscillation in a Plasma by a Beam of Electrons

In subsection 4 of section 6 we showed that low-frequency electron oscillations ($\omega_i \ll \omega \ll \omega_e$) can be propagated in a plasma located in a magnetic field (no matter whether it is hot or cold), their frequency being proportional to the square of the wave vector,

$$\omega = \alpha k^2,$$

where $\alpha = \omega_e |\cos\theta| c^2/\Omega_e^2$. Since $\omega/k \ll c$ these oscillations can interact effectively with a beam of charged particles passing through the plasma [Stepanov and Kitsenko, 1961; Kovner, 1961].

In order to investigate this interaction we must start with the general dispersion equation (4.6) in which the components of the tensor ε_{ij} are defined by the formulae (4.4). We shall not give the detailed calculations here, contenting ourselves with the final result.

If the resonance condition $\omega = \alpha k^2 \approx k_{\parallel}u$ is satisfied the growth rate of the oscillations is

$$\frac{\gamma}{\omega} = \frac{\sqrt{\pi}\sin^2\theta\,\omega^2 k^2 c^2 \Omega_e'^2}{k_{\parallel}^2 v_e'^2 \Omega_e^4}\, z\, e^{-z^2}, \tag{11.11}$$

where $z = (\alpha k^2 - k_{\parallel}u)/k_{\parallel}v'_e$. This formula is valied if $|\gamma| \ll k_{\parallel}v'_e \ll \omega_e$, i.e. for low-density beams with a high enough thermal scatter of the velocities; the plasma is assumed to be cold.

For the resonances $\omega = \alpha k^2 \approx k_{\|}u - l\omega_e (l = 1, 2, \ldots)$ the growth rate is $(\omega_e/kv'_e)^{2l+2}$ times less than the growth rate defined by the formula (11.11).

If a cold beam of electrons passes through a cold plasma the growth rate of the oscillations with the frequency $\omega = \alpha k^2$ for the Cherenkov resonance $\omega = \alpha k^2 = k_{\|}u$ is defined by the formula

$$\frac{\gamma}{\omega} = -\frac{\sqrt{3}}{2^{4/3}}\left(\frac{\Omega'_e kc \sin\theta}{\Omega_e^2}\right)^{2/3}. \tag{11.12}$$

This growth rate is proportional to $(n'_0)^{1/3}$ and not to n'_0 as in the case of a hot beam.

During cyclotron excitation by a cold beam of the oscillations of a cold plasma with the frequency $\omega = \alpha k^2$, when $\omega = \alpha k^2 = k_{\|}u - \omega_e$, the growth rate is

$$\frac{\gamma}{\omega} = -\frac{\Omega'_e \Omega_e}{2k^2c^2}\,\frac{1 - |\cos\theta|}{|\cos\theta|^{3/2}}. \tag{11.13}$$

3. *Cyclotron Excitation of Ion-Cyclotron and Magnetohydrodynamic Waves in a Cold Plasma by a Beam of Particles*

Let us examine the excitation of low-frequency ion-cyclotron and magnetohydrodynamic waves by a beam of particles.

When there is no beam the frequencies of these waves, as has been shown in section 7, are defined by the formulae

$$\omega_j^2(k, \theta) = \tfrac{1}{2} k^2 V_A^2 \left[1 + \cos^2\theta + r\cos^2\theta \pm \sqrt{(1 + \cos^2\theta + r\cos^2\theta)^2 - 4\cos^2\theta}\right], \tag{11.14}$$

where

$$r = \frac{k^2c^2}{\Omega_i^2}.$$

Since the ion-cyclotron and magnetohydrodynamic waves are low-frequency waves both the electrons and the ions in the beam take part in the interaction with them [Stepanov and Kitsenko, 1961].

The beam interacts particularly effectively with the ion-cyclotron and magnetohydrodynamic waves under conditions of cyclotron resonance. Here we must distinguish cyclotron resonance for the beam's electrons, when the condition $\omega = \omega_j(k, \theta) \approx k_{\|}u - \omega_e$ is satisfied, and cyclotron resonance for the beam's ions, when $\omega = \omega_j(k, \theta) \approx k_{\|}u - \omega_i$.

If the plasma is cold and the beam's velocities have considerable thermal spread the growth rate of the oscillations with the frequency $\omega_j(k, \theta)$ under the cyclotron resonance conditions $\omega_j(k, \theta) \approx k_{\|}u - \omega_\alpha$ is of the form

$$\gamma_j = \frac{\sqrt{\pi}\,\Omega_\alpha'^2}{4\omega_j Q}\left[(1 + \cos^2\theta)\,\frac{k^2c^2}{\omega_j^2} - \frac{2\Omega_j^2}{\omega_i(\omega_i \mp \omega_j)}\right] z_0\, e^{-z_i^2}, \tag{11.15}$$

where

$$Q = \frac{\Omega_i^4}{(\omega_j^2 - \omega_i^2)^2}\left[(1 + \cos^2\theta)\,\frac{k^2V_A^2}{\omega_j^2} + \frac{\omega_j^2}{\omega_i^2} - 2\right]; \tag{11.16}$$

$$z_n = \frac{\omega_j(k, \theta) + n\omega_\alpha - k_{\|}u}{k_{\|}v_\alpha'}.$$

The top sign in the formula for γ_j relates to the conditions of resonance for the beam's ions and the bottom one for the beam's electrons.

Therefore there is a growth in the oscillations if $u > \omega_j(k, \theta)/k_{\|}$. In the case of excitation of oscillations by an electron beam the increment is proportional to $\Omega_e'^2$ and in the case of excitation of oscillations by the beam's ions it is proportional to $\Omega_i'^2$.

The formulae (11.15) define the growth of ion-cyclotron and magnetohydrodynamic waves in a cold plasma when a hot beam is passing through it. If a cold beam passes through the plasma the growth of the oscillations with the frequency $\omega_j(k, \theta)$ is defined for the cyclotron resonance $\omega = \omega_j(k, \theta) = k_{\|}u - \omega_\alpha$ by the formula

$$\gamma_j = -\left\{\frac{\Omega_\alpha'^2\,\omega_\alpha}{4\omega_j\,|Q|}\left|(1 + \cos^2\theta)\,\frac{k^2c^2}{\omega_j^2} - \frac{2\Omega_i^2}{\omega_i(\omega_i \mp \omega_j)}\right|\right\}^{1/2}, \tag{11.17}$$

where Q is defined by the formula (11.16). This growth, unlike the growth of the oscillations excited when a hot beam passes through the plasma, is proportional to $(n_0')^{1/2}$ (just as in the case of cyclotron excitation of high-frequency longitudinal plasma oscillations by a cold beam).

4. Cherenkov Excitation of Magnetosonic Waves in a Hot Plasma by a Beam of Particles

In a strongly non-isothermal plasma ($T_e \gg T_i$), as has been shown in section 8, fast and slow magnetosonic waves and an Alfvén wave can be propagated in the low-frequency range ($\omega \ll \omega_i$). Since these are low-frequency waves both the electrons and the ions of the beam can take part in their excitation. The beam's particles interact particularly strongly with the magnetosonic waves at the Cherenkov resonance $\omega_j \approx k_{\parallel} u$, where ω_j is the frequencies of the magnetosonic waves [Akhiezer, Kitsenko and Stepanov, 1961].

We should point out that cyclotron excitation of magnetosonic waves in a hot plasma is generally less efficient than Cherenkov excitation. Therefore we shall not give the expressions here for the growth of magnetosonic waves during cyclotron excitation.

Let us examine the excitation of magnetosonic waves by a cold beam. In this case the part played by the beam's ions is small. The effect of the beam on the plasma oscillations will be particularly great if the frequency of the oscillations is close to $k_{\parallel} u$ (the beam density is assumed to be low). By putting $\omega = k_{\parallel} u + \eta$ we can show that for $|\eta| \ll |\omega|$

$$\eta = k_{\parallel} u \left\{ \frac{n_0' m_i}{n_0 m_e} \frac{V_s^2 \cos^2 \theta (u^2 \cos^2 \theta - V_A^2)}{(u^2 \cos^2 \theta - V_2^2)(u^2 \cos^2 \theta - V_3^2)} \right\}^{1/2}, \tag{11.18}$$

where the V_j are the velocities of fast ($j = 2$) and slow ($j = 3$) magnetosonic waves

$$V_j^2 = \tfrac{1}{2}(V_s^2 + V_A^2) \pm \tfrac{1}{2}\sqrt{(V_s^2 + V_A^2)^2 - 4V_A^2 V_s^2 \cos^2 \theta}. \tag{11.19}$$

We see that the oscillations will increase if $V_A < u \cos \theta < V_2$ or if $u \cos \theta < V_3$ (it is assumed here that $u \gg v_i, v_i', v_e'$). In order of magnitude $\operatorname{Im} \eta \sim ku\sqrt{n_0' m_i / n_0 m_e}$, if $V_A \sim V_s \sim u$ and $\theta \sim 1$.

The formula (11.18) becomes inapplicable when $u \cos\theta = V_j$. In this case the growth rate reaches a maximum

$$\frac{\gamma_j}{\omega_j} = -\frac{\sqrt{3}}{2^{4/3}} \left| \frac{n_0' m_i}{n_0 m_e} \frac{\cos^2\theta V_s^2 (V_j^2 - V_A^2)}{V_j^2 (V_2^2 - V_3^2)} \right|^{1/3}, \tag{11.20}$$

where $\omega_j = kV_j$. It is proportional to $(n_0')^{1/3}$.

We should mention that the magnetosonic waves for $V_A \lesssim V_s$ exist only in a strongly non-isothermal plasma when $T_e \gg T_i$. If $T_e \lesssim T_i$ the magnetosonic waves are strongly damped when there is no beam. However, when a beam with a low thermal scatter of its velocities and a directional velocity $u \sim V_A \sim V_s \sim v_i$ passes through such a plasma the oscillations at the frequency $\omega \approx k_{\|}u$ begin to increase. Here in order of magnitude $\gamma = ku(n_0' m_i/n_0 m_e)^{1/2}$. This estimate is valid if $T_e'/T_e \ll n_0'/n_0 \ll m_e/m_i$.

12. General Stability and Instability Conditions for Particle Distributions in a Plasma

1. Stability and Instability Criteria for Particle Distributions in a Free Plasma

In the preceding sections we have examined the interaction of beams of charged particles with a plasma and shown that under certain conditions this interaction leads to an increase in the oscillations, i.e. to instability of the plasma-beam system.

Let us now move on to a study of the general question of the conditions that the distribution functions of the particles in a plasma have to satisfy for the plasma oscillations (which we shall assume to be longitudinal) to be damped or increasing.

We shall first discuss a free plasma not acted upon by external magnetic fields. In this case, as was shown in section 2, the initial distribution function $F_0(w)$ (w is the component of the electron's velocity in the direction of the wave vector $\boldsymbol{k}$) will be stable if all the roots of the equation

$$\frac{i\Omega_e^2}{k} \int_C \frac{F_0'(w)\, dw}{p + ikw} = 1 \tag{12.1}$$

(where integration is along the real axis w indented round the possible pole $w = ip/k$) lie in the left-hand half-plane of p. (The function $F_0(w)$ is assumed in this section to be normalized to unity, $\int F_0(w)\, dw = 1$.) In this case the spatial Fourier component of the potential $\varphi_k(t)$ will approach zero for large t (see (2.6); we should mention that t should be small by comparison with the relaxation time τ). The deviation of the distribution function $f_k(w, t)$ from the initial function will be subject to undamped oscillations of constant amplitude with a frequency kw dependent on the particle velocity (see the expression (2.6)).

On the other hand, if at least one of the roots of the equation (12.1) lies in the right-hand half-plane of p the functions $\varphi_k(t)$ and $f_k(w, t)$ will rise unlimitedly with time and the initial distribution will be unstable.

If several kinds of particle take part in the oscillations, then $\Omega_e^2 F_0'(w)$ should be replaced in the formula (12.1) by $\psi'(w) \equiv \sum_\alpha \Omega_\alpha^2 F_\alpha'(w)$, where $F_\alpha(w)$ is the initial distribution function of particles of the α-th kind normalized to unity and $\Omega_\alpha^2 = 4\pi e_\alpha^2 n_\alpha / m_\alpha$.

Therefore the necessary and sufficient condition for stability of the particle distributions of a free plasma with respect to the longitudinal oscillations consists of the absence of roots of the equation

$$y = G(s) \equiv \int_{-\infty}^{\infty} \frac{\psi'(w)\, dw}{w - s} = k^2 \tag{12.2}$$

in the upper half-plane of s ($s = ip/k$) for any value of k ($k > 0$).

It is easy to see that the presence of roots in the equation (12.2) in the upper half-plane of s is equivalent to the fact that the curve K described by the point $y = G(s)$, when s runs through the real axis, intersects the positive y half-axis. In actual fact, if the curve K intersects the positive y half-axis, for example at the point A (see Fig. 7b), then near this point there is always another point B corresponding to $\operatorname{Im} s > 0$ for which $\operatorname{Re} y > 0$, $\operatorname{Im} y = 0$. The quantity s_B corresponding to the point B is a root of the equation (12.2) when $k^2 = \operatorname{Re} y_B$.

If the curve K does not intersect the positive y half-axis the equation (12.2) has no roots in the upper half-plane. In actual fact, the integral defining the function $y = G(s)$ exists for any values of s lying in the upper half-plane. Therefore the curve K should be closed and the region D, which is an image of the upper half-plane s, will be enclosed inside the curve K. It follows from this that the function $y = G(s)$ cannot equal any positive value of k^2 for any value of s lying in the upper half-plane, i.e. the equation (12.2) has no roots in the upper half-plane of s.

Three typical curves are shown in Fig. 7a, b, c [Gertsenshtein, 1952b; Penrose, 1960; Akhiezer, Lyubarskii and Polovin, 1961].

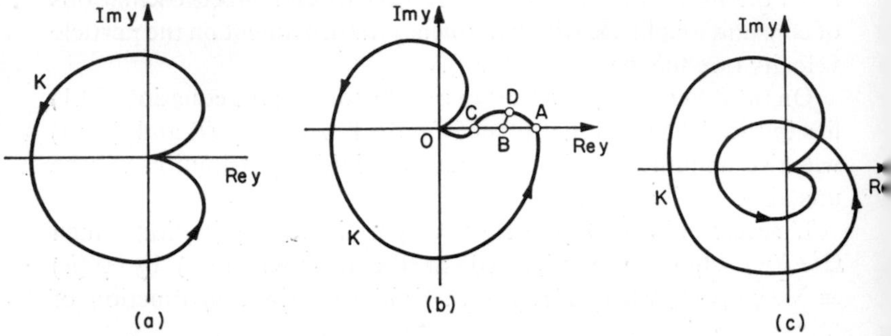

FIG. 7. Contour K: (a) stable distribution; (b) and (c) different types of unstable distribution.

Figure 7a corresponds to the absence of roots of the equation (12.2) in the upper half-plane, i.e. to stability. Figures 7b and c correspond to the presence of such roots, i.e. to instability.

Let us define the conditions under which the curve K intersects the positive y half-axis. This intersection means that for a certain real value of s the quantity

$$y = P\int_{-\infty}^{\infty} \frac{\psi'(w)\,dw}{w-s} + \pi i\psi'(s)$$

(P denotes the principal value) is positive, i.e.

$$\psi'(s) = 0, \quad P\int_{-\infty}^{\infty} \frac{\psi'(w)\,dw}{w-s} > 0.$$

The first of these conditions is satisfied at the extremum points $w_1, w_2, \ldots, w_n$ of the function $\psi(w)$. Therefore for instability of the distribution it is necessary and sufficient to satisfy at least one of the inequalities

$$\int_{-\infty}^{\infty} \frac{\psi'(w)\,dw}{w-w_j} > 0, \quad j = 1, 2, \ldots, n. \tag{12.3}$$

If at all the extremum points of the function $\psi(w)$ the inverse inequalities

$$\int_{-\infty}^{\infty} \frac{\psi'(w)\,dw}{w - w_j} < 0 \qquad (12.4)$$

are satisfied for all values $j = 1, 2, \ldots, n$, then the distribution $\psi(w)$ will be stable.

It is easy to show that if the conditions (12.4) are satisfied only at the minimum points they are satisfied at all the extremum points, i.e. the distribution $\psi(w)$ will in this case be stable.

In actual fact, when the point s moves along the real axis from $-\infty$ to $+\infty$ the upper half-plane of s stays on the left. Therefore when the point y moves along the curve K the region D lying inside the curve K also remains on the left. This means that the point y either does not intersect the positive half-axis at all or cuts it at least once moving from the lower to the upper half-plane (see Fig. 7b, c). In this case $\psi'(w)$ moves from negative to positive values, which is possible only in the neighbourhood of the minimum of $\psi(w)$.

Thus the criterion for stability of the distribution functions is of the form†

$$\int_{-\infty}^{\infty} \frac{\psi'(w)\,dw}{w - w_j} < 0, \quad \psi'(w_j) = 0, \quad \psi''(w_j) > 0. \qquad (12.5)$$

The stability condition (12.5) can be given another form if we integrate by parts [Penrose, 1960; Noerdlinger, 1960]

$$\int_{-\infty}^{\infty} \frac{\psi(w) - \psi(w_j)}{(w - w_j)^2}\,dw < 0, \quad \psi'(w_j) = 0, \quad \psi''(w_j) > 0. \qquad (12.6)$$

It can be concluded from this that the distribution will be unstable if the function $\psi(w)$ becomes zero at an isolated point (since by definition $\psi(w) \geq 0$, at this point $\psi(w)$ has a minimum).

We shall show that if the distribution $\psi(w)$ is unstable we have the inequality

$$\psi'(V_\varphi) > 0, \qquad (12.7)$$

where $V_\varphi = \mathrm{Re}\, s$ and s is a root of the equation (12.2).

† This criterion has been independently established in various papers [Gertsenshtein, 1952b; Penrose, 1960; Akhiezer, Lyubarskii and Polovin, 1961; Noerdlinger, 1960].

The proof follows directly from Fig. 7b. Let A be the point of the minimum of $\psi(w)$, B be the point at which s is a root of the equation (12.2) and C is the point of the maximum of $\psi(w)$. Through the point B we shall draw a line Re s = const. which intersects the curve K at the point D lying between the minimum A and the maximum C. Since the values of s rise as one moves along the arc AC the derivative $\psi'(s_D)$ will be positive at a value of s corresponding to the point D.

The instability condition (12.7) has a simple physical meaning. Since V_φ is obviously the phase velocity of a wave with the frequency $\omega = k$ Re s the condition (12.7) means that the number of particles that give up energy to the wave is larger than the number of particles receiving energy from the wave [Bohm and Gross, 1949]. We should mention that in an equilibrium plasma $F_0'(V_\varphi) < 0$, i.e. the number of particles receiving energy from the wave is larger than the number of particles giving up energy to the wave; thanks to this, as has already been pointed out above, the oscillations in an equilibrium plasma are damped.

It follows directly from the stability criterion (12.5) that a distribution function having only one maximum is stable [Gerstenshtein, 1952b; Walker, 1955; Auer, 1958]. In particular if the initial distribution functions $F_\alpha(v)$ are spherically symmetrical (with an arbitrary number of maxima and minima) and nowhere become zero, then the function $\psi(w)$ has a unique maximum (at the point $w = 0$). Therefore the spherically symmetrical particle distributions are stable [Ginzburg, 1959; Kovrizhnykh and Rukhadze, 1960].

When deriving the instability criterion of the distribution function (12.3) we made no allowance for collisions between particles. These collisions obviously prevent the development of instability. Therefore the increment of the oscillations' increase in the case of an unstable distribution function should exceed a certain minimum value determined by the effective frequency of the oscillations for instability really to develop.

If the distribution function is unstable, then at the same time as the increase in the oscillations there will be a change in the particle distribution leading to a decrease and finally to a cessation of the increase of the oscillations. An investigation of this phenomenon requires us to take account of non-linear effects which we shall not discuss here. We shall merely remark that the unstable "twin-hump" distribution (Fig. 8) is deformed into a distribution with a plateau as a result of the development of instability in a time of the order of $1/\gamma$, where γ is the increment of the oscillations' increase in the linear theory. This plateau distribution gradually approaches a

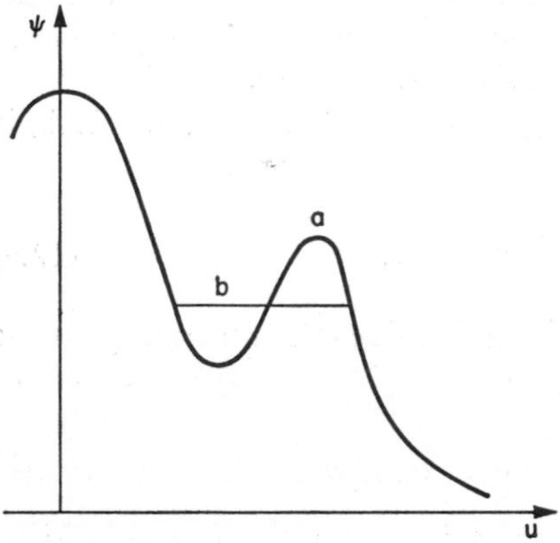

FIG. 8. Twin-hump distribution function (a) and distribution function with plateau (b).

Maxwellian distribution in a time of the order of the mean time between collisions τ [Vedenov, 1962; Vedenov, Velikhov and Sagdeyev, 1962; Drummond and Pines, 1963; Shapiro, 1963] (it is assumed that $\gamma\tau \gg 1$).

2. Two-Beam Instability

The conditions (12.5), (12.6) can be applied to an investigation of the question of the stability of a system of two infinite interpenetrating beams of charged particles moving with parallel or antiparallel velocities.

We shall use $F_1(w)$ and $F_2(w)$ to denote the distribution functions of the particles in these beams. If v_1 and v_2 are the thermal velocities of the particles in the beams and u_1, u_2 their directional velocities the values of the functions $F_{1,2}$ will be close to zero when $|w - u_{1,2}| \gg v_{1,2}$. If the difference between u_1 and u_2 is large enough, i.e. $|u_1 - u_2| \gg v_1 + v_2$, the minimum value of ψ will also be close to zero. It may be concluded from this, in accordance with the condition (12.6), that the distribution function will be unstable.

Therefore when the inequality

$$|u_1 - u_2| \gg v_1 + v_2 \tag{12.8}$$

is satisfied a system of two beams will be unstable.

The instability condition (12.8) is equally valid for a neutralized electron beam moving through a plasma (if we neglect the ion oscillations) and for a plasma whose electrons are moving relative to the ions (taking the ion oscillations into consideration). Unlike the results of the preceding sections we are not making any assumptions here about the lowness of the beam density.

Let us now examine different cases when the condition (12.8) is not satisfied.

If

$$|u_1 - u_2| \ll v_1 + v_2, \quad v_1 \sim v_2, \tag{12.9}$$

then a two-beam system will be stable since the function $\psi(w)$ has no minimum.

If

$$|u_1 - u_2| \ll v_1, \quad v_1 \gg v_2, \quad a_1 \lesssim a_2, \tag{12.10}$$

(where a_1, a_2 are the Debye radii of the particles in the beam), then, as can be seen directly from the condition (12.6), a two-beam system will be stable.

Finally, in the case

$$|u_1 - u_2| \ll v_1, \quad v_1 \gg v_2, \quad a_1 \gg a_2 \tag{12.11}$$

from the necessary stability condition—the existence of a minimum for the function $\psi(w)$— there follows the instability condition

$$|u_1 - u_2| \gg v_2. \tag{12.12}$$

TABLE 1. STABILITY AND INSTABILITY CONDITIONS OF A TWO-BEAM SYSTEM

<table>
<tr><td>$|u_1 - u_2| \gg v_1 + v_2$</td><td colspan="4">$|u_1 - u_2| \ll v_1 + v_2$</td></tr>
<tr><td rowspan="4">Instability</td><td>$v_1 \sim v_2$</td><td colspan="3">$v_1 \gg v_2$</td></tr>
<tr><td rowspan="3">Stability</td><td>$a_1 \lesssim a_2$</td><td colspan="2">$a_1 \gg a_2$</td></tr>
<tr><td rowspan="2">Stability</td><td>$|u_1 - u_2| < v_2$</td><td>$|u_1 - u_2| > v_2$</td></tr>
<tr><td>Stability</td><td>Instability</td></tr>
</table>

In the special case of a plasma with hot electrons which move relative to cold ions the instability, as is shown in subsection 4 of section 10, is connected with the excitation of ion Langmuir oscillations. It can be shown that this instability is connected with increasing oscillations with high values of $k(1/a_1 \ll k \ll 1/a_2)$.

The stability and instability conditions for a system of two beams under different conditions are shown in Table 1.

3. *Stability and Instability Criteria for Electron Distributions of a Plasma in a Magnetic Field*

Let us find the stability conditions for the distribution function of the electrons of a plasma located in an external magnetic field $\boldsymbol{H}_0$ in relation to the longitudinal electron oscillations.

Assuming the length of the plasma waves to be long enough $(kv_e/\omega_e \ll 1)$, we can put the longitudinal oscillation dispersion equation $A = 0$ in the form

$$1 - \frac{\Omega_e^2 \cos^2\theta}{k_{\|}} \int_{-\infty}^{\infty} \frac{F_0'(w)\, dw}{k_{\|} w - \omega} + \frac{\Omega_e^2 \sin^2\theta}{2\omega_e} \times$$

$$\times \int_{-\infty}^{\infty} \left(\frac{1}{k_{\|} w - \omega + \omega_e} - \frac{1}{k_{\|} w - \omega - \omega_e} \right) F_0(w)\, dw = 0, \quad (12.13)$$

where $F_0(w)$ is the electron distribution function with respect to the longitudinal component (relative to $\boldsymbol{H}_0$) of the velocity w; $k_{\|} = k \cos\theta$ and θ is the angle between $\boldsymbol{k}$ and $\boldsymbol{H}_0$.

Introducing the notation

$$\psi_H'(w) = F_0'(w) \cos^2\theta + \frac{F_0(w + s_H) - F_0(w - s_H)}{2 s_H} \sin^2\theta, \quad (12.14)$$

where $s_H = \omega_e/k_{\|}$, we can rewrite the equation (12.13) in the form

$$G_H(s) \equiv \int_{-\infty}^{\infty} \frac{\psi_H'(w)\, dw}{w - s} = \frac{k_{\|}^2}{\Omega_e^2}, \quad (12.15)$$

where $s = \omega/k_{\|}$.

By comparing this equation with the equation (12.2) it is easy to see that the necessary and sufficient stability condition for the distribution function $F_0(w)$ is that the roots s of the equation (12.15) should not lie in the upper half-plane of s.

In the case of instability, as has been shown above, the function $y = G_H(s)$ maps the real s axis onto a certain curve K intersecting the real positive half-axis (we should mention that as the value of s increases the curve K intersects the real positive y half-axis at least once, moving from the lower to the upper half-plane).

The electron distribution is stable if for all values of $s = w_j$ for which the function $\psi_H(w)$ defined by the formula (12.14) has a minimum the conditions

$$\int_{-\infty}^{\infty} \frac{\psi_H'(w)\, dw}{w - w_j} < 0 \qquad (12.16)$$

are satisfied [Akhiezer, Lyubarskii and Polovin, 1961].

We notice that if we put $\theta = 0$, $s_H = 0$ or $s_H = \infty$ in the expression (12.14) for $\psi_H'(w)$, then $\psi_H'(w)$ is the same as $F_H'(w)$. Therefore if $\theta = 0$ or $s_H = 0$ or $s_H = \infty$ the stability conditions (12.16) are the same as the stability conditions when there is no magnetic field. It follows from this that a magnetic field, generally speaking, reduces the size of the class of stable distribution functions.

It can be shown [Polovin, 1964] that the stability conditions (12.16) are satisfied only for an even distribution function with one maximum.†

Up to now in studying the distribution function stability condition we have not fixed the value of k (the quantities Ω_e and θ were not fixed either when investigating the distribution functions in a magnetic field).

The problem can, however, be put in another way [Ozawa, Kaji and Kito, 1961] by determining the stability conditions for fixed values of k, θ and Ω_e. When the question is put in this way the stability criterion can be obtained if we slightly alter the arguments in sub-section 1 of this section.

In the case when the value of k^2 in the right-hand side of the equation (12.2) is not fixed there is instability if the curve K which is a mapping of the real s axis onto the plane $y = G(s)$ intersects the y half-axis at an arbitrary point. In this case we must always

† In particular the anisotropic distribution $F_0(v) = f(v_\parallel^2, v_\perp^2)$ is stable relative to long-wave longitudinal electron oscillations. This function may, however, be unstable for longitudinal oscillations if we take into consideration the higher-order terms in the expansion of the dispersion equation in powers of kv_e/ω_e [Ozawa, Kaji and Kito, 1961; Sen, 1952; Harris, 1959; Burt and Harris, 1961].

select a value for k so that the region D bounded by the contour K contains the point Re $y = k^2$, which also means the presence of instability.

If the value of k is fixed, it is sufficient for instability for the contour K to intersect the positive y half-axis. It is also necessary for the point k^2 to lie in the region D. In other words, the stability criterion for fixed k consists in that the function

$$W(s) \equiv \int_{-\infty}^{\infty} \frac{\psi'(w)\,dw}{w - s} - k^2$$

maps the upper half-plane Im $s \geq 0$ onto the region D which does not contain the origin of the coordinates $W = 0$.

The stability criterion when there is a magnetic field is formulated in just the same way if the values of k, θ and Ω_e are fixed. In this case it is necessary merely to replace the function $W(s)$ by $W_H(s)$:

$$W_H(s) \equiv \int_{-\infty}^{\infty} \frac{\psi_H'(w)\,dw}{w - s} - \frac{k_{\|}^2}{\Omega_e^2}.$$

In order to find out whether the point $W = 0$ is in the region D it is sufficient to know the signs of the quantities $W(w_1)$, $W(w_2), \ldots,$ $W(w_n)$ [Ozawa, Kaji and Kito, 1961], where w_i are the extremum points of the function $\psi_H(w)$. If the signs of the quantities $W(w_i)$ are known the question of whether there is stability or instability of the distribution can be elucidated as follows.

We put the quantities $w_1, w_2, \ldots, w_n$ in increasing order: $w_1 < w_2 < \cdots < w_n$. In the same order we put the signs (plus or minus) of the quantities $W(w_1)$, $W(w_2)$, ..., $W(w_n)$. We cross out in turn two identical signs standing next to each other. If there is only one sign left after this crossing out (it may be only a minus) the distribution is stable. If after crossing out we have left a sequence of alternating signs (these can be only the sequences $-+-$, $-+-+-$, $-+-+-+-$, etc.) the distribution is unstable [Ozawa, Kaji and Kito, 1961].

For example, the sequence of signs $++-+-$ denotes instability and the sequence of signs $+--+-$ denotes stability.

13. Absolute and Convective Instabilities; Amplification and Blocking of Oscillations

1. Criteria of Absolute and Convective Instabilities

When investigating the question of the stability of the plasma particle distribution functions in the preceding sections we started with the linearized kinetic equations and the Maxwell equations and obtained as a condition of their solubility the dispersion equation $F(\boldsymbol{k}, \omega) = 0$ which connects the frequency ω and the wave vector $\boldsymbol{k}$ of the oscillations. If real values of $\boldsymbol{k}$ correspond to complex ω with $\operatorname{Im} \omega > 0$ the perturbations, which take the form of plane monochromatic waves $e^{i[(\boldsymbol{k}\cdot\boldsymbol{r})-\omega t]}$, grow without limit with time and the distribution function is unstable.

In actual fact, however, small perturbations do not take the form of individual plane monochromatic waves but are superpositions

$$u(\boldsymbol{r}, t) = \int a_k \, e^{i[(\boldsymbol{k}\cdot\boldsymbol{r})-\omega t]} \, d^3\boldsymbol{k}, \tag{13.1}$$

where ω and $\boldsymbol{k}$ are connected by the dispersion equation $F(\boldsymbol{k}, \omega) = 0$ and a_k is determined by the initial perturbation

$$a_k = (2\pi)^{-3} \int u(\boldsymbol{r}, 0) \, e^{-i(\boldsymbol{k}\cdot\boldsymbol{r})} \, d^3\boldsymbol{r}$$

($u(\boldsymbol{r}, t)$ denotes any one of a number of quantities, for example the density-, velocity-, field-, $\cdots$ perturbations).

If the individual Fourier components in the wave packet (13.1) grow without limit with time the whole packet may nevertheless remain limited at a fixed point in space. In order to explain this we expand $\omega(\boldsymbol{k})$ into the real and imaginary parts $\omega = \omega' + i\omega''$ and put $r = 0$ in (13.1)

$$u(0, t) = \int a_k \, e^{-i\omega'(k)t} \, e^{\omega''(k)t} \, d^3\boldsymbol{k}. \tag{13.2}$$

If $\omega'' > 0$ the factor $e^{\omega'' t}$ approaches infinity when $t \to \infty$. On the other hand, the factor $e^{-i\omega' t}$ is a rapidly oscillating function which averages to zero with time after multiplying by the continuous function and integrating with respect to $\boldsymbol{k}$. Therefore the expression (13.2) is an indeterminate quantity of the $0 \times \infty$ type, i.e. it may be infinitely great or zero.

Therefore when investigating the instability it is not enough to know that complex frequencies exist for the equation $F(\boldsymbol{k}, \omega) = 0$

and we still have to find out how the wave packet (13.1) behaves at a fixed point in space when $t \to \infty$. It is clear that this way of putting the question is not characteristic for a plasma alone. Therefore the results obtained below are applicable when studying the stability of any system, whether it be mechanical or electrodynamic.

If the perturbation $u(\boldsymbol{r}, t)$ for fixed $\boldsymbol{r}$ and $t \to \infty$ rises without limit the instability is called absolute. If, on the other hand, despite the presence in the packet (13.1) of Fourier components with $\operatorname{Im} \omega > 0$ the perturbation for $\boldsymbol{r} = \text{const.}$ and $t \to \infty$ remains limited (in this case it generally approaches zero) we speak of convective instability. It may be said that in this case the velocity of the packet as a whole is so great that the perturbation is, as it were, "carried away downstream" [Landau and Lifshitz, 1960b].

In order to explain what causes the difference between the absolute and convective instability let us take for the sake of simplicity the one-dimensional case and assume that the function $F(k, \omega)$ is a polynomial in k and ω. (The investigation of the general case when the equation $F(k, \omega) = 0$ is transcendental is full of mathematical difficulties.)

The assumption of the algebraic nature of the dispersion equation corresponds to replacing the system of the initial kinetic equations and Maxwell equations (which is integro-differential) by a system of equations in partial derivatives with constant coefficients

$$\sum_{k=1}^{n} \left(X_{ik} \frac{\partial u_k}{\partial x} + T_{ik} \frac{\partial u_k}{\partial t} + C_i u_i \right) = 0, \tag{13.3}$$

where X_{ik}, T_{ik}, C_i are constants ($i = 1, 2, \ldots, n$). This system should be hyperbolic since it describes unsteady processes so all its characteristics† should be real. Since the coefficients X_{ik}, T_{ik} and C_i are constant all the characteristics should be straight lines and the angle of inclination of the characteristics to the t axis should be the same at each point (x, t).

Let us assume at first that two characteristics pass through each point (x, t). In this case we can imagine the two cases shown in Fig. 9. The difference between these cases is that in Fig. 9a the char-

† Let us recall the definition of the characteristics. If the perturbation is given on a certain arc AB in the plane (x, t) it affects the solution $u(x, t)$ of the system only in the region bounded by the characteristics passing through the points A and B.

acteristics AA_1 and AA_2 starting from any point A run in one direction,† whilst in Fig. 9b they run in different directions (since in the case of a system of equations with constant coefficients the direction of the characteristics does not depend on the choice of

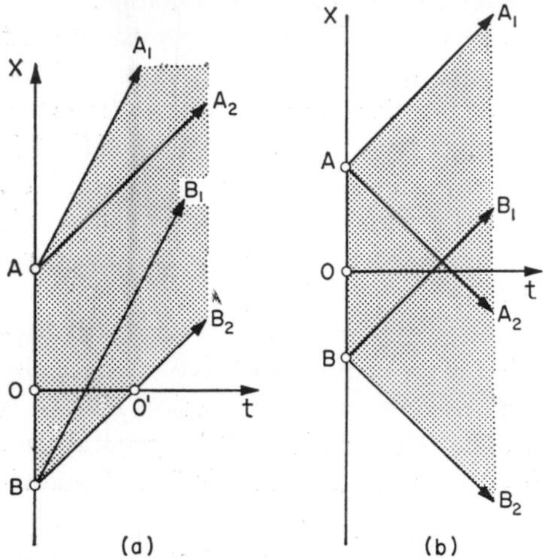

FIG. 9. Region of influence of perturbation given on section AB: (a) characteristics running in one direction; (b) characteristics running in opposite directions.

point the characteristics BB_1 and BB_2 will be parallel to the characteristics AA_1 and AA_2 at any other point).

Let the perturbation $u(x, 0)$ at $t = 0$ be non-zero on a finite section AB of the x axis‡ (see Fig. 9). Since the characteristics are lines separating the perturbed from the unperturbed region the perturbation at any point in time is non-zero in the region A_1ABB_2 bounded by the most "extreme" characteristics AA_1 and BB_2 and are zero outside this region [Courant and Hilbert, 1962].

In the case shown in Fig. 9a the perturbation at the point $x = 0$ is non-zero only for a finite time interval (on the section OO'), whilst in Fig. 9b the perturbation at the point $x = 0$ is always non-zero, so Fig. 9a corresponds to convective instability and Fig. 9b to absolute instability.

Therefore if the characteristics run in the same direction there is convective instability; if the characteristics run in opposite directions there is absolute instability.

† A positive direction on the characteristic corresponds to increasing time t.

‡ The criteria obtained below for absolute and convective instabilities are valid on a more general assumption: that the initial perturbation $u(x, 0)$ approaches zero rapidly enough as $|x|$ rises [Polovin, 1961, 1963].

Let us now determine the connexion between the direction of the characteristics and the nature of the dispersion curve $F(k, \omega) = 0$.

We shall first find the characteristics of the system (13.3). Since a characteristic separates a perturbed from an unperturbed region the normal derivatives $\partial u_i/\partial n$ cannot be determined unambiguously by the equations (13.3) if we are given all the quantities u_i along the characteristics (and thus also their derivatives $\partial u_i/\partial s$ along the direction of the characteristic). Denoting the tangent of the angle of inclination of the characteristic of the t axis by V we can express $\partial u_i/\partial x$ and $\partial u_i/\partial t$ in terms of $\partial u_i/\partial s$ and $\partial u_i/\partial n$:

$$\left.\begin{aligned} \frac{\partial u_i}{\partial t} &= \frac{1}{\sqrt{V^2+1}}\frac{\partial u_i}{\partial s} - \frac{V}{\sqrt{V^2+1}}\frac{\partial u_i}{\partial n}; \\ \frac{\partial u_i}{\partial x} &= \frac{V}{\sqrt{V^2+1}}\frac{\partial u_i}{\partial s} + \frac{1}{\sqrt{V^2+1}}\frac{\partial u_i}{\partial n}. \end{aligned}\right\}$$

Substituting these relations in the equations (13.3) we obtain

$$\sum_{k=1}^{n} (X_{ik} - VT_{ik}) \frac{\partial u_k}{\partial n} = - \sum_{k=1}^{n} (VX_{ik} + T_{ik}) \frac{\partial u_k}{\partial s} - C_i u_i \sqrt{V^2+1}. \tag{13.4}$$

The unknowns are in the right-hand side of the equations (13.4). For us to be unable to determine the normal derivatives $\partial u_i/\partial n$ from these equations it is necessary for the determinant of the system to be equal to zero:

$$\det (X_{ik} - VT_{ik}) = 0. \tag{13.5}$$

This equation, which is an n-th order polynomial in V, defines the tangents of the inclination of the n characteristics.

On the other hand we must find the solution of the system (13.3) in the form $u_i = u_i^0 e^{i(kx-\omega t)}$ in order to obtain the dispersion equation $F(k, \omega) = 0$. In this case the system (13.3) becomes

$$\sum_{k=1}^{n} (i\,kX_{ik} - i\,\omega T_{ik} + C_i\delta_{ik})\, u_k^0 = 0.$$

Putting the determinant of this system equal to zero we obtain the dispersion equation

$$F(k, \omega) \equiv \det (i\, kX_{ik} - i\, \omega T_{ik} + C_i \delta_{ik}) = 0. \qquad (13.6)$$

For large k and ω the term $C_i \delta_{ik}$ can be neglected in this equation:

$$\det \left(X_{ik} - \frac{\omega}{k} T_{ik} \right) = 0, \quad k \to \infty.$$

A comparison of this equation with the equation (13.5) for determining the tangent of the inclination of the characteristics V shows that

$$\lim_{k \to \infty} \frac{\omega}{k} = V,$$

i.e. the angle of inclination of the characteristics is equal to the angle of inclination of the dispersion curve asymptote.

It follows from this that the nature of the instability can be determined at once if we have a graph of the dispersion function $F(k, \omega) = 0$. Four typical dispersion curves are shown in Fig. 10. In Fig. 10a the straight line k = const. intersects the dispersion curve for any values of the constant, i.e. each real value of k corresponds to real values of ω. Therefore Fig. 10a corresponds to a stable state.

On the other hand, in Fig. 10b, c and d there is a range of values of k ($k_A < k < k_B$) for which the straight line k = const. does not cut the dispersion curve, i.e. these values of k correspond to complex values of ω, so in these cases there is instability.

The difference between Fig. 10b, c and Fig. 10d is that Fig. 10b, c correspond to characteristics running in one direction and Fig. 10d to characteristics running in different directions. Figures 10b, c therefore correspond to a convective instability and Fig. 10d to absolute instability (Fig. 10b corresponds to characteristics directed towards increasing values of x, and Fig. 10c to characteristics directed towards decreasing values of x).

The difference between the convective and absolute instabilities may be formulated slightly differently. In Fig. 10b there is a range of real frequencies ($\omega_D < \omega < \omega_C$) which does not correspond to real k, whilst there is no such range in Fig. 10d. Therefore

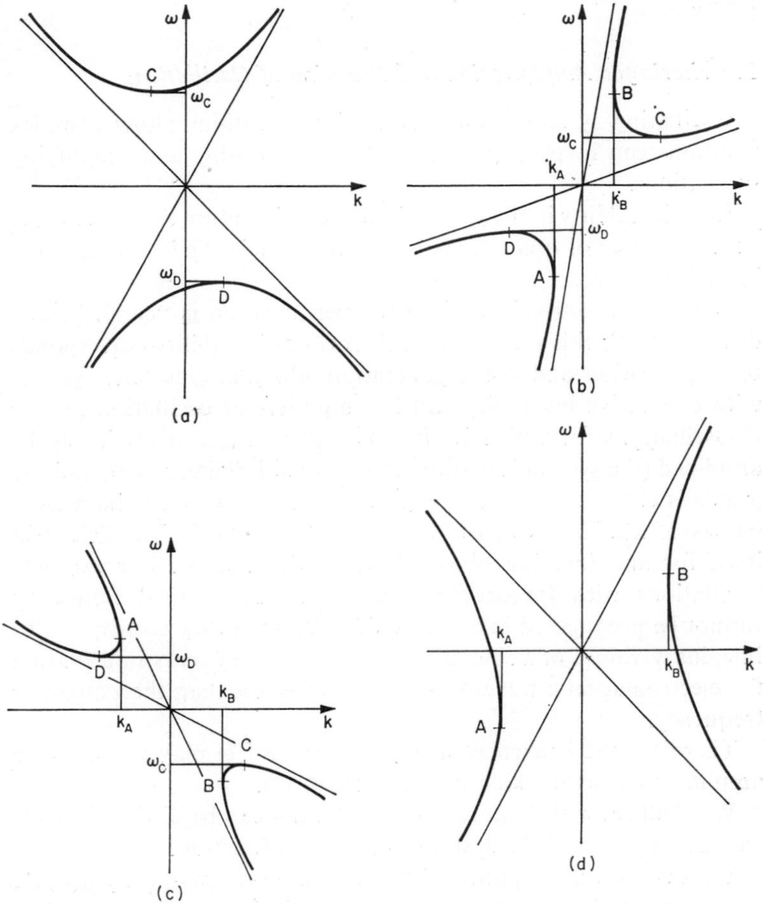

FIG. 10. Dispersion curves: (a) stability, blocking; (b) convective instability and amplification of waves moving in positive direction of the x axis; (c) convective instability and amplification of waves moving in negative direction of the x axis; (d) absolute stability, passing.

with convective instability real ω correspond to complex k, and with absolute instability real ω correspond to real k [Sturrock, 1960].

2. *Criteria for Amplification and Blocking of Oscillations*

Oscillating systems whose dispersion equations allow complex solutions can in principle be used for generating and amplifying oscillations.

If the instability in the system is absolute in nature the system may be a generator of oscillations whose frequencies lie in the absolute instability range.

With a convective instability the perturbation is "carried away downstream"; this means that this form of instability corresponds to amplification and not to generation of oscillations,† i.e. systems with convective instability can be amplifiers of oscillations.

Oscillations for which $\text{Im}\, k < 0$ with real ω can obviously be amplified (the system is assumed to be semi-infinite, $x > 0$, and the x axis is chosen so that the characteristics run towards increasing values of x). However, the condition $\text{Im}\, k < 0$ is insufficient in itself for amplification of oscillations with real ω. For example oscillations with frequencies lower than the critical frequency cannot be propagated in a waveguide although they correspond to imaginary values of k. An analogous situation occurs in a plasma for electromagnetic waves with frequencies less than the Langmuir frequency.

Therefore the existence of real k with real ω may mean either amplification or blocking of the oscillations.

We shall show that these two possibilities can be distinguished if we have a graph of the system's dispersion function.

We denote the amplified signal at the point $x = 0$ by $u(0, t)$, where $u(0, t)$ in any one of the system's independent dynamic variables. Then the value of the signal at the point x at the time t will be

$$u(x, t) = \int_{-\infty}^{\infty} b(\omega)\, e^{i(kx - \omega t)}\, d\omega, \qquad (13.7)$$

† Nevertheless systems with convective instability can also be used for generating oscillations if we connect their input and output; thanks to this there is feedback and the perturbation which has been "carried away" returns, i.e. the instability in the system becomes absolute.

where $k = k(\omega)$ is the solution of the dispersion equation $F(k, \omega) = 0$ and $b(\omega)$ is a Fourier component of the function $u(0, t)$:

$$b(\omega) = \frac{1}{2\pi} \int_{-\infty}^{\infty} u(0, t)\, e^{i\omega t}\, dt.$$

For the sake of simplicity we shall assume that $u(0, t)$ is equal to zero for large enough values of $|t|$. Since the signal is propagated from the point $x = 0$ towards increasing values of x and its propagation velocity is finite, for any finite t and $x \to \infty$ the quantity u should become zero:

$$u(\infty, t) = 0. \tag{13.8}$$

This condition imposes certain requirements on the nature of the dispersion function. To establish them we notice that the condition $u(\infty, t) = 0$ is formally analogous to the condition $u(x, \infty) = 0$ which is satisfied in the case of convective instability and the form (13.7) of the function $u(x, t)$ is analogous to the form (13.1) of the function $u(x, t)$ with convective instability.

If we make the replacement $x \rightleftarrows t, \omega \rightleftarrows k$ in the relations relating to the convective instability case we obtain the relations relating to the case of amplification of oscillations. Since convective instability occurs if real k corresponds to complex ω and real ω corresponds to complex k, amplification of the oscillations occurs if real ω corresponds to complex k and real k corresponds to complex ω.

We see that the criteria are formulated in the same way, in other words convective stability and oscillation amplification corresponds to exactly the same type of dispersion curve shown in Fig. 10b. (The dispersion curve shown in Fig. 10c corresponds to amplified waves being propagated towards decreasing values of x.)

Therefore systems with convective instability can be oscillation amplifiers.

We notice that the band of amplified frequencies, as can be seen from Fig. 10b, is narrower than the band of frequencies corresponding to convective instability, and the band of amplified wave vectors is broader than the band of wave vectors corresponding to convective instability.

By establishing the amplification criterion we have also established the oscillation blocking criterion. In actual fact, since both these possibilities correspond to complex values of k for real ω and amplification requires in addition that real k corresponds to complex ω, suppression of oscillations occurs if real ω corresponds to complex k and real k corresponds to real ω.

Figure 10a shows that the dispersion function corresponds to oscillation blocking. In fact, in the range $\omega_D < \omega < \omega_C$ real ω corresponds to complex k and real k always corresponds to real ω.

Therefore if all the real values of k correspond to real ω and all the real values of ω to real k, then there is stability and transmission of the oscillations.

If, however, some real values of k correspond to real ω and all real values of ω to real k, we have absolute instability and blocking of the oscillations.

If all real values of k correspond to real ω and certain real values of ω to complex k, then stability and blocking of the oscillations occur.

Finally, if certain real values of k correspond to complex ω and certain real values of ω to complex k, then there is convective instability and amplification of the oscillations.†

All these criteria are listed in Table 2.

TABLE 2. CRITERIA OF ABSOLUTE AND CONVECTIVE INSTABILITIES, AMPLIFICATION AND BLOCKING OF OSCILLATIONS

		Real ω correspond to	
		real k	complex k
Real k correspond to	real ω	passing / stability	blocking / stability
	complex ω	passing / absolute instability	amplification / convective instability

The corresponding processes are shown in this table at the intersection of the rows and columns corresponding to the different cases of real and complex ω and k. The cells are divided by diagonals into two parts to stress that stability and instability are determined by the nature of ω (i.e. its reality or complexity) and the passing and amplification (or blocking) by the nature of k.

† These criteria have been derived in Sturrock's paper [1959]; a strict proof has been given in Polovin's papers [1961, 1963].

Let us now examine the difference in the ways of posing the problems of stability and amplification (or blocking) of the oscillations.

In the problem of the stability the initial data are given on a straight line $t = 0$ from which all the characteristics originate so all the quantities in $u(x, 0)$ are independent. It follows in particular from this that for absolute instability the perturbation $u(0, t)$ at the point $x = 0$ (or at any other fixed point) rises infinitely when $t \to \infty$ [Polovin, 1961, 1963].

In the amplification problem the initial data are given on the straight line $x = 0$. The characteristics may issue to the right and the left of this straight line. If wave amplification is investigated in the half-space $x > 0$ the number of independent components of the function $u(0, t)$ on the straight line $x = 0$ is equal to the number of characteristics issuing to the right of this straight line. For example, in the case of passing corresponding to Fig. 10a the number of independent components is two. In the case of amplification corresponding to Fig. 10b the number of independent components is one. Finally in the case of amplification of waves running in the opposite direction corresponding to Fig. 10c the number of independent components is nought. In this case not a single wave is emitted by sources located on the straight line $x = 0$ on the side of increasing values of x.

Up to now it has been assumed that there are two characteristics, i.e. that the dispersion equation is a quadratic polynomial. However, the criteria of absolute and convective instabilities, amplification and blocking given in Table 2 are valid no matter what the power of the polynomial.

If the polynomial is more than quadratic there may be several ranges of real values of ω which correspond to complex values of k, for example the ranges (A, B), (C, D) and (E, F) in Fig. 11c.† Each of these ranges is bounded by the points where two real bran-

† Here we are splitting the branching points $A, B, C, D, E, F,$ of the function $k(\omega)$ into pairs. This breakdown is not, generally speaking, unambiguous. For example Fig. 11c also corresponds to the breakdown (A, D), (E, B), (C, F). In order to establish the correct breakdown into pairs one of the parameters in the dispersion equation (13.10) corresponding to Fig. 11c must be altered so that the branching points merge. For example when $\Omega \to 0$ the pairs of points (A, B) and (C, D) merge, which defines the correct breakdown into pairs. (It can be shown that the selection of the correct breakdown does not depend upon the selection of the parameter [Polovin, 1961, 1963].)

ches of the dispersion curve merge. If the asymptotes of these two branches point in the same direction amplification occurs, whilst if they point in opposite directions blocking of the oscillations

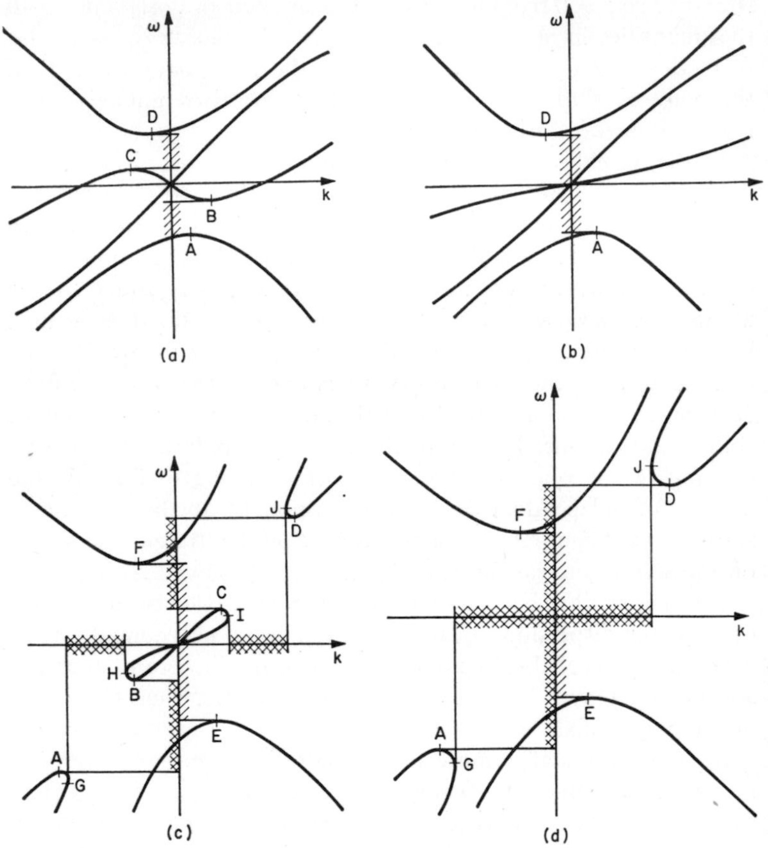

FIG. 11. Dispersion curve for interaction of cold beam with hot plasma ($\Omega' < \Omega$): (a) $u_0 < v_e \Omega'/\Omega$; (b) $v_e \Omega'/\Omega < u_0 < v_e$; (c) $v_e < u_0 < v_e \sqrt{1 + (\Omega'/\Omega)^2}$; (d) $v_e \sqrt{1 + (\Omega'/\Omega)^2} < u_0$.

occurs (for example, in Fig. 11c the frequency range (E, F) is the blocking band and the ranges (A, B) and (C, D) the amplification bands).

3. *Non-Invariant Nature of Concepts of Absolute and Convective Instabilities*

It is easy to see that the concepts of absolute and convective instabilities are not invariant with regard to the selection of the coordinate system. In actual fact, when changing to a coordinate system moving at a velocity v the frequency and wave vector are transformed by the formulae (in the non-relativistic case)

$$\omega' = \omega - kv, \qquad k' = k.$$

When the velocity v changes the asymptotes of the dispersion curves shown in Fig. 10 will rotate through the horizontal but not through the vertical. Therefore the dispersion curve shown in Fig. 10b can change into the dispersion curve shown in Fig. 10d. It follows from this that absolute instability can change into convective instability and vice versa. In particular convective instability becomes absolute if we change to a coordinate system moving at the wave's group velocity [Feix, 1963].

On the other hand, when changing to a moving coordinate system the dispersion curves shown in Fig. 10a, b cannot change into each other since the asymptote would pass through the vertical in this change. Therefore when changing to a moving coordinate system the amplification and blocking bands may disappear but they cannot change into each other.

4. *Nature of Beam Instability*

We shall illustrate the theory we have expounded by the example of a twin-beam tube [Sturrock, 1960] whose dispersion equation takes the form

$$\frac{\Omega_1^2}{(\omega - ku_1)^2} + \frac{\Omega_2^2}{(\omega - ku_2)^2} = 1, \tag{13.9}$$

where $\Omega_{1,2}^2 = 4\pi e^2 n_{1,2}/m_{1,2}$; $n_{1,2}$ and $u_{1,2}$ are the densities and velocities of the particles in the two beams and $m_{1,2}$ are the masses of the particles. This equation corresponds to the dispersion curve shown in Fig. 12a if the velocities u_1 and u_2 are in the same direction, and to the dispersion curve shown in Fig. 12b if the velocities u_1 and u_2 are in opposite directions. It can be immediately seen from these figures that when the signs of u_1 and u_2 are the same there is an amplification band and a convective instability band, whilst for u_1 and u_2 with different signs there is a blocking band and a band of absolute instability.

Let us now elucidate the nature of the instability that arises when a beam interacts with a plasma.

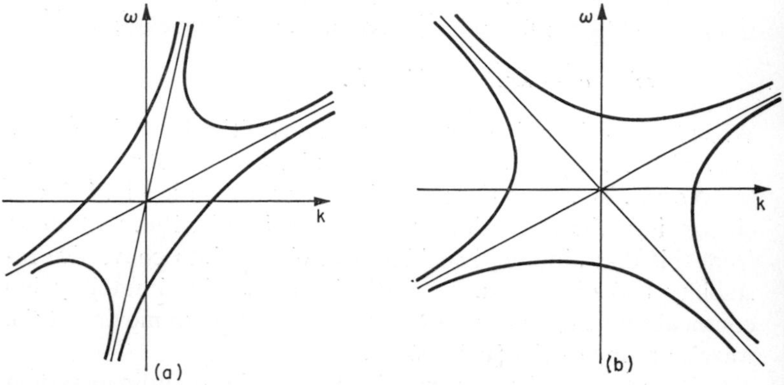

FIG. 12. Dispersion curve of twin-beam tube: (a) velocities of beams parallel; (b) velocities of beams anti-parallel.

If we use the kinetic equations to describe the plasma and beam, then, as we have seen in section 10, the dispersion of the plasma-beam system will be transcendental. We shall therefore simplify the problem and describe the plasma hydrodynamically (the plasma pressure is assumed to be n_0T); we shall take the beam to be cold. With these assumptions the dispersion equation of the plasma-beam system becomes

$$\frac{\Omega^2}{\omega^2 - k^2 v_e^2} + \frac{\Omega'^2}{(\omega - ku_0)^2} = 1, \tag{13.10}$$

where Ω, Ω' are the Langmuir frequencies of the plasma and the beam; v_e is the thermal velocity of the plasma electrons; u_0 is the velocity of the beam. This equation is algebraic so we can use the results obtained in the previous section.

The dispersion curves corresponding to the equation (13.10) are shown in Fig. 11 (for the sake of definition we are making $\Omega' < \Omega$). Figures 11a and b relate to the case $u_0 < v_e$, and Fig. 11c and d to the case $u_0 > v_e$; Fig. 11a corresponds to the beam velocity $u_0 < v_e\Omega'/\Omega$, Fig. 11b corresponds to $v_e\Omega'/\Omega < u_0 < v_e$, Fig. 11c corresponds to $v_e < u_0 < v_e\sqrt{1 + (\Omega'/\Omega)^2}$ and, lastly, Fig. 11d corresponds to $v_e\sqrt{1 + (\Omega'/\Omega)^2} < u_0$.

We see that in the case shown in Fig. 11a there are two blocking bands between the points (A, B) and (C, D) (the blocking bands are shown by shading on the ω axis). In Fig. 11b these two blocking bands merge into one (A, D).

It can be seen from Fig. 11a, b that when $u_0 < v_e$ the plasma-beam system is stable and wave amplification in this system is impossible.†

If $u_0 > u_e$ there is a blocking band in the range (E, F) (see Fig. 11c, d). In addition there are two amplification bands in the ranges (A, B) and (C, D) (see Fig. 11c; the amplification bands are shown by cross-hatching on the ω axis), or one amplification band (A, D) (see Fig. 11d). In Fig. 11c we can also see two convective instability bands (G, H) and (I, J) (they are marked by cross-hatching on the k axis), whilst in Fig. 11d these two bands of convective instability merge into one band (G, I)‡ [Sturrock 1960; Fainberg, Kurilko and Shapiro, 1961]. There are no regions of absolute instability.

We notice that an equation of the same type as (13.10) describes the oscillations of a beam passing through a waveguide. In this case all we have to do is to replace Ω by the boundary frequency of the waveguide and v_e by the velocity of a wave in the waveguide when there is no beam. If $u_0 > v_e$ there is convective instability or amplification of the oscillations (depending on the excitation conditions). If $u_0 < v_e$, then the motion of the beam is stable and amplification of the oscillations is impossible, although in this case the dispersion equation leads to complex values of k for real values of ω.

† This statement is valid only in the hydrodynamic approximation. When the kinetic effects are allowed for the plasma-beam system may be unstable even if $u_0 < v_e$ (see sub-section 3 of section 10).

‡ We note that this conclusion is not connected with the assumption of the low density of the beam.

CHAPTER IV

Fluctuations in a Plasma

14. Electromagnetic Fluctuations in an Equilibrium Plasma

1. Fluctuations in a Free Equilibrium Plasma

Knowing the spectra of the plasma oscillations we can move on to investigating the fluctuations in a plasma. As has already been pointed out at the beginning of the monograph such phenomena as thermal radiation and the various processes of electromagnetic wave and charged particle scattering in a plasma are connected with the fluctuations. A study of the correlations between the fluctuations may also be of interest in its own right for the purposes of plasma diagnostics.

Let us first examine the electromagnetic fluctuations in an equilibrium plasma.

We shall use $\boldsymbol{E}_{k\omega}$ and $\boldsymbol{j}_{k\omega}$ to denote the Fourier components of the electric and current density fluctuations. These quantities are connected by the Maxwell equations for a vacuum

$$\hat{\Lambda}^0 \boldsymbol{E}_{k\omega} = -\frac{4\pi i}{\omega} \boldsymbol{j}_{k\omega}, \tag{14.1}$$

where

$$\Lambda_{ij}^0 = n^2 \left(\frac{k_i k_j}{k^2} - \delta_{ij} \right) + \delta_{ij}; \quad n = \frac{ck}{\omega}.$$

In order to find the fluctuating fields and currents we must, as is well known [Callen and Welton, 1951; Leontovich and Rytov, 1952; Landau and Lifshitz, 1957b], formally introduce into the relations connecting the current and the field the subsidiary field $\mathscr{E}_{k\omega}$:

$$\boldsymbol{j}_{k\omega} = \frac{i\,\omega}{4\pi}\,(1 - \hat{\varepsilon})\,(\boldsymbol{E}_{k\omega} + \mathscr{E}_{k\omega}) \tag{14.2}$$

where $\hat{\varepsilon} \equiv \varepsilon_{ij}(\boldsymbol{k}, \omega)$ is the plasma's dielectric permittivity tensor. Next we must determine the alteration of the plasma's energy caused by the action of the subsidiary field. This alteration is, in unit time, obviously

$$\dot{U} = \frac{1}{2c}\,\mathrm{Re}\sum_{k\omega} i\omega\mathfrak{A}_{k\omega}\boldsymbol{j}^{*}_{k\omega}, \tag{14.3}$$

where $\mathfrak{A}_{k\omega}$ is a Fourier component of the subsidiary field's vector potential

$$\mathfrak{A}_{k\omega} = -i(c/\omega)\mathscr{E}_{k\omega}.$$

Using the equations (14.1) and (14.2) we can, by eliminating $\boldsymbol{E}_{k\omega}$, express the current $\boldsymbol{j}_{k\omega}$ by the subsidiary field $\mathfrak{A}_{k\omega}$:

$$\boldsymbol{j}_{k\omega} = \frac{1}{c}\,\hat{\alpha}\,\mathfrak{A}_{k\omega}, \tag{14.4}$$

where

$$\hat{\alpha} = \frac{\omega^2}{4\pi}\,(\hat{\Lambda}^0 - \hat{\Lambda}^0\hat{\Lambda}^{-1}\hat{\Lambda}^0) \tag{14.5}$$

and $\hat{\Lambda}^{-1}$ is the inverse tensor to the tensor $\hat{\Lambda}$ (see the formula (3.6′)),

$$\hat{\Lambda} = n^2\left(\frac{k_i k_j}{k^2} - \delta_{ij}\right) + \varepsilon_{ij};\quad \hat{\Lambda}^{-1} = \Delta^{-1}\hat{\lambda},\quad \Delta = \det\hat{\Lambda}. \tag{14.5′}$$

Substituting the expression (14.4) in the equation (14.3) we obtain

$$\dot{U} = \frac{1}{4c^2}\sum_{k\omega} i\omega(\alpha^{*}_{ij} - \alpha_{ji})\,\mathfrak{A}_i\mathfrak{A}^{*}_j. \tag{14.3′}$$

Having obtained the expression for the alteration in the plasma's energy due to the action of the subsidiary field and knowing the connexion (14.4) between the fluctuating quantity $\boldsymbol{j}_{k\omega}$ and the "random" force $\mathfrak{A}_{k\omega}$ we can at once find on the basis of the fluctuation–dissipation theorem the spectral distribution of the current fluctuations (see, for example, Landau and Lifshitz, 1957a, formulae (88.6), (88.9))‡

$$\langle j_i j_j \rangle_{k\omega} \equiv \int e^{-i(k\cdot r - r') + i\omega(t-t')} < j_i(r, t)\, j_j(r', t') > d^3r\, dt$$

$$= \frac{i\hbar}{1 - e^{\hbar\omega/T}} \{\alpha^*_{ji}(k, \omega) - \alpha_{ij}(k, \omega)\}. \qquad (14.6)$$

Therefore the current fluctuations in an equilibrium plasma are determined by the anti-Hermitian part of the tensor $\hat{\alpha}$ which in its turn is determined by the plasma's dielectric permittivity tensor.†

It is significant that the relation (14.6) is valid both for a free plasma and for a plasma located in an external magnetic field; it is merely necessary for the plasma to be in a state of statistical equilibrium.

It is easy to conclude from the form of the tensor $\hat{\alpha}$ that its singularities coincide with the zeros of the determinant Δ. But the equation

$$\Delta(k, \omega) = 0$$

defines, as we have seen in section 3, the eigen oscillation spectrum of a plasma $\omega_r(k)$ (the suffix r denotes the branches of the oscillations). Therefore the spectral distribution of the plasma fluctuations has singularities at frequencies that are the same as the frequencies of its eigen oscillations.

It is easy to determine the nature of these singularities. Since the damping of the eigen oscillations in a "collisionless" plasma is

† Various papers [Tolmachev, 1957a, 1957b; Tyablikov and Tolmachev, 1957; Klimontovich, 1958] deal with the derivation of the equations for the spatial correlation functions of systems of particles with electromagnetic interaction. The correlation functions of microcurrents are calculated from the laws of motion by Shafranov [1958a]. Bass and Kaganov [1958] and Silin [1959] deal with the allowance to be made for spatial dispersion when investigating fluctuations. The correlation of the electromagnetic quantities in a plasma have also often been discussed [Pines and Bohm, 1952; Salpeter, 1960c; Akhiezer, A. I., Akhiezer, I. A., and Sitenko, 1961; Salpeter, 1961; Rostoker, 1961; Akhiezer, I. A., 1962; Aleksin and Stepanov, 1962, 1963a, 1963b; Bogdankevich, Rukhadze and Silin, 1962; Ichimura, Pines and Rostoker, 1962; Ichimura, 1962].

‡ Note that $\langle j_i(k, \omega)\, j_j^*(k', \omega')\rangle = (2\pi)^4 \langle j_i j_j \rangle_{k\omega}\, \delta(k - k')\, \delta(\omega - \omega')$.

very slight, when determining the anti-Hermitian part of the tensor α we can use the well-known formula

$$\operatorname{Im} \frac{1}{x - i0} = \pi\delta(x).$$

Remembering the definition (14.5) we find

$$\langle j_i j_j \rangle_{k\omega} = \frac{1}{2} \frac{\hbar\omega^2}{e^{\hbar\omega/T} - 1} (\hat{\Lambda}^0 \hat{\lambda} \hat{\Lambda}^0)_{ij}\, \delta(\Lambda(\boldsymbol{k}, \omega)), \quad \omega_r \approx \omega(\boldsymbol{k}). \tag{14.7}$$

We can see that near the eigen frequencies the spectral distribution of the current fluctuations has δ-type maxima.

We should point out the following properties of the tensor $\hat{\alpha}$:

$$\alpha_{ij}(\boldsymbol{k}, \omega) = \alpha_{ji}(-\boldsymbol{k}, \omega); \; \alpha_{ij}(\boldsymbol{k}, \omega) = \alpha_{ij}^*(-\boldsymbol{k}, -\omega). \tag{14.8}$$

If the plasma is located in an external magnetic field $\boldsymbol{H}_0$, then in the first of these formulae we must at the same time change the sign of $\boldsymbol{H}_0$.

The real ($\hat{\alpha}'$) and imaginary ($\hat{\alpha}''$) parts of the tensor $\hat{\alpha}$ are connected by Kramers–Kronig dispersion relations

$$\left.\begin{aligned} \alpha'_{ij}(\boldsymbol{k}, \omega) &= \alpha_{ij}(\boldsymbol{k}, \infty) + \frac{1}{\pi} P \int_{-\infty}^{\infty} \frac{\alpha'_{ij}(\boldsymbol{k}, \omega')\, d\omega'}{\omega' - \omega}, \\ \alpha''_{ij}(\boldsymbol{k}, \omega) &= -\frac{1}{\pi} P \int_{-\infty}^{\infty} \frac{\alpha'_{ij}(\boldsymbol{k}, \omega')\, d\omega'}{\omega' - \omega}. \end{aligned}\right\} \tag{14.9}$$

In the high-temperature range ($T \gg \hbar\omega$), which is all we shall be interested in the following, the relation (14.6) becomes

$$\langle j_i j_j \rangle_{k\omega} = i \frac{T}{\omega} \{\alpha_{ji}^*(\boldsymbol{k}, \omega) - \alpha_{ij}(\boldsymbol{k}, \omega)\}. \tag{14.10}$$

It is easy to find the correlation function of the current density at coincident points in time (assuming that $T \gg \hbar\omega$). We integrate equation (14.10) with respect to the frequency; using the equality (14.9) we obtain

$$\langle j_i j_j \rangle_k = \frac{T}{2}\{\alpha_{ij}(\boldsymbol{k},0) - \alpha_{ij}(\boldsymbol{k},\infty) + \alpha_{ji}^*(\boldsymbol{k},0) - \alpha_{ji}(\boldsymbol{k},\infty)\}. \tag{14.11}$$

For a free plasma the tensor $\hat{\alpha}$, in just the same way as the dielectric permittivity tensor $\hat{\varepsilon}$, can be split into the longitudinal and transverse parts α_l and α_t:

$$\alpha_{ij} = \frac{k_i k_j}{k^2}\alpha_l + \left(\delta_{ij} - \frac{k_i k_j}{k^2}\right)\alpha_t,$$

where

$$\alpha_l = \frac{\omega^2}{4\pi}\frac{\varepsilon_l - 1}{\varepsilon_l}; \quad \alpha_t = \frac{\omega^2}{4\pi}(1 - n^2)\frac{\varepsilon_t - 1}{\varepsilon_t - n^2}, \tag{14.12}$$

where ε_l and ε_t are the longitudinal and transverse dielectric constants of the plasma. Using these expressions we can put the spectral distribution of the current fluctuations in an isotropic plasma in the form

$$\langle j_i j_j \rangle_{k\omega} = \frac{\omega T}{2\pi}\left\{\frac{k_i k_j}{k^2}\frac{\operatorname{Im}\varepsilon_l}{|\varepsilon_l|^2} + \left(\delta_{ij} - \frac{k_i k_j}{k^2}\right)(1 - n^2)^2 \frac{\operatorname{Im}\varepsilon_t}{|\varepsilon_t - n^2|^2}\right\}. \tag{14.13}$$

Here the first term defines the fluctuations of the longitudinal current and the second the fluctuations of the transverse current.

The longitudinal current fluctuations are connected with the charge density fluctuations. By using the continuity equation it is easy to find the charge density fluctuations in an isotropic plasma

$$\langle \varrho^2 \rangle_{k\omega} = \frac{k^2 T}{2\pi\omega}\frac{\operatorname{Im}\varepsilon_l}{|\varepsilon_l|^2}. \tag{14.14}$$

Integrating this expression with respect to frequency we find the instantaneous correlation function of the charge density at

$$\langle \varrho^2 \rangle_k = \frac{k^2 T}{4\pi}\left\{1 - \frac{1}{\varepsilon_l(\boldsymbol{k},0)}\right\}. \tag{14.15}$$

The relations (14.6) and (14.10) taken together with the Maxwell equations permit us to find the spectral distributions of the field fluctuations. The fluctuations of the electric field at high temperature are defined by the formula

$$\langle E_i E_j \rangle_{k\omega} = 4\pi i \frac{T}{\omega} (\Lambda_{ij}^{-1} - \Lambda_{ij}^{*-1}). \tag{14.16}$$

By virtue of (14.12) this relation becomes for an isotropic plasma

$$\langle E_i E_j \rangle_{k\omega} = 8\pi \frac{T}{\omega} \left\{ \frac{k_i k_j}{k^2} \frac{\operatorname{Im} \varepsilon_l}{|\varepsilon_l|^2} + \left(\delta_{ij} - \frac{k_i k_j}{k^2} \right) \frac{\operatorname{Im} \varepsilon_t}{|\varepsilon_t - n^2|^2} \right\}. \tag{14.17}$$

The magnetic field fluctuations are defined by a similar relation

$$\langle H_i H_j \rangle_{k\omega} = 8\pi \frac{T}{\omega} \left(\delta_{ij} - \frac{k_i k_j}{k^2} \right) n^2 \frac{\operatorname{Im} \varepsilon_t}{|\varepsilon_t - n^2|^2}. \tag{14.17'}$$

The expressions for the spectral distributions are considerably simpler in the high-frequency range when we must not take the movement of the ions into consideration. Using in this case the formula (3.11) for the plasma's dielectric permittivity tensor we obtain

$$\langle \varrho^2 \rangle_{k\omega} = \sqrt{2\pi} \frac{e^2 n_0}{\Omega} \frac{(ak)^3 e^{-z^2}}{|a^2 k^2 + 1 + i\sqrt{\pi}\, z w(z)|^2} \tag{14.18}$$

where

$$z = \omega / kv, \quad v^2 = 2T/m.$$

When $\omega \gg kv$ this formula gives

$$\langle \varrho^2 \rangle_{k\omega} = \frac{T\Omega^2 k^2}{2\omega} \delta(\omega^2 - \omega_L^2(k)), \tag{14.19}$$

where

$$\omega_L(k) = \Omega(1 + \tfrac{3}{2} a^2 k^2).$$

Therefore in the high-frequency range the charge density fluctuations occur chiefly at frequencies close to the eigen frequencies of the longitudinal electron oscillations.

Figure 13 shows the spectral distribution of the charge density fluctuations as a function of the frequency ($\omega = kvz$) for different values of the parameter $(ak)^2$. For large $(ak)^2$ low-frequency fluctuations play a major part. As the parameter $(ak)^2$ decreases the effective frequency of the fluctuations rises. When $(ak)^2 \ll 1$ only frequencies close to the eigen frequencies of the density oscillations of the plasma remain in the fluctuation spectrum.

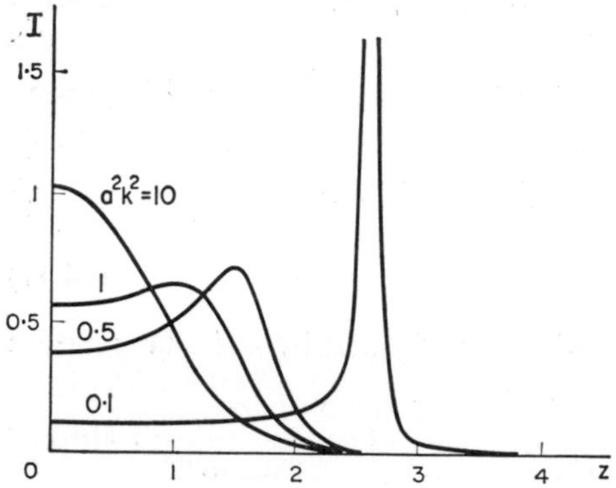

FIG. 13. Spectral distribution of charge density fluctuations

$$I(z) = \langle \varrho^2 \rangle_{k\omega} \Big/ \int_{-\infty}^{\infty} \langle \varrho^2 \rangle_{k\omega} \, d\omega \quad (z = \omega / kv)$$

for $a^2k^2 = 10, 1, 0{\cdot}5, 0{\cdot}1$.

The spectral distributions of the transverse current density fluctuations in the extreme cases of low and high frequencies are defined by the formulae

$$\left.\begin{aligned} \langle j_t^2 \rangle_{k\omega} &= \frac{\Omega^2}{k}\sqrt{\frac{mT}{2\pi}} \exp\left\{-\frac{m\omega^2}{2Tk^2}\right\} \quad (\omega \ll ck); \\ \langle j_t^2 \rangle_{k\omega} &= \frac{T\Omega^4}{\omega}\, \delta(\omega^2 - \Omega^2 - c^2k^2) \quad (\omega \sim ck \gg kv). \end{aligned}\right\} \tag{14.20}$$

Finally we give the spectral distributions integrated with respect to the frequency:

$$\left.\begin{aligned} \langle \varrho^2 \rangle_k &= \frac{2\, e^2 n_0 k^2}{k^2 + (8\pi e^2 n_0)/T}; \quad \langle j^2 \rangle_k = \frac{3e^2 n_0 T}{m}; \\ \langle \boldsymbol{E}^2 \rangle_k &= 8\pi T \frac{3 + a^2k^2}{2 + a^2k^2}; \quad \langle \boldsymbol{H}^2 \rangle_k = 8\pi T. \end{aligned}\right\} \tag{14.21}$$

These expressions allow not only for the motion of the electrons but also for the motion of the ions which make a significant contribution to the electric field and charge density correlators (this is connected with the large contribution of the low-frequency fluctuations to the correlators $\langle \boldsymbol{E}^2 \rangle_k$, $\langle \varrho^2 \rangle_k$).

Using the formulae (14.21) it is easy to find the spatial correlation functions:

$$\left.\begin{aligned}
\langle \varrho^2 \rangle_r &= 2e^2 n_0 \left\{ \delta(\boldsymbol{r}) - \frac{e^{-r/\bar{a}}}{4\pi a^2 r} \right\}; \\
\langle \boldsymbol{j}^2 \rangle_r &= \frac{3e^2 n_0 T}{m} \delta(\boldsymbol{r}); \\
\langle \boldsymbol{E}^2 \rangle_r &= 8\pi T \left\{ \delta(\boldsymbol{r}) + \frac{e^{-r/\bar{a}}}{4\pi a^2 r} \right\}; \\
\langle \boldsymbol{H}^2 \rangle_r &= 8\pi T \delta(\boldsymbol{r}),
\end{aligned}\right\} \tag{14.22}$$

where $\bar{a} = a/\sqrt{2}$ $(a = (4\pi e^2 n_0/T)^{-1/2}$ is the Debye radius).

2. *Fluctuations in an Equilibrium Plasma Located in a Magnetic Field*

The fluctuations of a plasma located in a constant and uniform magnetic field $\boldsymbol{H}_0$ are defined by the general formulae (14.6) and (14.5) [Akhiezer, A.I., Akhiezer, I.A. and Sitenko, 1961; Salpeter, 1961]. In particular the spectral distribution of the charge density fluctuations is

$$\langle \varrho^2 \rangle_{k\omega} = -\frac{k^2 T}{2\pi\omega} \operatorname{Im} \frac{D(\boldsymbol{k}, \omega)}{\Delta(\boldsymbol{k}, \omega)}, \tag{14.23}$$

where

$$\begin{aligned}
D(\boldsymbol{k}, \omega) = n^4 &- (\varepsilon_{11} \cos^2\theta + \varepsilon_{22} + \varepsilon_{33} \sin^2\theta - 2\varepsilon_{13} \sin\theta \cos\theta) n^2 \\
&+ (\varepsilon_{11}\varepsilon_{22} + \varepsilon_{12}^2) \cos^2\theta + (\varepsilon_{22}\varepsilon_{33} + \varepsilon_{23}^2) \sin^2\theta \\
&+ 2(\varepsilon_{12}\varepsilon_{23} - \varepsilon_{21}\varepsilon_{13}) \sin\theta \cos\theta;
\end{aligned}$$

$$\Delta(\boldsymbol{k}, \omega) = An^4 + Bn^2 + C;$$

A, B, C are defined by the formulae (4.7) ($\cos\theta = (\boldsymbol{k}\cdot\boldsymbol{H}_0)/kH_0$).

When $n^2 \gg 1$ the expression for $\langle\varrho^2\rangle$ is considerably simplified to

$$\langle\varrho^2\rangle_{k\omega} = \frac{k^2T}{2\pi\omega}\,\frac{\operatorname{Im} A}{|A|^2}. \qquad (14.24)$$

By integrating the expression (14.23) over the frequencies and using the expression (14.9) when doing this we can find the instantaneous correlation function of the charge density

$$\langle\varrho^2\rangle_k = \frac{k^2T}{4\pi}\left\{1 - \frac{1}{A(k,0)}\right\}.$$

Since $A(k, 0) = 1 + 8\pi e^2 n_0/k^2T$,

$$\langle\varrho^2\rangle_k = \frac{2e^2 n_0 k^2}{k^2 + 8\pi e^2 n_0/T}. \qquad (14.25)$$

This formula is not different from the first of the formulae (14.21).

Therefore the magnetic field does not affect the spatial correlation function of the charge density fluctuations. It has a considerable effect, however, on the spectral distribution of the density fluctuations.

If $\omega \gg kv$ the spectral distribution of the charge density fluctuations can be determined by the formula

$$\langle\varrho^2\rangle_{k\omega} = \left(\frac{k\omega}{2\Omega}\right)^2 T \frac{(\omega^2-\omega_e^2)^2}{\omega^4\sin^2\theta + (\omega^2-\omega_e^2)^2\cos^2\theta} \times$$
$$\times \{\delta(\omega-\omega_1) + \delta(\omega-\omega_2) + \delta(\omega+\omega_1) + \delta(\omega+\omega_2)\}, \qquad (14.26)$$

where ω_1 and ω_2 are the eigen frequencies of the longitudinal electron oscillations of a plasma in a magnetic field.

15. Fluctuations in a Two-Temperature Plasma

1. "Random Forces" Method

In the preceding section we have determined the fluctuations of the electromagnetic quantities in an equilibrium plasma. A knowledge of the plasma's dielectric permittivity tensor is sufficient for finding these fluctuations.

In a number of problems it is necessary to know the fluctuations of the electron and ion densities separately (for example, when studying the scattering of electromagnetic waves in a plasma) and also the fluctuations of the particle distribution functions. Here the plasma may be equilibrium or non-equilibrium.

If the plasma is an equilibrium or quasi-equilibrium plasma (characterized by Maxwellian distributions for the electrons and ions at different temperatures), the fluctuations of all the quantities of interest to us can be found by using the fluctuation–dissipation theorem as before. To do this we must introduce additional quantities—so-called "random forces"—into the equations describing the system under discussion. It is most convenient to introduce these additional terms in such a form that the fluctuations of the random forces at different points in space and time do not correlate with each other. Since we are interested in the fluctuations of the particle distribution functions this can be achieved if we introduce the random forces into the right-hand sides of the kinetic equations defining the distribution functions [Abrikosov and Khalatnikov, 1958]. Therefore in the case of a plasma consisting of electrons and ions of one kind we shall start with the equations [Akhiezer, A.I., Akhiezer, I.A. and Sitenko 1961]:

$$\left.\begin{aligned}
&\left[\frac{\partial}{\partial t} + \left(\boldsymbol{v}\cdot\frac{\partial}{\partial \boldsymbol{r}}\right) + \frac{e}{m}\left(\boldsymbol{E}\cdot\frac{\partial}{\partial \boldsymbol{v}}\right)\right] F_e(\boldsymbol{v}, \boldsymbol{r}, t)\\
&= \frac{-1}{\tau_e} f_e(\boldsymbol{v}, \boldsymbol{r}, t) + y_e(\boldsymbol{v}, \boldsymbol{r}, t);\\
&\left[\frac{\partial}{\partial t} + \left(\boldsymbol{v}\cdot\frac{\partial}{\partial \boldsymbol{r}}\right) + \frac{z_i e}{M}\left(\boldsymbol{E}\cdot\frac{\partial}{\partial \boldsymbol{v}}\right)\right] F_i(\boldsymbol{v}, \boldsymbol{r}, t)\\
&= \frac{-1}{\tau_i} f_i(\boldsymbol{v}, \boldsymbol{r}, t), + y_i(\boldsymbol{v}, \boldsymbol{r}, t),
\end{aligned}\right\} \qquad (15.1)$$

where $f_{e,i} = F_{e,i} - F^0_{e,i}$ are the deviations of the distribution functions from the Maxwellian functions $F^0_{e,i}$; $y_{e,i}$ are the random forces; $z_i e$ is the ion charge.

The quantities $-f/\tau$ introduced into the right-hand sides of the equations (15.1) allow schematically for particle collisions ($\tau_{e,i}$ are certain mean relaxation times of the electrons and ions for the distributions $F^0_{e,i}$). The exact form of the collision integrals is unimportant to us since when investigating the fluctuations in a collisionless plasma (which is all we are interested in) we allow the collision time τ to approach infinity in the final formulae.

Following the general rules of fluctuation theory [Landau and Lifshitz, 1958b] we shall select as the "generalized thermodynamic velocities" $\dot{x}$ figuring in this theory the functions

$$\dot{x}_\alpha(\boldsymbol{v}, \boldsymbol{r}, t) = \frac{-1}{\tau_\alpha} f_\alpha(\boldsymbol{v}, \boldsymbol{r}, t) + y_\alpha(\boldsymbol{v}, \boldsymbol{r}, t) \tag{15.2}$$

(the suffix α denotes the kind of particle; $\alpha = e, i$) and we find the "generalized thermodynamic forces" $X = -\delta\dot{S}/\delta\dot{x}$ corresponding to them, where $\dot{S}$ is a time derivative of the system's entropy

$$\dot{S}(t) = \int d^3\boldsymbol{r}\, d^3\boldsymbol{v} \left\{ \frac{f_e}{\tau_e} \ln \frac{F^0_e}{G_e} + \frac{f_i}{\tau_i} \ln \frac{F^0_i}{G_i} \right\}$$
$$- \int d^3\boldsymbol{r}\, d^3\boldsymbol{v} \left\{ \frac{f_e}{F^0_e} \left(y_e - \frac{f_e}{\tau_e} \right) + \frac{f_i}{F^0_i} \left(y_i - \frac{f_i}{\tau_i} \right) \right\} \tag{15.3}$$

($G_{e,i}$ are the densities of the electron and ion states). The quantity $\dot{S}$ must be found for given values of the system's energy and numbers of particles of each kind.

If we examine the fluctuations near the state of thermodynamic equilibrium the first term in the equation (15.3) becomes zero and the function $\dot{S}$ is bilinear (when $y = 0$) with respect to the quantities $\dot{x}$ characterizing the deviation of the system from equilibrium. In this case the quantities $\dot{x}$ can be expressed in the form $\dot{x}_\alpha = -\gamma_\alpha X_\alpha + y_\alpha$. The "kinetic coefficients" γ in these relations directly determine the averaged products of the random forces:

$$\langle y_\alpha(\boldsymbol{v}, \boldsymbol{r}, t)\, y_{\alpha'}(\boldsymbol{v}', \boldsymbol{r}', t') \rangle$$
$$= 2\delta_{\alpha\alpha'} \gamma_\alpha(\boldsymbol{v})\, \delta(\boldsymbol{v} - \boldsymbol{v}')\, \delta(\boldsymbol{r} - \boldsymbol{r}')\, \delta(t - t'). \tag{15.4}$$

Knowing the standard deviation of the random forces we can, by using the kinetic equations (15.1) and the Maxwell equations, express the distribution functions of the particles and the different physical quantities defined by them in terms of the random forces and then use the equality (15.4) to average with respect to the random forces.

The method described can be generalized to the case of a two-temperature plasma [Akhiezer, A.I., Akhiezer, I.A. and Sitenko, 1961]. This generalization is possible because, due to the large difference in the masses of the electrons and the ions, the exchange of energy between particles of one kind proceeds far more rapidly than the exchange of energy between particles of different kinds. If we neglect the exchange of energy between particles of different kinds the state of a plasma with different electron and ion temperatures will correspond to the entropy maximum (for given values of the numbers of particles and energies of the electrons and ions separately).

The time derivative of the entropy of a two-temperature plasma is defined by the general expression (15.3); in this case the quantity $\dot{S}$ must be found for given values of the electron and ion energies. Because of this condition the first term in the equation (15.3) becomes zero so the time derivative of the entropy is (when $y = 0$), just as in the case of an equilibrium system, bilinear in the $\dot{x}$ which characterize the deviation of the system from the state with two Maxwell distributions. Continuing in the same way as in the case of a completely equilibrium plasma we find the quantities

$$X_\alpha(\boldsymbol{v}, \boldsymbol{r}, t) \equiv \frac{\delta \dot{S}}{\delta \dot{x}_\alpha(\boldsymbol{v}, \boldsymbol{r}, t)} = \frac{f_\alpha(\boldsymbol{v}, \boldsymbol{r}, t)}{F^0_\alpha(v)}$$

and put $\dot{x}$ in the form

$$\dot{x}_\alpha(\boldsymbol{v}, \boldsymbol{r}, t) = -\gamma_\alpha(\boldsymbol{v})\, X_\alpha(\boldsymbol{v}, \boldsymbol{r}, t) + y_\alpha(\boldsymbol{v}, \boldsymbol{r}, t),$$

$$\gamma_\alpha(\boldsymbol{v}) = \frac{1}{\tau_\alpha} F^0_\alpha(v). \tag{15.5}$$

Substituting the expressions (15.5) for the coefficients γ in the expression (15.4) we determine the standard deviation of the random forces

$$\langle y_\alpha(\boldsymbol{v}, \boldsymbol{r}, t)\, y_{\alpha'}(\boldsymbol{v}', \boldsymbol{r}', t')\rangle$$
$$= \frac{2}{\tau_\alpha} \delta_{\alpha\alpha'} F^0_\alpha(v)\, \delta(\boldsymbol{v} - \boldsymbol{v}')\, \delta(\boldsymbol{r} - \boldsymbol{r}')\, \delta(t - t'). \tag{15.6}$$

By using the expression (15.6) we can, just as in the case of an equilibrium plasma, find the correlation functions of the various physical quantities.

2. *Spectral Distribution of Fluctuations*

We give below the expressions for the correlators of the electron and ion densities [Salpeter, 1960c; Akhiezer, A.I., Akhiezer, I.A. and Sitenko, 1961]:

$$e^2\langle\delta n_e^2\rangle_{k\omega} = \frac{2k^2}{\omega|\varepsilon_l|^2}\{A_e|1 + 4\pi\varkappa_l^i|^2 + A_i|4\pi\varkappa_l^e|^2\};$$

$$(z_i e)^2\,\langle\delta n_i^2\rangle_{k\omega} = \frac{2k^2}{\omega|\varepsilon_l|^2}\{A_e|4\pi\varkappa_l^i|^2 + A_i|1 + 4\pi\varkappa_l^e|^2\};$$

$$z_i e^2\,\langle\delta n_e \delta n_i\rangle_{k\omega} = z_i e^2\,\langle\delta n_i\,\delta n_e\rangle_{k\omega}^*$$

$$= \frac{-2k^2}{\omega|\varepsilon_l|^2}\{A_e(1 + 4\pi\varkappa_l^i)\,(4\pi\varkappa_l^i)^* + A_i(4\pi\varkappa_l^e)\,(1 + 4\pi\varkappa_l^e)^*\}. \tag{15.7}$$

Here $z_\alpha e$ is the charge of particles of a kind α; $\varepsilon_l = 1 + 4\pi(\varkappa_l^e + \varkappa_l^i)$ is the longitudinal dielectric permittivity of the plasma; $\varkappa_l^{e,i}$ are the longitudinal electric susceptibilities of the electrons and the ions

$$\varkappa_l^\alpha(\boldsymbol{k}, \omega) = \frac{(z_\alpha e)^2}{m_\alpha k^2}\int \frac{(\boldsymbol{k}\cdot\partial/\partial\boldsymbol{v})\,F_\alpha^0(\boldsymbol{v})}{\omega - (\boldsymbol{k}\cdot\boldsymbol{v}) + i0}\,d^3\boldsymbol{v} \tag{15.8}$$

and the quanties A_α are defined by the relation

$$A_\alpha(\boldsymbol{k}, \omega) = \frac{\pi(ez_\alpha)^2\omega}{k^2}\int F_\alpha^0(\boldsymbol{v})\,\delta(\omega - (\boldsymbol{k}\cdot\boldsymbol{v}))\,d^3\boldsymbol{v}. \tag{15.9}$$

It is easy to obtain the spectral distribution of the charge density fluctuations from the equation (15.7):

$$\langle\varrho^2\rangle_{k\omega} = \frac{2k^2}{\omega|\varepsilon_l|^2}\{A_e + A_i\}. \tag{15.10}$$

The spectral distributions of the fluctuations of the longitudinal electric field and the longitudinal current can be expressed in terms of $\langle \varrho^2 \rangle$ by means of the Poisson equation and the continuity equation.

In the case under discussion, when the unperturbed distribution functions F_α^0 are Maxwellian distributions (it is not necessary for the temperatures of the electrons and the ions to be the same), the quantities A_α can be expressed in terms of the electrical susceptibilities and temperatures of the electrons and the ions:

$$A_\alpha(\boldsymbol{k}, \omega) = T_\alpha \operatorname{Im} \varkappa_l^\alpha(\boldsymbol{k}, \omega). \tag{15.11}$$

Substituting the expression (15.11) in the equation (15.10) it is easy to see that when $T_i = T_e$ the latter relation changes into (14.14).

Let us examine in greater detail the charge density fluctuations. In the low-frequency region ($\omega \ll kv_i$) the charge density correlator is, in accordance with (15.10), (15.11),

$$\langle \varrho^2 \rangle_{k\omega} = |z_i|\, e^2 n_0 \left(\frac{2\pi M}{T_i}\right)^{1/2} \bar{a}(\bar{a}k)^3\, (1 + \bar{a}^2 k^2)^{-2}, \tag{15.12}$$

where $\bar{a} = a_e a_i (a_e^2 + a_i^2)^{-1/2}$ is the screening radius,

$$a_\alpha^2 = T_\alpha (4\pi e^2 |z_\alpha|\, n_0)^{-1},$$

and n_0 is the plasma electron density (we assume $v_e \gg v_i$).

In the high-frequency region ($\omega \gg kv_e$) it is the electrons that play the major part in the charge density oscillations so the correlator $\langle \varrho^2 \rangle$ is defined, just as in the case of an isothermal plasma, by the formula (14.19) (with $T = T_e$). In this case the correlator has sharply defined maxima at the frequencies $\omega = \pm\Omega(1 + \frac{3}{2} a_e^2 k^2)$ corresponding to the possibility of propagation of longitudinal electron oscillations in the plasma.

It can be seen from the relation (14.14) that in an isothermal plasma the charge density fluctuation correlator in the "medium-frequency" range ($kv_i \ll \omega \ll kv_e$) is small. As the temperature ratio T_e/T_i rises the part played by the "medium" frequencies in the fluctuation spectrum increases; when $T_e \gg T_i$ a sharply defined maximum appears in this frequency region (if $z_i \ll M/m$) connected with the possibility of propagation of low-frequency oscillations in the plasma.

Near the maximum we have (for $\bar{a}k \ll 1$)

$$\langle \varrho^2 \rangle_{k\omega} = \tfrac{1}{2} T_e (a_e k)^2 \omega^3 V_s^{-2} \delta(\omega^2 - V_s^2 k^2), \tag{15.13}$$

where $V_s = \sqrt{T_e/M}$ is the velocity of non-isothermal sound ($|z_i| = 1$).

We now give the expression for the distribution function fluctuation correlator [Akhiezer, A.I., Akhiezer, I.A. and Sitenko, 1961]:

$$\begin{aligned}\langle f_\alpha(\boldsymbol{v}) f_{\alpha'}(\boldsymbol{v}') \rangle_{k\omega} &= 2\pi \delta_{\alpha\alpha'} F_\alpha^0(\boldsymbol{v})\, \delta(\boldsymbol{v} - \boldsymbol{v}')\, \delta(\omega - (\boldsymbol{k} \cdot \boldsymbol{v})) \\ &+ 2\pi \frac{4\pi e^2 z_\alpha z_{\alpha'}}{k^2} F_\alpha^0(\boldsymbol{v})\, F_{\alpha'}^0(\boldsymbol{v}')\, S_l^{\alpha\alpha'}(\boldsymbol{v}, \boldsymbol{v}') \\ &+ 2\pi \frac{4\pi e^2 z_\alpha z_{\alpha'}}{\omega^2} F_\alpha^0(\boldsymbol{v})\, F_{\alpha'}^0(\boldsymbol{v}')\, [(\boldsymbol{v} \cdot \boldsymbol{v}') \\ &- k^{-2}(\boldsymbol{k} \cdot \boldsymbol{v})(\boldsymbol{k} \cdot \boldsymbol{v}')]\, S_t^{\alpha\alpha'}(\boldsymbol{v}, \boldsymbol{v}').\end{aligned} \tag{15.14}$$

The first term in this expression is the same as the correlator for the distribution function fluctuations in a gas of neutral particles [Kadomtsev, 1957]; the second and third terms allow for the interaction between the particles by a self-consistent field.

The second term is connected with the longitudinal (electrostatic) part of the self-consistent field; the function

$$\begin{aligned}S_l^{\alpha\alpha'} &= T_\alpha^{-1} \frac{(\boldsymbol{k} \cdot \boldsymbol{v})}{\omega - (\boldsymbol{k} \cdot \boldsymbol{v}) + i0} \varepsilon_l^{-1} \delta(\omega - (\boldsymbol{k} \cdot \boldsymbol{v}')) \\ &+ T_{\alpha'}^{-1} \frac{(\boldsymbol{k} \cdot \boldsymbol{v}')}{\omega - (\boldsymbol{k} \cdot \boldsymbol{v}') - i0} \varepsilon_l^{*-1} \delta(\omega - (\boldsymbol{k} \cdot \boldsymbol{v})) \\ &+ 4 T_\alpha^{-1} T_{\alpha'}^{-1} \frac{(\boldsymbol{k} \cdot \boldsymbol{v})}{\omega - (\boldsymbol{k} \cdot \boldsymbol{v}) + i0} \times \\ &\times \frac{(\boldsymbol{k} \cdot \boldsymbol{v}')}{\omega - (\boldsymbol{k} \cdot \boldsymbol{v}') - i0} \cdot \frac{\operatorname{Im}(T_e \varkappa_l^e + T_i \varkappa_l^i)}{\omega\, |\varepsilon_l|^2}\end{aligned} \tag{15.15}$$

contained in it has sharply defined maxima at the frequencies of the plasma's longitudinal oscillations.

Lastly, the third term allows for the transverse part of the self-consistent field; the function

$$S_t^{\alpha\alpha'} = T_\alpha^{-1} \frac{\omega}{\omega - (\boldsymbol{k} \cdot \boldsymbol{v}) + i0} (\varepsilon_t - n^2)^{-1} \delta(\omega - (\boldsymbol{k} \cdot \boldsymbol{v}'))$$

$$+ T_{\alpha'}^{-1} \frac{\omega}{\omega - (\boldsymbol{k} \cdot \boldsymbol{v}') - i0} (\varepsilon_t^* - n^2)^{-1} \delta(\omega - (\boldsymbol{k} \cdot \boldsymbol{v}))$$

$$+ 4T_\alpha^{-1} T_{\alpha'}^{-1} \omega(\omega - (\boldsymbol{k} \cdot \boldsymbol{v}) + i0)^{-1} \times$$

$$\times (\omega - (\boldsymbol{k} \cdot \boldsymbol{v}') - i0)^{-1} \frac{\operatorname{Im}(T_e \varkappa_t^e + T_i \varkappa_t^i)}{|\varepsilon_t - n^2|^2} \qquad (15.16)$$

contained in it (where $n = ck/\omega$ and ε_t, $\varkappa_t^{e,i}$ are the transverse dielectric constant of the plasma and the transverse electrical susceptibilities of the electrons and ions) becomes infinite at the transverse electromagnetic wave frequencies $\omega = \sqrt{c^2k^2 + \Omega^2}$.

Near these frequencies

$$S_t^{\alpha\alpha'}(\boldsymbol{v}, \boldsymbol{v}') = \frac{\omega}{T_e} \delta(\omega^2 - c^2k^2 - \Omega^2). \qquad (15.17)$$

By using the equations (15.14), (15.16) it is easy to find the correlators of the fluctuations of the transverse current and the transverse electric and magnetic fields. These quantities are chiefly of interest at high frequencies ($\omega \gg kv_e$); in this case the ion motion is insignificant and the correlators are defined by the formulae (14.17), (14.20) in which we must put $T = T_e$.

3. *Fluctuations in a Two-Temperature Plasma Located in a Magnetic Field*

Let us pause to examine the question of the fluctuations in a two-temperature plasma located in a constant uniform magnetic field $\boldsymbol{H}_0$ [Akhiezer, A. I., Akhiezer, I. A. and Sitenko, 1961]. In this case we can proceed as before from the kinetic equations with the random forces (15.1) to calculate the correlation functions; all that we have to do is to introduce into the left-hand sides of these equations the terms $(z_\alpha e/m_\alpha c)([\boldsymbol{v} \wedge \boldsymbol{H}_0] \cdot (\partial/\partial \boldsymbol{v})) F_\alpha$ which allow for the action of the magnetic field. Because of these additional terms the expressions connecting the averaged products of the various physical quantities and the averaged products of the random forces are altered; the standard deviation of the random forces is determined as before, as can easily be checked, by the expression (15.6).

We now give the final expression for the current density correlator

$$\langle j_i j_j \rangle_{k\omega} = 2\omega B_{il} B^*_{jm} \sum_\alpha A^\alpha_{lm}, \tag{15.18}$$

where the tensor $\hat{A}^\alpha$ is connected with the anti-Hermitian part of the electrical susceptibility of particles of the α-th kind (compare with equation (15.11))

$$A^\alpha_{ij} = \frac{1}{2i} T_\alpha (\varkappa^\alpha_{ij} - \varkappa^{\alpha *}_{ji}), \tag{15.19}$$

and the tensor $\hat{B}$ is of the form

$$B_{ij} = \delta_{ij} - (\varepsilon_{il} - \delta_{il}) \Lambda^{-1}_{lj}. \tag{15.20}$$

When $T_e = T_i$ the expression (15.18) changes into (14.10).

Finally we give the expression for the correlator for the current density of particles of different kinds $\boldsymbol{j}^\alpha = z_\alpha e \int \boldsymbol{v} F_\alpha(\boldsymbol{v})\, d^3\boldsymbol{v}$:

$$\langle j^\alpha_i j^{\alpha'}_j \rangle_{k\omega} = 2\omega \sum_{\alpha''} B^{\alpha\alpha''}_{il} B^{\alpha'\alpha''*}_{jm} A^{\alpha''}_{lm}, \tag{15.21}$$

where

$$B^{\alpha\alpha'}_{ij} = \begin{cases} \delta_{ij} - 4\pi\varkappa^\alpha_{il}\Lambda^{-1}_{lj} & (\alpha = \alpha'), \\ \quad - 4\pi\varkappa^\alpha_{il}\Lambda^{-1}_{lj} & (\alpha \neq \alpha'). \end{cases} \tag{15.22}$$

By using the Maxwell equations and the continuity equation we can obtain from the expressions (15.18) and (15.21) the correlation functions for all the macroscopic quantities. The following are the expressions for the field correlation functions:

$$\left. \begin{aligned} \langle E_i E_j \rangle_{k\omega} &= \frac{32\pi^2}{\omega^3} \Lambda_{im} \Lambda^{-1*}_{jn} \sum_\alpha A^\alpha_{mn}, \\ \langle H_i H_j \rangle_{k\omega} &= \frac{32\pi^2 c^2}{\omega^3} \varepsilon_{imn} \varepsilon_{klj} k_m k_l \Lambda^{-1}_{ns} \Lambda^{-1*}_{jp} \sum_\alpha A^\alpha_{sp}. \end{aligned} \right\} \tag{15.23}$$

We notice that the correlation functions (15.18), (15.21) have a δ-type singularity if ω and $\boldsymbol{k}$ are connected by the relation $\Delta(\boldsymbol{k}, \omega) \equiv \det \Lambda = 0$, i.e. at the frequencies of the plasma's eigen oscillations.

16. Fluctuations in a Non-Equilibrium Plasma

1. Fluctuations in a Plasma with Stable Distribution Functions

Let us move on to investigate the fluctuations in plasmas with non-equilibrium (and not necessarily stable) distribution functions. For plasmas of this kind we cannot, of course, use the fluctuation-dissipation theorem since the non-equilibrium distribution function does not correspond to the entropy maximum. Therefore when investigating the fluctuations in a non-equilibrium plasma we use another method; we take given random perturbations of the velocity distributions of the particles at a certain (initial) point in time and follow how the initial fluctuations develop with time. In the case of a plasma characterized by a stable distribution function, and also in the case of a plasma through which a low-density beam of charged particles is passing, after the passage of a certain space of time, the correlation functions of the fluctuations no longer depend on the initial perturbations, but are also determined only by the unperturbed distribution functions of the particles in the system.

In order to determine distribution functions F_α of particles of a kind α we use the kinetic equation without the collision integral (2.1) with the initial conditions

$$F_\alpha(\boldsymbol{u}, \boldsymbol{r}, t)|_{t=0} - F_\alpha^0(\boldsymbol{v}) = g_\alpha(\boldsymbol{v}, \boldsymbol{r}),$$

where F_α^0 is the distribution function averaged over the fluctuations and g_α is the fluctuation of the distribution function at the initial point in time.

By applying a Laplace transform with respect to the time to the kinetic equation and the Poisson equation we can express the particle distribution functions and the various physical quantities determined by them at the time t in terms of the initial values of the distribution function fluctuations g. In particular, for the spatial Fourier component of the charge density we obtain

$$\varrho(\boldsymbol{k}, t) = \frac{ie}{2\pi} \int_{-\infty+i\sigma}^{\infty+i\sigma} \frac{d\omega e^{-i\omega t}}{\varepsilon(\boldsymbol{k}, \omega)} \sum_\alpha z_\alpha \int \frac{g_\alpha(\boldsymbol{v}, \boldsymbol{k})\, d^3v}{\omega - (\boldsymbol{k} \cdot \boldsymbol{v})}, \quad (16.1)$$

where ε is the longitudinal dielectric permittivity of the system

$$\varepsilon(\boldsymbol{k}, \omega) = 1 + 4\pi \sum_{\alpha} \varkappa^{\alpha}(\boldsymbol{k}, \omega)$$

and $\varkappa^{\alpha}$ is the electrical susceptibility of its α-th component defined by the formula (15.8). Integration with respect to ω in (16.1) is carried out along the straight line $\operatorname{Im} \omega = \sigma$ which passes above all the poles of the function ε^{-1}.

We now construct the quadratic combinations of the different physical quantities (relating to the not necessarily coincident times t, t') and average these combinations with respect to the random quantities g_{α}. The quantities obtained in this way are the correlation functions for the system under discussion; knowing them allows us in particular to determine the squares of the oscillation amplitudes of the physical quantities at the time t (it is sufficient to take $t' = t$ in the correlation functions for this).

As an example we give the expression for the charge density correlation function (which we shall denote by C in this section)

$$C(\boldsymbol{k}, t, t') \equiv \int d^3\boldsymbol{r} \exp\{-i(\boldsymbol{k} \cdot (\boldsymbol{r} - \boldsymbol{r}'))\} \langle \varrho(\boldsymbol{r}, t)\, \varrho(\boldsymbol{r}', t') \rangle$$

$$= (2\pi)^{-2} \iint_{-\infty + i\sigma}^{\infty + i\sigma} d\omega\, d\omega' \exp\{-i\omega t - i\omega' t'\} \times$$

$$\times\, \varepsilon^{-1}(\boldsymbol{k}, \omega)\, \varepsilon^{-1}(-\boldsymbol{k}, \omega')\, B(\boldsymbol{k}, \omega, \omega'), \tag{16.2}$$

where

$$B = -e^2 \sum_{\alpha, \alpha'} z_{\alpha} z_{\alpha'} \int \frac{d^3\boldsymbol{v}\, d^3\boldsymbol{v}'}{(\omega - (\boldsymbol{k} \cdot \boldsymbol{v}))\, (\omega' + (\boldsymbol{k} \cdot \boldsymbol{v}'))} \times$$

$$\times \int d^3\boldsymbol{r}\, e^{-i(\boldsymbol{k} \cdot (\boldsymbol{r} - \boldsymbol{r}'))} \langle g_{\alpha}(\boldsymbol{v}, \boldsymbol{r})\, g_{\alpha'}(\boldsymbol{v}', \boldsymbol{r}') \rangle. \tag{16.2'}$$

The Fourier component of the averaged product of the initial values of the distribution functions' fluctuations contained in this formula can be given in the following general form:

$$\int d^3\boldsymbol{r} \exp\{-i(\boldsymbol{k} \cdot (\boldsymbol{r} - \boldsymbol{r}'))\} \langle g_{\alpha}(\boldsymbol{v}, \boldsymbol{r})\, g_{\alpha'}(\boldsymbol{v}', \boldsymbol{r}') \rangle$$

$$= \delta_{\alpha\alpha'} \delta(\boldsymbol{v} - \boldsymbol{v}')\, F_{\alpha}^{0}(\boldsymbol{v}) + Y_{\alpha\alpha'}(\boldsymbol{v}, \boldsymbol{v}', \boldsymbol{k}), \tag{16.3}$$

where the first term corresponds to an ideal gas (each particle is "correlated only with itself", see (15.14)), whilst the second term is caused by the interaction between the particles. It is significant that the second term is a smooth function of the velocities, whilst the first contains $\delta(\boldsymbol{v} - \boldsymbol{v}')$.

In the case of an equilibrium plasma the function Y is, in accordance with the formula (15.15), of the form

$$Y_{\alpha\alpha'} = \frac{-4\pi e^2}{T} z_\alpha z_{\alpha'} F_\alpha^0(\boldsymbol{v})\, F_{\alpha'}^0(\boldsymbol{v}')\, (\bar{a}^{-2} + k^2)^{-1}, \tag{16.4}$$

where $\bar{a}$ is the screening radius. Using the kinetic equation and the Poisson equation to express the fluctuations of the distribution function at the time t in terms of the initial fluctuations and averaging the latter by means of the expressions (16.3), (16.4) we return to the same relations (16.3), (16.4) for the averaged values of the distribution function fluctuations. It may be said that the equilibrium fluctuations reproduce themselves. In this case the relation (16.2), in accordance with (14.14), gives

$$C(\boldsymbol{k}, t - t') = \frac{k^2 T}{(2\pi)^2} \int_{-\infty}^{\infty} \frac{d\omega}{\omega} \exp\{-i\omega(t - t')\} \operatorname{Im} \frac{-1}{\varepsilon(\boldsymbol{k}, \omega)}. \tag{16.5}$$

Let the averaged distribution functions F_α^0 be equilibrium functions as before but the initial perturbations g_α be such that the function Y is no longer defined by the formula (16.4). We substitute (16.3) in (16.2) and use Cauchy's theorem to integrate with respect to ω, ω'. In this case we obtain other terms as well as the terms of (16.5) which describe the equilibrium fluctuations. These terms, however, become damped in time with a decrement $\operatorname{Im}\omega_k$, where ω_k is a root of the equation $\varepsilon(\boldsymbol{k}, \omega_k) = 0$. Therefore, despite the non-equilibrium nature of the initial fluctuations, after the passage of a time $t \sim (\operatorname{Im}\omega_k)^{-1}$ equilibrium fluctuations of the charge density and the other macroscopic quantities are established in the plasma.

For weakly damped natural plasma oscillations the quantity $\operatorname{Im}\omega_k$ is small so the plasma states for which the eigen oscillation amplitudes are far from equilibrium amplitudes may exist for a very long time and be looked upon as quasi-equilibrium states.

Let us examine the more general case of a plasma with non-equilibrium, but stable, particle distribution functions. Substituting (16.3) in (16.2′) we obtain

$$B(\boldsymbol{k}, \omega, \omega') =$$
$$= -e^2(\omega + \omega')^{-1} \sum_{\alpha} z_\alpha^2 \int F_\alpha^0(\boldsymbol{v}) \{(\omega - (\boldsymbol{k} \cdot \boldsymbol{v}) + i0)^{-1}$$
$$+ (\omega' + (\boldsymbol{k} \cdot \boldsymbol{v}) + i0)^{-1}\} \, d^3\boldsymbol{v}$$
$$+ \delta B(\boldsymbol{k}, \omega, \omega'). \tag{16.6}$$

Here the first term has appeared from the δ-type term in the equation (16.3), whilst δB denotes the contribution from the quantity Y to the function B. It is significant that the first term in the equation (16.6) has a pole when $\omega + \omega' = 0$, whilst the quantity δB, in just the same way as ε^{-1}, has no poles in the upper half-planes of the variables ω, ω' or for real values of these variables. Thanks to this circumstance the undamped contribution to the correlator C defined by the formula (16.2) gives only the pole of the function B at $\omega + \omega' = 0$; the remaining terms in the expression for C will decrease with time.

Therefore after the passage of a time $t \sim (\text{Im}\,\omega_k)^{-1}$ in a non-equilibrium, but stable, plasma charge density fluctuations which are independent of the initial perturbations are established; they are defined by the correlation function [Rostoker, 1961]:

$$\left.\begin{aligned} C(\boldsymbol{k}, t - t') &= \int_{-\infty}^{\infty} e^{-i\omega(t-t')} \langle \varrho^2 \rangle_{k\omega} \frac{d\omega}{2\pi}; \\ \langle \varrho^2 \rangle_{k\omega} &= \frac{2k^2(A_e + A_i)}{\omega |\varepsilon|^2}, \end{aligned}\right\} \tag{16.7}$$

where the quantities A_α are given by the formula (15.9).

We should point out that the relation (16.7) is formally the same as the relation (15.10) for the correlation function of the charge density in a quasi-equilibrium plasma (although with arbitrary distribution functions F_α^0 the quantities A_α are no longer expressed, of course, in terms of the imaginary parts of the electrical susceptibilities).

Just as in the case of equilibrium distribution functions, fluctuations with the frequencies of the plasma's eigen oscillations continue longer than any others to depend on the initial perturbations, so the plasma states characterized by eigen oscillation amplitudes that differ from those defined by the formula (16.7) may exist for a very long time.

In a similar way we can find the correlation functions of the plasma electron and ion density fluctuations. These correlation functions are defined by the formulae (15.7)–(15.9) in which F_α^0 must be taken as a non-Maxwellian unperturbed distribution function. The electric field fluctuations can be expressed in terms of the charge density fluctuations by the Poisson equation.

2. *Critical Fluctuations near the Onset of a Plasma Instability*

The formulae (16.7), (15.7) correctly describe the correlations of the fluctuations in a plasma with arbitrary stable particle distribution functions. In this case the directional velocities of the particles do not have to be equal to zero, so these relations are applicable for investigating the fluctuations in a plasma through which a beam of particles is passing and also in a plasma with electrons moving relative to the ions provided that the beam velocity (or the electron velocity) does not exceed the critical value at which instability starts.

The relations (16.7), (15.7) allow us to follow how the magnitude and nature of the fluctuations alter as the directional velocity of any kind of particle increases. It turns out in this case that as we approach the boundary of the stability region the fluctuations increase considerably, becoming infinite on the boundary of this region (if we limit ourselves to the linear theory, of course). This phenomenon is analogous to the rise in the fluctuations near the critical point well known in statistical physics (the phase transition point, see, for example, Landau and Lifshitz, 1958b).

Let us take as an example the fluctuations in a plasma consisting of cold ions and hot electrons moving relative to the ions [Bogdankevich, Rukhadze and Silin, 1962; Ichimura, Pines and Rostoker, 1962; Ichimura, 1962]. The correlator of the charge density fluctuations in such a plasma is, in accordance with (16.7) and (15.9), of the form

$$\langle \varrho^2 \rangle_{k\omega} = 2k^2 |\varepsilon_l(\boldsymbol{k}, \omega)|^{-2} \times$$
$$\times \left\{ \frac{T_e}{\omega - (\boldsymbol{k} \cdot \boldsymbol{u})} \operatorname{Im} \varkappa_l^e (k, \omega - (\boldsymbol{k} \cdot \boldsymbol{u})) + \frac{T_i}{\omega} \operatorname{Im} \varkappa_l^i (k, \omega) \right\}, \tag{16.8}$$

where $\boldsymbol{u}$ is the directional velocity of the electrons; $\varepsilon_l(\boldsymbol{k}, \omega)$ is the dielectric constant of the plasma defined by the formula (10.15); $\varkappa_l^e(k, \omega)$ is the electrical susceptibility of the plasma's electron component in the coordinate system in which the electrons are at rest, and $\varkappa_l^i(k, \omega)$ is the electrical susceptibility of the plasma's ion component (the quantities $\varkappa_l^{e,i}$ are defined by the formulae (3.9)).

The function $\langle \varrho^2 \rangle_{k\omega}$ has a pole if ω and $\boldsymbol{k}$ are connected by the relation $\varepsilon_l(k, \omega) = 0$, which is the dispersion equation of the plasma's longitudinal oscillations. It has been shown in sub-section 4 of section 10 that this equation has a solution corresponding to low-frequency oscillations with the frequency $\omega = V_s k \times (1 + a_e^2 k^2)^{-1/2}$. The decrement $\gamma(\boldsymbol{k})$ of these oscillations defined by the formula (10.16) becomes zero at a certain value of the electrons' directional velocity $u_{\|} = u_c(k)$ $(u_{\|} = k^{-1}(\boldsymbol{u} \cdot \boldsymbol{k}))$; when $u_{\|} > u_c(k)$ the oscillations with the wave vector $\boldsymbol{k}$ increase.

When $kv_i \ll \omega \ll kv_e$ the expression (16.8) can be put in the form

$$\langle \varrho^2 \rangle_{k\omega} = \frac{\Omega_i^4}{8V_s} \cdot \frac{(a_e k)^6}{\gamma(\boldsymbol{k})} \sqrt{2\pi m T_e}\, R \delta \left(\omega^2 - \frac{V_s^2 k^2}{1 + a_e^2 k^2} \right), \tag{16.9}$$

where

$$R = \left[1 + \left(\frac{M T_e}{m T_i} \right)^{1/2} \exp \left\{ \frac{-M V_s^2}{2T_i(1 + a_e^2 k^2)} \right\} \right] (1 + a_e^2 k^2)^{-7/2}.$$

We see that the quantity $\langle \varrho^2 \rangle_{k\omega}$ (just as always if weakly damped charge density oscillations are possible in the system) is proportional to the δ-function expressing the dependence of the frequency of the oscillations on the wave vector. It is significant that the factor in front of the δ-function contains in the denominator the oscillations' damping decrement $\gamma(\boldsymbol{k})$ which depends on the directional velocity of the electrons $\boldsymbol{u}$ and approaches zero when the quantity $u_{\parallel}$ approaches the critical velocity $u_c(k)$.

If we are interested in the long-wave fluctuations of the charge density ($a_e k \ll 1$) we can (neglecting the exponentially small contribution of the ions to the quantity γ) put (16.9) in the form

$$\langle \varrho^2 \rangle_{k\omega} = \frac{T_e (a_e k)^2 \, \omega^4}{2V_s^2 \, |\omega - (\boldsymbol{k} \cdot \boldsymbol{u})|} \, \delta(\omega^2 - V_s^2 k^2). \qquad (16.10)$$

If the component of the electron velocity in the direction of the wave vector $u_{\parallel}$ is close to the velocity of non-isothermal sound V_s, the coefficient of the δ-function in this expression rises without limit.

The correlation functions of the longitudinal electrical field and the densities of both kinds of particles behave similarly. In particular for the correlators of the electron density in the long-wave region ($a_e k \ll 1$), by using (15.7), we obtain

$$\langle \delta n_e^2 \rangle_{k\omega} = \frac{2\pi n_0 \omega^2}{|\omega - (\boldsymbol{k} \cdot \boldsymbol{u})|} \, \delta(\omega^2 - V_s^2 k^2). \qquad (16.11)$$

We should bear in mind that the formulae (16.8)–(16.11) are based on the linear theory (within the framework of which we derived the general expressions (16.7), (15.7) for the correlation functions) and relate to the fluctuations with wave vectors that satisfy the condition $u_{\parallel} < u_c(k)$. Fluctuating oscillations for which $u_{\parallel} > u_c(k)$ lead, as is shown in section 10, to plasma instability. Because of the non-linear effects these oscillations affect the oscillations for which $u_{\parallel} < u_c(k)$; we shall not touch on this question here, however.

3. Fluctuations in a Plasma-Beam System

If the distribution functions of the plasma particles are not only non-equilibrium but also unstable the situation becomes far more complicated. The function ε^{-1} in this case has poles in the upper half-plane of ω, so the contribution of the quantities Y (determined by the prehistory of the system and unknown in the general case) to the correlation functions do not decrease with time but increase. Nevertheless in the case of a system consisting of a plasma and a low-density beam ($n_0' \ll n_0$; n_0' is the beam density) the main terms in the correlation function do not depend on the random initial perturbations.†

In actual fact we substitute (16.3), (16.6) in (16.2) and use Cauchy's theorem to integrate. It is easy to see that the main terms in the correlation function C are the terms defined by the first terms in (16.3) and thus by the first terms in (16.6) containing $\omega + \omega'$ in the denominator. These terms are proportional to n_0' to a power less than the first, whilst the remaining terms contain n_0' to a power not less than the first.

In the general case the correlation functions and the squares of the oscillations' amplitudes in a plasma-beam system contain terms which increase exponentially with time with an increment proportional to $n_0'^{1/2}$, the pre-exponential factor also being proportional to $n_0'^{1/2}$. If the beam velocity is great compared with the mean thermal velocity of the plasma electrons, then, as we have seen in section 10, resonance appears between the beam oscillations and the plasma's Langmuir oscillations. In this case the correlation functions rise with an increment proportional to $n_0'^{1/3}$, the pre-exponential factor being independent of the beam density.

Without pausing to examine the general expressions for the correlation functions‡ we shall give only the formula for the correlation function of the charge density with a resonant wave vector value ($|(\boldsymbol{k}\cdot\boldsymbol{u})| \approx \Omega$) for the case $t, t' \gg \Omega^{-1}(n_0/n_0')^{1/3}$

$$C(\boldsymbol{k}, t, t') = \frac{k^2}{72\pi} \exp\left\{\Omega(t+t')\frac{\sqrt{3}}{2}\left(\frac{n_0'}{2n_0}\right)^{1/3} - i\Omega(t-t')\,\mathrm{sign}\,(\boldsymbol{k}\cdot\boldsymbol{u})\left[1-\frac{1}{2}\left(\frac{n_0'}{2n_0}\right)^{1/3}\right]\right\}, \tag{16.12}$$

where T is the temperature of the plasma (the beam is assumed to be cold) and $\boldsymbol{u}$ is the velocity of the beam.

† It is assumed that the perturbations did not increase too much during the time taken to "introduce" the beam so that the initial fluctuations are of the same order of magnitude as the equilibrium fluctuations although they differ from them.

‡ The fluctuations in a plasma-beam system are studied in detail by Akhiezer [1962].

Putting $t = t'$ in this expression and using the Poisson equation we can find the mean quadratic amplitude of the resonance oscillations of the electrical field in a plasma-beam system:

$$\langle E^2(\boldsymbol{k}, t)\rangle^{1/2} = \frac{1}{3}\sqrt{2\pi T}\exp\left\{\Omega t\,\frac{\sqrt{3}}{2}\left(\frac{n_0'}{2n_0}\right)^{1/3}\right\}. \quad (16.13)$$

CHAPTER V

Wave Scattering and Transformation and Scattering of Charged Particles in a Plasma

17. Scattering of Electromagnetic Waves in a Free Plasma

1. Current Causing Scattered Waves

When deriving the eigen oscillation spectra of a plasma we started with the linearized kinetic equations where we neglected the non-linear terms

$$\frac{e_\alpha}{m_\alpha}\left(\left\{E + \frac{1}{c}[v \wedge H]\right\} \cdot \frac{\partial}{\partial v}\right) f^\alpha,$$

where $f^\alpha = F^\alpha - F_0^\alpha$ is the deviation of the distribution function F^α from the initial distribution F_0^α. The equation for the electric field obtained as a result of this is

$$\text{curl curl}\, E + \frac{\hat{\varepsilon}}{c^2}\frac{\partial^2}{\partial t^2} E = 0, \tag{17.1}$$

where $\hat{\varepsilon}$ is the operator of the plasma's dielectric constant. This equation, being linear, satisfies the principle of superposition and therefore corresponds to the possibility of the independent propagation of different oscillations in the plasma.

In actual fact, however, the different oscillations are not propagated in a plasma independently but interact with one another. This interaction is contained in the original kinetic equations and is described by the non-linear terms $(e_\alpha/m_\alpha)(\{\boldsymbol{E}+([\boldsymbol{v}\wedge\boldsymbol{H}]/c)\}\cdot(\partial/\partial\boldsymbol{v}))f^\alpha$ which were dropped when deriving the equation (17.1).

The interaction between the oscillations leads to different processes of wave scattering and transformation in the plasma. Let us examine, for example, the propagation of a transverse electromagnetic wave in a plasma. Because of its interaction with the fluctuating oscillations of the plasma wave scattering occurs, which may be accompanied by a change in frequency. The intensity of the scattered waves is determined by the intensity of the incident wave and the level of the plasma fluctuations.

Since the fluctuation spectrum has sharply defined maxima at the frequencies of the plasma's eigen oscillations there will also be sharply defined maxima in the scattered wave spectrum at frequencies that differ from the frequency of the incident wave by the frequencies of the plasma's eigen oscillations (or by multiples of their frequencies).

The interaction of waves propagated in a plasma with the fluctuating oscillations may also lead to transformation of the waves, for example the conversion of a transverse wave into a longitudinal one and a longitudinal one into a transverse one. The probabilities of these processes as well as the probabilities of the scattering processes are determined by the level of the fluctuations in the plasma.

Since we have studied the fluctuations let us move on to the wave scattering and transformation processes in a plasma which we shall consider at first to be free.

We notice first that the non-linear interaction between the different oscillations of a plasma is small. Because of this we can approximately pick out the field of the incident wave which, by definition, satisfies the equation (17.1). We shall consider the field of the incident wave to be given and denote it by $\boldsymbol{E}^0(\boldsymbol{r}, t)$.

Because of the interaction of the incident wave $\boldsymbol{E}^0$ with the fluctuating field scattered waves appear, so the total electric field in the plasma during the propagation of a wave can be given in the form

$$\boldsymbol{E}(\boldsymbol{r}, t) = \boldsymbol{E}^0(\boldsymbol{r}, t) + \delta\boldsymbol{E}(\boldsymbol{r}, t) + \boldsymbol{E}'(\boldsymbol{r}, t),$$

where $\delta\boldsymbol{E}$ is the fluctuating field and $\boldsymbol{E}'$ is the field of the scattered wave. Since the interaction between the waves is small the field $\boldsymbol{E}'$ may be considered to be proportional to the product of the strengths of the incident wave field and the fluctuating field, $E' \sim E^0\delta E$.

Our problem is to determine the field of the scattered wave $\boldsymbol{E}'$. This field obviously satisfies the Maxwell equation

$$\text{curl curl}\,\boldsymbol{E}' + \frac{1}{c^2}\frac{\partial^2}{\partial t^2}\boldsymbol{E}' = -\frac{4\pi}{c^2}\frac{\partial}{\partial t}\boldsymbol{j}', \tag{17.2}$$

where $\boldsymbol{j}'$ is the density of all the currents producing the field $\boldsymbol{E}'$.

In accordance with (1.3) the currents in the plasma are connected with the distribution function by the relation

$$\boldsymbol{j} = \sum_\alpha e_\alpha \int \boldsymbol{v} f^\alpha d^3\boldsymbol{v}.$$

We must therefore find out what form the distribution function takes when a wave $\boldsymbol{E}^0$ is propagated in the plasma. The deviation of the distribution function f^α from the original function F_0^α can be put in the form

$$f^\alpha = f_\alpha^0 + \delta f_\alpha + f_\alpha',$$

where f_α^0 is the deviation of the distribution function connected with the incident wave; δf_α is the distribution function fluctuation and f_α' is the deviation of the distribution function connected with the scattered wave. The functions f_α^0 and f_α' satisfy the equations

$$\frac{\partial}{\partial t} f_\alpha^0 + \left(\boldsymbol{v}\cdot\frac{\partial}{\partial \boldsymbol{r}}\right) f_\alpha^0 + \frac{e_\alpha}{m_\alpha}\left(\left\{\boldsymbol{E}_0 + \frac{1}{c}[\boldsymbol{v}\wedge \boldsymbol{H}_0]\right\}\cdot\frac{\partial}{\partial \boldsymbol{v}}\right) F_0^\alpha = 0; \tag{17.3}$$

$$\begin{aligned}\frac{\partial}{\partial t} f_\alpha' + \left(\boldsymbol{v}\cdot\frac{\partial}{\partial \boldsymbol{r}}\right) f_\alpha' &+ \frac{e_\alpha}{m_\alpha}\left(\left\{\boldsymbol{E}' + \frac{1}{c}[\boldsymbol{v}\wedge \boldsymbol{H}']\right\}\cdot\frac{\partial}{\partial \boldsymbol{v}}\right) F_0^\alpha \\ &+ \frac{e_\alpha}{m_\alpha}\left(\left\{\boldsymbol{E}^0 + \frac{1}{c}[\boldsymbol{v}\wedge \boldsymbol{H}^0]\right\}\cdot\frac{\partial}{\partial \boldsymbol{v}}\right)\delta f_\alpha \\ &+ \frac{e_\alpha}{m_\alpha}\left(\left\{\delta\boldsymbol{E} + \frac{1}{c}[\boldsymbol{v}\wedge \delta\boldsymbol{H}]\right\}\cdot\frac{\partial}{\partial \boldsymbol{v}}\right) f_\alpha^0 = 0,\end{aligned} \tag{17.4}$$

where $\boldsymbol{H}^0$ and $\boldsymbol{H}'$ are the magnetic fields of the incident and scattered waves and $\delta\boldsymbol{H}$ is the fluctuating magnetic field.

We shall assume that the incident wave is a plane monochromatic wave

$$\boldsymbol{E}^0(\boldsymbol{r}, t) = \boldsymbol{E}^0 \exp\{i(\boldsymbol{k}\cdot\boldsymbol{r}) - i\omega t\}.$$

Then the solution of the equation (17.3) is of the form

$$(f'_\alpha)_{k\omega} = -i\,\frac{e_\alpha}{m_\alpha}\,(\omega - (\boldsymbol{k}\cdot\boldsymbol{v}))^{-1} \times$$
$$\times \left(\left\{\boldsymbol{E}^0 + \frac{1}{c}\,[\boldsymbol{v}\wedge\boldsymbol{H}^0]\right\}\cdot\frac{\partial}{\partial\boldsymbol{v}}\right) F_0^\alpha \tag{17.5}$$

(here the factor exp $\{i(\boldsymbol{k}\cdot\boldsymbol{r}) - i\omega t\}$ is omitted). The current connected with this part of the distribution function is

$$\boldsymbol{j}_{k\omega} = -i\omega\,\frac{\varepsilon(\boldsymbol{k},\omega)^{-1}}{4\pi}\,\boldsymbol{E}^0. \tag{17.6}$$

Changing in the equation (17.4) to the Fourier components we obtain

$$(f'_\alpha)_{k'\omega'} = -i\,\frac{e_\alpha}{m_\alpha}\,(\omega' - (\boldsymbol{k}'\cdot\boldsymbol{v}))^{-1} \times$$
$$\times \left\{\left(\left[\boldsymbol{E}'_{k'\omega'} + \frac{1}{c}\,[\boldsymbol{v}\wedge\boldsymbol{H}'_{k'\omega'}]\right]\cdot\frac{\partial}{\partial\boldsymbol{v}}\right) F_0^\alpha\right.$$
$$+ \left(\left[\boldsymbol{E}^0 + \frac{1}{c}\,[\boldsymbol{v}\wedge\boldsymbol{H}^0]\right]\cdot\frac{\partial}{\partial\boldsymbol{v}}\right)(\delta f_\alpha)_{q,\Delta\omega}$$
$$\left. + \left(\left[\delta\boldsymbol{E}_{q,\Delta\omega} + \frac{1}{c}\,[\boldsymbol{v}\wedge\delta\boldsymbol{H}]_{q,\Delta\omega}\right]\cdot\frac{\partial}{\partial\boldsymbol{v}}\right)(f_\alpha^0)_{k\omega}\right\}, \tag{17.7}$$

where

$$\Delta\omega = \omega' - \omega \quad \text{and} \quad \boldsymbol{q} = \boldsymbol{k}' - \boldsymbol{k}.$$

It is easy to determine the current connected with the function f'_α:

$$\boldsymbol{j}'_{k'\omega'} = -i\omega'\,\frac{\varepsilon(\boldsymbol{k}',\omega') - 1}{4\pi}\,\boldsymbol{E}'_{k'\omega'} + \boldsymbol{J}_{k'\omega'}, \tag{17.8}$$

where

$$\boldsymbol{J}_{k'\omega'} = -i\sum_\alpha \frac{e_\alpha^2}{m_\alpha}\int d^3v\,\frac{\boldsymbol{v}}{\omega' - (\boldsymbol{k}'\cdot\boldsymbol{v})} \times$$
$$\times \left\{\left(\left[\boldsymbol{E}^0 + \frac{1}{c}\,[\boldsymbol{v}\wedge\boldsymbol{H}^0]\right]\cdot\frac{\partial}{\partial\boldsymbol{v}}\right)(\delta f_\alpha)_{q,\Delta\omega}\right.$$
$$\left. + \left(\left[\delta\boldsymbol{E}_{q,\Delta\omega} + \frac{1}{c}\,[\boldsymbol{v}\wedge\delta\boldsymbol{H}_{q,\Delta\omega}]\right]\cdot\frac{\partial}{\partial\boldsymbol{v}}\right)(f_\alpha^0)\right\}_{k\omega}. \tag{17.9}$$

Substituting the expression (17.8) for the current $\boldsymbol{j}'$ in the equation (17.2) for the field of the scattered wave we obtain

$$\text{curl curl}\, \boldsymbol{E}' + \frac{\hat{\varepsilon}}{c^2}\frac{\partial^2}{\partial t^2}\boldsymbol{E}' = -\frac{4\pi}{c^2}\frac{\partial}{\partial t}\boldsymbol{J}. \tag{17.10}$$

We see that the quantity $\boldsymbol{J}$ can be looked upon as a current causing scattered waves. This current is proportional to the field of the incident wave and the quantities characterizing the fluctuations in the plasma.

The equation (17.10) describes all the wave scattering and transformation processes in a free plasma.

In the following we shall examine the scattering (and transformation) only of high-frequency (transverse electromagnetic and longitudinal Langmuir) waves. These processes are basically caused by the plasma's electron component. Therefore $\boldsymbol{J}$ in (17.10) must be understood as the electron current density.

Since the phase velocities of the waves under discussion are far greater than the thermal velocity of the electrons, when calculating the integral contained in the expression for the current $\boldsymbol{J}$ we can use the expansions

$$(\omega - (\boldsymbol{k}\cdot\boldsymbol{v}))^{-1} = \omega^{-1}\left(1 + \frac{(\boldsymbol{k}\cdot\boldsymbol{v})}{\omega} + \cdots\right);$$

$$(\omega' - (\boldsymbol{k}'\cdot\boldsymbol{v}))^{-1} = \omega'^{-1}\left(1 + \frac{(\boldsymbol{k}'\cdot\boldsymbol{v})}{\omega'} + \cdots\right).$$

As a result we obtain

$$\begin{aligned} \boldsymbol{J}_{k'\omega'} = i\frac{e}{m\omega}\Bigg\{ & \left[e\delta n^e_{q,\Delta\omega} + \frac{1}{\omega'}(\boldsymbol{k}'\cdot\delta\boldsymbol{j}^e_{q,\Delta\omega}) - \frac{1}{\omega}(\boldsymbol{k}\delta\boldsymbol{j}^e_{q,\Delta\omega})\right]\boldsymbol{E}^0 \\ & + \frac{\boldsymbol{k}}{\omega}(\boldsymbol{E}_0\cdot\delta\boldsymbol{j}^e_{q,\Delta\omega}) + \frac{1}{\omega'}(\boldsymbol{k}'\cdot\boldsymbol{E}^0)\,\delta\boldsymbol{j}^e_{q,\Delta\omega} \\ & + \frac{i}{4\pi}\frac{\Omega^2}{\omega\omega'}(\boldsymbol{k}'\cdot\delta\boldsymbol{E}_{q,\Delta\omega})\,\boldsymbol{E}^0 + \frac{\omega'}{\Delta\omega}(\boldsymbol{E}^0\cdot\delta\boldsymbol{E}_{q,\Delta\omega})\,\boldsymbol{q} \\ & + \left[(\boldsymbol{k}'\cdot\boldsymbol{E}^0) - \frac{\omega'}{\Delta\omega}(\boldsymbol{q}\cdot\boldsymbol{E}^0) + \frac{\omega'}{\omega}(\boldsymbol{k}\cdot\boldsymbol{E}^0)\right]\delta\boldsymbol{E}_{q,\Delta\omega}\Bigg\}, \end{aligned} \tag{17.11}$$

where δn^e and $\delta \boldsymbol{j}^e$ are the fluctuations of the electron density and the electron current density

$$\delta n^e = \int \delta f_e \, d^3 v; \quad \delta \boldsymbol{j}^e = e \int \boldsymbol{v} \delta f_e \, d^3 \boldsymbol{v}.$$

We notice that the fluctuating field $\delta \boldsymbol{E}$ contained in the expression (17.11) is determined by the fluctuations of both the electron and ion currents.

Neglecting the small relativistic corrections we can express the fluctuations of the current $\delta \boldsymbol{j}^e$ and the field $\delta \boldsymbol{E}$ in terms of the fluctuations of the electron and ion densities δn^e and δn^i:

$$\delta \boldsymbol{j}^e_{\boldsymbol{q}, \Delta\omega} = \frac{\Delta\omega}{q^2} \boldsymbol{q} \delta n^e_{\boldsymbol{q}, \Delta\omega},$$

$$\delta \boldsymbol{E}_{\boldsymbol{q}, \Delta\omega} = -i \frac{4\pi e}{q^2} \boldsymbol{q} (\delta n^e_{\boldsymbol{q}, \Delta\omega} - \delta n^i_{\boldsymbol{q}, \Delta\omega}). \tag{17.12}$$

Substituting these relations in (17.11) we obtain

$$\boldsymbol{J}_{\boldsymbol{k}'\omega'} = \frac{ie^2}{m\omega} \left\{ \left[\boldsymbol{E}^0 + \frac{\Delta\omega}{\omega'} \frac{\boldsymbol{k}'}{q^2} (\boldsymbol{q} \cdot \boldsymbol{E}^0) + \frac{\Delta\omega}{\omega} \frac{\boldsymbol{q}}{q^2} (\boldsymbol{k} \cdot \boldsymbol{E}^0) \right] \delta n^e_{\boldsymbol{q}, \Delta\omega} \right.$$

$$- \left(\frac{\Delta\omega}{q\omega'} \right)^2 \left[(\boldsymbol{k}' \cdot \boldsymbol{q}) \boldsymbol{E}^0 + (\boldsymbol{k}' \cdot \boldsymbol{E}^0) \boldsymbol{q} + \frac{\omega'}{\omega} (\boldsymbol{k} \cdot \boldsymbol{E}^0) \boldsymbol{q} \right] \delta n^e_{\boldsymbol{q}, \Delta\omega}$$

$$+ \left(\frac{\Omega}{q\omega'} \right)^2 \left[(\boldsymbol{k}' \cdot \boldsymbol{q}) \boldsymbol{E}^0 + (\boldsymbol{k}' \cdot \boldsymbol{E}^0)_q + \frac{\omega'}{\omega} (\boldsymbol{k} \cdot \boldsymbol{E}^0) \boldsymbol{q} \right] \times$$

$$\left. \times (\delta n^e_{\boldsymbol{q}, \Delta\omega} - \delta n^i_{\boldsymbol{q}, \Delta\omega}) \right\}. \tag{17.13}$$

It is easy to see that we need not take the last two terms into consideration in the expression for the current $\boldsymbol{J}$. To prove this we recall that the longitudinal fluctuations in a plasma occur largely at the frequencies $\Delta\omega \ll \Omega$ and $\Delta\omega \approx \Omega$. Let us first examine the fluctuations with the frequencies $\Delta\omega \ll \Omega$. For them

$$\langle (\delta n^e - \delta n^i)^2 \rangle_{\boldsymbol{q}, \Delta\omega} \sim (aq)^4 \langle (\delta n^e)^2 \rangle_{\boldsymbol{q}, \Delta\omega}.$$

Therefore when $\Delta\omega \ll \Omega$ the ratio of the third term in (17.13) to the first is $(kv_e/\omega)^2$ in order of magnitude, i.e. is far less than unity (it is assumed that $\omega/k \gg v_e$). The second term in (17.13) when $\Delta\omega \ll \Omega$ can also be neglected since it contains $(\Delta\omega/\omega')^2$ $(\omega' > \Omega)$.

We shall now assume that the fluctuating oscillation is a Langmuir oscillation, i.e. $\Delta\omega \approx \Omega$. In this case $(\delta n^i_{q,\Delta\omega}) \ll (\delta n^e_{q,\Delta\omega})$ and the second term in (17.13) cancels with the third.

We can thus proceed from the following expression for the current causing the scattered waves

$$\boldsymbol{J}_{k'\omega'} = \frac{ie^2}{m\omega}\left\{\boldsymbol{E}^0 + \frac{\Delta\omega}{\omega'}\frac{\boldsymbol{k}'}{q^2}(\boldsymbol{q}\cdot\boldsymbol{E}^0) + \frac{\Delta\omega}{\omega}\frac{\boldsymbol{q}}{q^2}(\boldsymbol{k}\cdot\boldsymbol{E}^0)\right\}\delta n^e_{q,\Delta\omega}. \tag{17.14}$$

This expression is valid if the phase velocities of the incident and scattered waves are far greater than the thermal velocity of the electrons.

We shall show that upon this assumption we can obtain the expression (17.14) by proceeding from the simple hydrodynamic picture if we introduce the hydrodynamic velocity of the electrons $\boldsymbol{v}(\boldsymbol{r}, t)$ and their density $n(\boldsymbol{r}, t)$. These quantities, with which the density of the electron current is connected by the relation

$$\boldsymbol{j} = en\boldsymbol{v}, \tag{17.15}$$

satisfy the equations

$$\left(\frac{\partial}{\partial t} + (\boldsymbol{v}\cdot\nabla)\right)\boldsymbol{v} = \frac{e}{m}\left(\boldsymbol{E} + \frac{1}{c}[\boldsymbol{v}\wedge\boldsymbol{H}]\right),$$

$$\frac{\partial}{\partial t}n + \operatorname{div}(n\boldsymbol{v}) = 0. \tag{17.16}$$

If a wave $\boldsymbol{E}^0$ is propagated in the plasma the density and hydrodynamic velocity of the electrons can be given in the form

$$n = n_0 + n^0 + \delta n + n', \tag{17.15'}$$

$$\boldsymbol{v} = \boldsymbol{v}^0 + \delta\boldsymbol{v} + \boldsymbol{v}',$$

where n^0 is the density variation and $\boldsymbol{v}^0$ is the electron velocity caused by the field of the incident wave; n' and $\boldsymbol{v}'$ are the analogous quantities connected with the scattered wave $\boldsymbol{E}'$; δn and $\delta \boldsymbol{v}$ are the density and hydrodynamic velocity fluctuations.

The quantities n^0 and $\boldsymbol{v}^0$ satisfy the equations

$$\frac{\partial}{\partial t} \boldsymbol{v}^0 = \frac{e}{m} \boldsymbol{E}^0, \quad \frac{\partial}{\partial t} n^0 + n_0 \operatorname{div} \boldsymbol{v}^0 = 0, \tag{17.17}$$

and the quantities n' and $\boldsymbol{v}'$ satisfy the equations

$$\left.\begin{aligned} \frac{\partial}{\partial t} \boldsymbol{v}' &= \frac{e}{m} \boldsymbol{E}' + \frac{e}{mc} [\delta \boldsymbol{v} \wedge \boldsymbol{H}^0] \\ &\quad - (\boldsymbol{v}^0 \cdot \nabla)\, \delta \boldsymbol{v} - (\delta \boldsymbol{v} \cdot \nabla)\, \boldsymbol{v}^0, \\ \frac{\partial}{\partial t} n' &+ n_0 \operatorname{div} \boldsymbol{v}' + n_0 \operatorname{div} \delta \boldsymbol{v} + \delta n \operatorname{div} \boldsymbol{v}^0 = 0. \end{aligned}\right\} \tag{17.18}$$

Putting $\boldsymbol{E}^0(\boldsymbol{r}, t) = \boldsymbol{E}^0 \exp\{i(\boldsymbol{k} \cdot \boldsymbol{r}) - i\omega t\}$ and $\boldsymbol{E}'(\boldsymbol{r}, t) = \boldsymbol{E}' \exp\{i(\boldsymbol{k}' \cdot \boldsymbol{r}) - i\omega' t\}$ in these equations we find

$$\begin{aligned} \boldsymbol{v}^0 &= \frac{ie}{m\omega} \boldsymbol{E}^0, \quad n^0 = \frac{ie}{m\omega^2} n_0 (\boldsymbol{k} \cdot \boldsymbol{E}^0), \\ \boldsymbol{v}' &= \frac{ie}{m\omega'} \left(\boldsymbol{E}' + \frac{1}{c} [\delta \boldsymbol{v}_{\boldsymbol{q},\Delta\omega} \wedge \boldsymbol{H}^0] \right. \\ &\quad \left. + \frac{1}{\omega'} \{ (\boldsymbol{q} \cdot \boldsymbol{v}^0)\, \delta \boldsymbol{v}_{\boldsymbol{q},\Delta\omega} + (\boldsymbol{k} \cdot \delta \boldsymbol{v}_{\boldsymbol{q},\Delta\omega})\, \boldsymbol{v}^0 \} \right), \end{aligned} \tag{17.19}$$

where $\boldsymbol{q} = \boldsymbol{k}' - \boldsymbol{k}$; $\Delta\omega = \omega' - \omega$ and $\delta \boldsymbol{v}_{\boldsymbol{q},\Delta\omega}$ is the Fourier component of the electron velocity fluctuation. The velocity fluctuations are connected with the electron density fluctuations by the continuity relation

$$\frac{\partial}{\partial t} \delta n + n_0 \operatorname{div} \delta \boldsymbol{v} = 0. \tag{17.20}$$

For the longitudinal fluctuations, which are the only significant ones,

$$\delta \boldsymbol{v}_{\boldsymbol{q},\Delta\omega} = \frac{\Delta\omega}{n_0 q^2} \boldsymbol{q} \delta n_{\boldsymbol{q},\Delta\omega}.$$

Substituting this expression in (17.19) we obtain

$$v' = \frac{ie}{m\omega'}\left\{E' + \frac{\Delta\omega \cdot \delta n_{q,\Delta\omega}}{n_0\omega q^2}([q \wedge [k \wedge E^0]] + q(q \cdot E^0) + E^0(k \cdot q))\right\}. \quad (17.21)$$

Let us now determine the current causing the scattered waves. It can clearly be put in the form

$$j' = e(n_0 v' + n^0 \delta v + v^0 \delta n). \quad (17.22)$$

If there were no fluctuations the current j' would be

$$j'|_{\delta n = 0} = e n_0 v'|_{\delta n=0} = \frac{ie^2 n_0}{m\omega'} E'.$$

By subtracting this expression from the expression (17.22) we find the current we are interested in:

$$J = j' - j'|_{\delta n=0}. \quad (17.23)$$

By using (17.21) we can obtain from this the current's Fourier component $J_{k'\omega'}$:

$$J_{k'\omega'} = \frac{ie^2}{m\omega}\left\{E^0 + \frac{\Delta\omega}{\omega'}\frac{k'}{q^2}(q \cdot E^0) + \frac{\Delta\omega}{\omega}\frac{q}{q^2}(k \cdot E^0)\right\}\delta n_{q,\Delta\omega}.$$

This expression is the same as the expression (17.14) which was derived from the kinetic standpoint.

2. Scattering Cross Section

Having the expression for the current J we can, in accordance with (17.10), find the field of the scattered waves. It is clear that the current J will contain both transverse and longitudinal parts independently of the polarization properties of the incident wave. Therefore the field of the scattered waves will also contain transverse and longitudinal components. By isolating these components we shall be able to study the scattering of transverse waves (i.e. their change into transverse waves), the transformation of transverse waves into longitudinal waves, the scattering of longitudinal waves and the transformation of longitudinal waves into transverse waves.

Let us first examine the scattering of transverse waves in a plasma $[(\boldsymbol{k}\cdot\boldsymbol{E}^0)=0,\ (\boldsymbol{k}'\cdot\boldsymbol{E}')=0)]$ [Akhiezer, Prokhoda and Sitenko, 1957; Dougherty and Farley, 1960; Salpeter, 1960a, 1960b; Akhiezer, A.I., Akhiezer, I.A. and Sitenko, 1961]. Taking the transverse component of the current $\boldsymbol{J}$ we can find the Fourier component of the field of a scattered transverse wave

$$\boldsymbol{E}'_{k'\omega'} = -\frac{4\pi e^2\omega'}{mc^2\omega}\left(k'^2 - \frac{\omega'^2}{c^2}\varepsilon(\omega')\right)^{-1}\boldsymbol{E}^0_\perp \delta n_{q,\Delta\omega}, \tag{17.24}$$

where $\boldsymbol{E}^0_\perp$ is the component of $\boldsymbol{E}^0$ at right angles to the vector $\boldsymbol{k}'$ and $\varepsilon(\omega) = 1 - \Omega^2/\omega^2$.

The mean energy increment of the scattered wave field in unit time is obviously defined by the formula

$$I = -\tfrac{1}{2}\,\mathrm{Re}\int d^3\boldsymbol{r}\langle \boldsymbol{E}'(\boldsymbol{r},t)\cdot\boldsymbol{J}(\boldsymbol{r},t)\rangle. \tag{17.25}$$

By substituting the expressions (17.24) and (17.14) for $\boldsymbol{E}'$ and $\boldsymbol{J}$ in this we find the energy increment of the scattered transverse wave field†

$$I^{(t\to t')} = \frac{V}{(2\pi)^3}\frac{e^4}{m^2c^2\omega^2}\times$$
$$\times\ \mathrm{Im}\int d\omega'\, d^3\boldsymbol{k}'\,\frac{\omega'\boldsymbol{E}^{02}_\perp\langle\delta n^2\rangle_{q,\Delta\omega}}{\boldsymbol{k}'^2 - (\omega'^2/c^2)\varepsilon(\omega')}, \tag{17.26}$$

where V is the volume of the plasma.

It is obvious that only the poles of the integrand make a contribution to $I^{(t\to t')}$. After integrating with respect to the modulus of the vector $\boldsymbol{k}'$ we find the scattering intensity in the frequency range $d\omega'$ and in the element of a solid angle do'

$$dI^{(t\to t')} = \frac{Vc}{16\pi^2}\left(\frac{e^2}{mc^2}\right)^2\left(\frac{\omega'}{\omega}\right)^2\sqrt{\varepsilon(\omega')}\,E^{02}_\perp\times$$
$$\times\ \langle\delta n^2\rangle_{q,\Delta\omega}\,d\omega'\,do'. \tag{17.27}$$

† Editor's Note. In equation (17.26) the symbol $t\to t'$ refers to the scattering of transverse into transverse waves. Later we shall meet $I^{(t\to l)}$ for the scattering of transverse into longitudinal waves.

(The frequency ω' and the wave vector $\boldsymbol{k}'$ of the scattered wave are connected by the relation $k'^2 = (\omega'/c)^2 \varepsilon(\omega')$.)

If the incident wave is unpolarized the formula (17.27) must be averaged with respect to the different orientations of the vector $\boldsymbol{E}^0$. In this case the mean value of the square of the field $E_\perp^{0^2}$ is

$$\overline{E_\perp^{0^2}} = \tfrac{1}{2}(1 + \cos^2\vartheta)\, E^{0^2},$$

where ϑ is the scattering angle (the angle between the vectors $\boldsymbol{k}'$ and $\boldsymbol{k}$).

Dividing the scattering intensity $\overline{dI}$ by the flux density of the incident wave's energy $S_0 = (c/8\pi)\sqrt{\varepsilon(\omega)}\, E^{0^2}$ and the magnitude of the scattering volume V we find the differential scattering cross section or the scattering coefficient $d\Sigma$

$$d\Sigma = dI/S_0 V.$$

For a non-polarized wave the differential scattering cross section per element of solid angle do' for the frequency range $d\omega'$ is of the form

$$d\Sigma^{(t\to t')} = \left(\frac{e^2}{mc^2}\right)^2 \left(\frac{\omega'}{\omega}\right)^2 \sqrt{\frac{\varepsilon(\omega')}{\varepsilon(\omega)}} \times$$

$$\times (1 + \cos^2\vartheta)\, \langle \delta n^2 \rangle_{q,\Delta\omega}\, d\omega' \,\frac{do'}{4\pi} \qquad (17.28)$$

(it is assumed that the frequencies ω and ω' are greater than Ω).

Although when deriving the formula (17.28) we took into consideration the scattering of electromagnetic waves only on the electron density fluctuations $d\Sigma^{(t\to t')}$ (the scattering cross section) proves to be dependent on the motion of the ions as well. This can be explained by the fact that the spectral distribution of the electron density fluctuations $\langle \delta n^2 \rangle_{q,\Delta\omega}$ depends essentially on the motion of the plasma ions because of the self-consistent interaction between the electrons and the ions.

We should point out that the formula (17.28) is valid for an arbitrary change in frequency. If $\Delta\omega \ll \omega$ the factor $(\omega'/\omega)^2 \sqrt{\varepsilon(\omega')/\varepsilon(\omega)}$ becomes unity and the formula (17.28) changes into the well-known formula determining the cross section of scattering on density fluctuations with a small frequency variation (see, for example, Landau and Lifshitz, 1957a).

The spectral distribution of the scattered waves is thus determined by the spectral distribution of the electron density fluctuations. In an isothermal plasma the scattered radiation spectrum consists of the Doppler-broadened basic line ($|\Delta\omega| \lesssim qv_i$) and the sharply defined maxima when $\Delta\omega = \pm\Omega$ (if $aq \ll 1$). Therefore in the most interesting case of high frequencies ($\omega \gg \Omega$) the factor $(\omega'/\omega)^2 \sqrt{\varepsilon(\omega')/\varepsilon(\omega)}$ may be considered to be unity. In this case the scattering cross section can be integrated with respect to the frequencies by using the relation (14.9). As a result we obtain the expression for the scattering cross section in an isothermal plasma per unit solid angle

$$d\Sigma = \frac{n_0}{2}\left(\frac{e^2}{mc^2}\right)^2 \frac{1 + a^2q^2}{2 + a^2q^2}(1 + \cos^2\vartheta)\, do',$$

$$q = \frac{2\omega}{c}\sin\frac{\vartheta}{2}. \tag{17.29}$$

Integrating (17.29) with respect to the angles we find the total scattering cross section

$$\Sigma = n_0\sigma_0\left\{1 - \frac{3}{4(ak)^2} + \frac{3\ln(1 + 2a^2k^2)}{8(ak)^2} + \frac{3}{4\sqrt{2}}\,\frac{1-(ak)^2}{(ak)^3}\arctan(\sqrt{2}\cdot ak)\right\}, \tag{17.30}$$

where $\sigma_0 = (8\pi/3)(e^2/mc^2)^2$ is the Thomson scattering cross section of electromagnetic waves by a free electron. In the extreme cases of short and long wavelengths the scattering cross section is of the form

$$\Sigma = n_0\sigma_0 \quad (ak \gg 1), \tag{17.31}$$

$$\Sigma = \tfrac{1}{2}n_0\sigma_0 \quad (ak \ll 1). \tag{17.32}$$

3. Spectral Distribution of Scattered Radiation

Let us examine in greater detail the spectral distribution of the scattered radiation in a free plasma.† In the case of short wavelengths ($aq \gg 1$) the correlator $\langle\delta n^2\rangle_{q,\Delta\omega}$ takes the form of a

† The spectral distribution of the scattered radiation in the case of an equilibrium plasma has been investigated in various papers [Dougherty and Farley, 1960; Salpeter, 1960a, 1960b; Akhiezer, A.I., Akhiezer, I.A. and Sitenko, 1961] and in the case of a two-temperature plasma in Akhiezer, A.I., Akhiezer, I.A. and Sitenko's paper [1961].

Gaussian function of the frequency shift $\Delta\omega$, so the spectral distribution of the scattering is also Gaussian

$$d\Sigma = \frac{n_0}{q}\left(\frac{e^2}{mc^2}\right)^2\left(\frac{m}{8\pi T_e}\right)^{1/2} \times$$
$$\times (1+\cos^2\vartheta)\exp\left\{\frac{-m\,\Delta\omega^2}{2q^2T_e}\right\} d\omega'\, do'. \qquad (17.33)$$

(This formula is valid if $\Delta\omega \neq \Omega_i$.)

We can see that the Doppler broadening of the line is determined by the thermal velocity of the electrons. The total scattering cross section (17.31) is equal to the sum of the scattering cross sections on the individual electrons. The Coulomb interaction between the electrons and the ions is insignificant and the scattering is not coherent.

In the case of long wavelengths ($ak \ll 1$) the collective properties of the plasma are manifested. This case occurs in particular in experiments on the scattering of radio waves on the density fluctuations in the upper layers of the ionosphere ($k^{-1} \sim 10$ cm, $a \sim 1$ cm, see Dougherty and Farley, 1960).

We give below the expressions for the spectral distribution of the scattered radiation in the various frequency ranges, assuming that $ak \ll 1$.

If the change in frequency upon scattering is small ($\Delta\omega \ll qv_i$) the scattering cross section is defined by the formula

$$d\Sigma = \frac{n_0}{\sqrt{8\pi}}\left(\frac{e^2}{mc^2}\right)^2 \frac{\sqrt{m}\,T_e^{3/2}+\sqrt{M}\,T_i^{3/2}}{q(T_e+T_i)^2} \times$$
$$\times (1+\cos^2\vartheta)\, d\omega'\, do'. \qquad (17.34)$$

In the case of a strongly non-isothermal plasma the scattering cross section with a small change in frequency is $\frac{1}{4}\sqrt{M/m}$ times less than the corresponding cross section for an isothermal plasma with a temperature T_e.

If $\Delta\omega \ll qv_i$ the scattering cross section in an isothermal plasma is

$$d\Sigma = \frac{n_0}{\sqrt{4\pi}}\left(\frac{e^2}{mc^2}\right)^2 (qv_i)^{-1} f\left(\frac{\Delta\omega}{qv_i}\right)(1+\cos^2\vartheta)\, d\omega'\, do', \qquad (17.35)$$

$$f(z) = e^{-z^2}\,|2+i\sqrt{\pi}\,zw(z)|^{-2},$$

where $w(z)$ is defined by the formula (2.16). The scattering cross section decreases sharply when $\Delta\omega \sim qv_i$ so the quantity $\Delta\omega \sim qv_i$ characterizes the width of the spectral distribution of the scattered radiation in an isothermal plasma. This quantity is determined by the thermal velocity of the ions although the scattering occurs on the electrons.

If $qv_i \ll \Delta\omega \ll qv_e$ the scattering cross section for an isothermal plasma is very small. For a strongly non-isothermal plasma the scattering cross section has sharply defined maxima if the frequency shift coincides with the frequency of the low-frequency oscillation of the plasma with the wave vector $\boldsymbol{q}$.

In particular if $aq \ll 1$ there are maxima when $\Delta\omega = \pm V_s q$, where V_s is the velocity of non-isothermal sound. The scattering cross section near the maxima is of the form

$$d\Sigma = \frac{n_0}{4}\left(\frac{e^2}{mc^2}\right)^2 (1 + \cos^2\vartheta)\,\{\delta(\Delta\omega - V_s q) + \delta(\Delta\omega + V_s q)\}\, d\omega'\, do'. \tag{17.36}$$

Integrating (17.36) with respect to the angles and frequencies we find the total scattering cross section in a non-isothermal plasma

$$\Sigma \simeq n_0 \sigma_0. \tag{17.37}$$

This formula is valid if $(T_e/T_i)^3 \gg M/m$ and $ak \ll 1$. We see that the cross section (17.37) is twice as great as the scattering cross section in an isothermal plasma (17.32).

In the case of large changes in frequency $\Delta\omega \gg qv_e$ the scattering cross section has sharply defined maxima when $\Delta\omega \approx \pm\Omega$ connected with the scattering of electromagnetic waves on the longitudinal electron oscillations. For an arbitrary relation between the temperatures of the electrons and the ions the differential scattering cross section in this range of frequencies is defined by the formula

$$d\Sigma = \frac{n_0}{4}\left(\frac{e^2}{mc^2}\right)^2 \left(\frac{\omega'}{\omega}\right)^2 \sqrt{\frac{\varepsilon(\omega')}{\varepsilon(\omega)}}\,(aq)^2 (1 + \cos^2\vartheta) \times \{\delta(\Delta\omega - \Omega) + \delta(\Delta\omega + \Omega)\}\, d\omega'\, do'. \tag{17.38}$$

The total scattering cross section of electromagnetic waves on the Langmuir oscillations when $\omega \gg \Omega$ is of the form

$$\Sigma = 2(ak)^2\, n_0 \sigma_0 \quad (ak \ll 1). \tag{17.39}$$

We see that the collective phenomena in a plasma are particularly strongly manifested in the scattering if $ak \ll 1$. In this case the spectra of the scattered electromagnetic waves differ considerably for an isothermal and a non-isothermal plasma.

In an isothermal plasma there is a central maximum in the scattered radiation spectrum caused by non-coherent scattering on the electron density fluctuations with a width determined by the ion velocities, and lateral satellites caused by scattering on the electron oscillations. The relative weight of the satellites (in relation to the main maximum) is $\sim(2ak)^2$.

There is no central maximum in a strongly non-isothermal plasma. There are two maxima located symmetrically about $\Delta\omega = 0$ caused by scattering on the sonic oscillations, and lateral satellites with scattering on the Langmuir oscillations. The relative weight of these satellites in relation to the sonic maxima is $2(ak)^2$.

4. Critical Opalescence

Let us examine the scattering of electromagnetic waves in a plasma in which the mean directional velocities of the particles are not zero; this may be so when studying a plasma whose electrons are moving relative to the ions or a plasma through which a beam of charged particles is passing.

Let us first examine the case when the directional velocity of the electrons (or the beam) is less than the critical velocity at which instability starts [Rosenbluth and Rostoker, 1962]. In this case the scattering coefficient is defined by the general formula (17.28) into which we must put the expression (15.7) as the electron density correlation function.

It has been shown in section 16 that as the directional velocity approaches its critical value defining the boundary of the stability region the correlation function of the density of the plasma electrons rises without limit. In accordance with (17.28) the light scattering coefficient rises at the same time.

In particular, if the electrons of a two-temperature plasma are moving relative to the ions at a velocity approaching the velocity of non-isothermal sound V_s, the differential scattering coefficient for scattering of light by sonic oscillations is, in accordance with (16.11), of the form [Ichimura, Pines and Rostoker, 1962]

$$d\Sigma = \frac{n_0}{2}\left(\frac{e^2}{mc^2}\right)^2 (qV_s)^2 \frac{1+\cos^2\vartheta}{|\Delta\omega - (\boldsymbol{q}\cdot\boldsymbol{u})|} \times$$

$$\times\ \delta(\Delta\omega^2 - q^2V_s^2)\, d\omega'\, do'. \qquad (17.40)$$

If $|(\boldsymbol{q}\cdot\boldsymbol{u})| \to qV_s$ the coefficient of the δ-function in this expression approaches infinity.

Integrating the expression (17.40) with respect to ω' we find the cross section for light scattering on the sonic oscillations per unit solid angle

$$\frac{d\Sigma}{do'} = \frac{n_0}{4}\left(\frac{e^2}{mc^2}\right)^2 (1+\cos^2\vartheta)\left[1 - \frac{u(\cos\theta' - \cos\theta)}{2V_s \sin\vartheta/2}\right]^{-1}, \qquad (17.41)$$

where $\theta(\theta')$ is the angle between the vector $\boldsymbol{k}(\boldsymbol{k}')$ and $\boldsymbol{u}$ (to fix the ideas we assume that $\theta < \pi/2$).

It is easy to see that when $u \gtrsim V_s$ there are directions of the vector $\boldsymbol{k}'$ for which $d\Sigma/do'$ is anomalously great. If $|1 - V_s/u| \ll 1$ the vectors $\boldsymbol{k}$, $\boldsymbol{k}'$ and $\boldsymbol{u}$ must be almost in the same plane and the condition $\theta + \theta' \approx \pi$ be satisfied. In this case $d\Sigma/do' \to \infty$ when the angle φ between the planes $(\boldsymbol{k}', \boldsymbol{u})$ and $(\boldsymbol{k}, \boldsymbol{u})$ approach $\pm\varphi_c$,

$$\varphi_c^2 = \cot^2\theta \left\{4\left(\frac{u^2}{V_s^2} - 1\right) - (\pi - \theta - \theta')^2\right\} \qquad (17.42)$$

when θ, θ' are not close to $\pi/2$ and

$$\varphi_c^2 = 4\left(\frac{u^2}{V_s^2} - 1\right)(\theta - \theta')^2 \qquad (17.42')$$

when $\theta, \theta' \approx \pi/2$.

The anomalous rise in the scattering coefficient near the boundary of the plasma's instability is connected with the existence of critical fluctuations and may be called critical opalescence by analogy with the well-known phenomenon of critical opalescence in condensed bodies near the phase transition point.

5. Scattering of Electromagnetic Waves in a Plasma-Beam System

Let us now examine the specific nature of the scattering of light in a plasma through which a beam of charged particles is passing at a velocity greater than critical [Akhiezer, 1963].

As has been shown in section 16, the times t, t' are contained in the correlation functions for such a system not only in the combination $t - t' \equiv \Delta t$ but also separately; in this case the correlators contain terms that rise both with an increase in $\bar{t} \equiv \frac{1}{2}(t + t')$ and with an increase in $|\Delta t|$. It is significant that the correlators oscillate rapidly when Δt changes (with a frequency of the order of $|(\boldsymbol{q} \cdot \boldsymbol{u})|$; $\boldsymbol{q}$ is the wave vector of the fluctuations; $\boldsymbol{u}$ is the velocity of the beam) and rise when Δt and $\bar{t}$ increase slowly (with an increment $\gamma \sim \Omega(n_0'/n_0)^{1/2}$ in the non-resonance case and with an increment $\gamma \sim \Omega(n_0'/n_0)^{1/3}$ in the resonance case; n_0' is the density of the beam). Therefore if each of the frequencies ω, ω', $\Delta\omega$ is large when compared with the increment the formula (17.28) can be used as before for the scattering cross section. It is difficult to neglect the non-oscillatory dependence of the correlation function on Δt ($\gamma\Delta t \to 0$) and to consider the Fourier component of the correlator with respect to the variable Δt to be a slowly varying function of $\bar{t}$.

Therefore we come to the conclusion that when electromagnetic waves are scattered in a plasma-beam system the spectrum of the scattered radiation contains as well as the Doppler-broadened basic line and the Langmuir satellites an additional line connected with the possibility of the propagation in this system of oscillations with a frequency close to $(\boldsymbol{q} \cdot \boldsymbol{u})$. This line is at maximum intensity if $|(\boldsymbol{q} \cdot \boldsymbol{u})| \approx \Omega$; in this case it is superimposed on the Langmuir line.

Unlike the scattering of light in a free plasma the scattering of light in a plasma-beam system is anisotropic in nature. The scattering will be particularly great for directions of $\boldsymbol{k}'$ that satisfy the condition $(\boldsymbol{k}' \cdot \boldsymbol{u}) = (\boldsymbol{k} \cdot \boldsymbol{u}) + \Omega$. For these directions the scattering cross section is

$$d\Sigma = \{1 + h(\bar{t})\}\, d\Sigma^0, \tag{17.43}$$

where $d\Sigma^0$ is the scattering cross section of electromagnetic waves on the plasma oscillations defined by the formula (17.38) and

$$h(t) = \tfrac{1}{9}\{2\cosh 2\gamma t + 4\cosh \gamma t + 3\},$$

$$\gamma = \frac{\sqrt{3}}{2}\left(\frac{n_0'}{2n_0}\right)^{1/3}\Omega. \tag{17.44}$$

The term $h(\bar{t})\, d\Sigma^0$ is connected with scattering on specific oscillations of the plasma-beam system which are absent in a free plasma. If $\bar{t} = 0$, then $h = 1$; as the time t increases the quantity $h(t)$ rises.

The scattering cross section continues to increase until the amplitudes of the increasing fluctuations in the plasma reach a saturation point determined by the non-linear effects.

In directions for which the condition $(\boldsymbol{k}' \cdot \boldsymbol{u}) = (\boldsymbol{k} \cdot \boldsymbol{u}) + \Omega$ is not satisfied, the scattering cross section is little different from the scattering cross section in a plasma when there is no beam.

18. Transformation of Transverse and Longitudinal Waves in a Plasma

1. Transformation of a Transverse Wave into a Longitudinal One

Let us move on to an examination of the transformation of a transverse wave into a longitudinal one [Ginzburg and Zheleznyakov, 1958; Bass and Blank, 1962]. By isolating the longitudinal component of the current $\boldsymbol{J}$ in (17.10) we can find the Fourier component of the longitudinal component of a scattered wave's electric field

$$\boldsymbol{E}'_{k'\omega'} = \frac{4\pi e^2 \boldsymbol{k}'(\boldsymbol{k} \cdot \boldsymbol{E}^0)}{mk'^2 \omega\omega' \varepsilon_l(k', \omega')} \left(1 + \frac{\Delta\omega k'^2}{\omega' q^2}\right) \delta n_{q,\Delta\omega}, \tag{18.1}$$

where ε_l is the plasma's longitudinal dielectric permittivity defined by the formula (3.9). Substituting the expression for $\boldsymbol{E}'$ in the formula (17.25) and using the expression (17.14) for the current $\boldsymbol{J}$ we find the longitudinal wave excitation intensity

$$I^{(t\to l)} = \frac{V}{(2\pi)^3} \frac{e^4}{m^2\omega^2} \times$$

$$\times \operatorname{Im} \int d\omega'\, d^3k' \, \frac{(\boldsymbol{k}' \cdot \boldsymbol{E}^0)^2 \left(1 + \dfrac{\Delta\omega}{\omega'} \dfrac{k'^2}{q^2}\right)^2}{\omega' k'^2 \varepsilon_l^*(k', \omega')} \langle \delta n^2 \rangle_{q,\Delta\omega}. \tag{18.2}$$

Only frequencies for which the denominator of the integrand becomes zero, i.e. $\varepsilon_l(k', \omega') = 0$, make a contribution to this expression. This means that as a result of absorption of the transverse electromagnetic wave plasma eigen oscillations are excited.

Using (18.2) and assuming that the incident wave is not polarized we can find the coefficient of transformation of electromagnetic transverse waves into longitudinal plasma waves:

$$d\Sigma^{(t\to l)} \equiv dI^{(t\to l)}/S_0 V$$
$$= \left(\frac{e^2}{mc^2}\right)^2 \left(\frac{mc^2}{3T}\right)^{3/2} \left(\frac{\omega'}{\omega}\right)^2 \sqrt{\frac{\varepsilon(\omega')}{\varepsilon(\omega)}} \times$$
$$\times \left(1 + \frac{k'^2 \Delta\omega}{\omega' q^2}\right) \sin^2 \vartheta \langle \delta n^2 \rangle_{q,\Delta\omega} d\omega' \frac{do'}{4\pi}. \tag{18.3}$$

We stress that this formula can be used only in the frequency range $\omega' \approx \Omega$ where the plasma wave damping is slight.

The ratio of the transformation coefficient (18.3) to the scattering coefficient (17.28) is of the form

$$\frac{d\Sigma^{(t\to l)}}{d\Sigma^{(t\to t)}} = \left(\frac{mc^2}{3T}\right)^{3/2} \frac{\sin^2 \vartheta}{1 + \cos^2 \vartheta} \left(1 + \frac{k'^2 \Delta\omega}{\omega' q^2}\right)^2. \tag{18.4}$$

In the frequency range $\omega' \approx \Omega$ this quantity may be considerably greater than unity.

2. *Transformation and Scattering of Longitudinal Waves*

Let us now examine the transformation and scattering of longitudinal waves on the density fluctuations in a plasma [Ginzburg and Zheleznyakov, 1958]. The scattered wave field in this case is determined as before by the equations (17.10) and (17.14) in which $\boldsymbol{E}^0$ must be considered parallel to $\boldsymbol{k}$.

Isolating the transverse (in relation to $\boldsymbol{k}'$) part of the current $\boldsymbol{J}$ we can, in accordance with (17.25), find the intensity of the transverse waves excited. Dividing the intensity by the density of the energy flux in the incident wave

$$S_0 = \frac{v_g}{16\pi} \frac{d}{d\omega} (\omega\varepsilon(\omega)) E_0^2,$$

where $v_g = d\omega/dk$ is the group velocity of the longitudinal waves, we can find the coefficient for the transformation of a longitudinal wave into a transverse one

$$d\Sigma^{(l\to t)} = \frac{1}{2\pi}\left(\frac{e^2}{mc^2}\right)^2\left(\frac{mc^2}{3T}\right)^{1/2}\left(\frac{\omega'}{\omega}\right)^2\sqrt{\frac{\varepsilon(\omega')}{\varepsilon(\omega)}}\times$$

$$\times\left(1-\frac{k^2\Delta\omega}{\omega q^2}\right)^2\sin^2\vartheta\,\langle\delta n^2\rangle_{q,\Delta\omega}\,d\omega'\,do'. \tag{18.5}$$

Since the spectral distribution of the density fluctuations is characterized by the maxima when $\Delta\omega = 0$ and $\Delta\omega = \pm\Omega$, the transverse electromagnetic waves will chiefly radiate at frequencies close to Ω and 2Ω.

Isolating in (17.14) the longitudinal (in relation to $\boldsymbol{k}'$) part of the current we can determine the coefficient for scattering of longitudinal waves on density fluctuations

$$d\Sigma^{(l\to l)} = \frac{1}{2\pi}\left(\frac{e^2}{mc^2}\right)^2\left(\frac{mc^2}{3T}\right)^2\left(\frac{\omega'}{\omega}\right)^2\sqrt{\frac{\varepsilon(\omega')}{\varepsilon(\omega)}}\times$$

$$\times\left(\cos\vartheta+\frac{\Delta\omega}{\omega'}\frac{k'^2\cos\vartheta-kk'}{q^2}+\frac{\Delta\omega}{\omega}\frac{kk'-k^2\cos\vartheta}{q^2}\right)^2\times$$

$$\times\langle\delta n^2\rangle_{q,\Delta\omega}\,d\omega'\,do'. \tag{18.6}$$

The ratio of the Langmuir wave scattering coefficient to the coefficient of their transformation into transverse ones is equal in order of magnitude to $(mc^2/T)^{3/2}\cot^2\vartheta$.

19. Incoherent Reflexion of Electromagnetic Waves from a Plasma

1. Coefficient of Reflexion

An electromagnetic wave incident on a bounded plasma is subject to incoherent reflexion, when the frequency of the reflected wave is not equal to the frequency of the incident wave and the angle of reflexion is not equal to the angle of incidence [Akhiezer, 1963], as well as the ordinary reflexion described by the Fresnel formulae. Incoherent reflexion is caused by interaction of the electromagnetic wave with the fluctuations in the plasma and can be used for the experimental determination of the spectral distribution of the fluctuations and finding the various plasma parameters from this distribution (see Dougherty and Farley, 1960, in this connexion).

In order to investigate the reflexion of electromagnetic waves from a plasma (which we shall consider to fill the half-space $z > 0$) we must find the electric field $\boldsymbol{E}$ that satisfies the Maxwell equations with the following boundary conditions: when $z = -\infty$ the field $\boldsymbol{E}$ should be the superposition of the incident plane wave

$$\boldsymbol{E}_0 \exp\{i(\boldsymbol{k} \cdot \boldsymbol{r}) - i\omega t\} \quad (k_z > 0)$$

and the reflected waves; when $z = +\infty$ the field should become zero.

We shall consider that the wave vector components of the incident and reflected waves k_z, k_z' normal to the boundary satisfy the inequalities $ak_z \ll 1$, $ak_z' \ll 1$, where a is the electron Debye radius. Under these conditions we need not allow for the structure of the boundary layer with a thickness of the order of a and we may treat the boundary as a separation plane on which the ordinary boundary conditions of macroscopic electrodynamics are satisfied, i.e. the quantities $\boldsymbol{E}_t$, curl $\boldsymbol{E}$ and $dE_z/dt + 4\pi j_z$ are continuous ($\boldsymbol{E}_t$ is the component of the vector $\boldsymbol{E}$ parallel to the boundary).

If the phase velocities of the incident and reflected waves are large compared with the thermal velocities of the plasma particles, then for the current we can use the expression $\boldsymbol{j} = en\boldsymbol{v}$, where n is the electron density and $\boldsymbol{v}$ their hydrodynamic velocity connected with the fields $\boldsymbol{E}$ and $\boldsymbol{H}$ by the equation

$$\left(\frac{d}{dt} + \frac{1}{\tau}\right)\boldsymbol{v} = \frac{e}{m}\left(\boldsymbol{E} + \frac{1}{c}\,[\boldsymbol{v} \wedge \boldsymbol{H}]\right) \tag{19.1}$$

(τ is the mean time between collisions which we shall make approach infinity whenever this is possible). Putting $n = n_0 + \delta n$, where n_0 is the mean value and δn is the fluctuation of the density, we shall try to find the field $\boldsymbol{E}$ defined by the Maxwell equations and the equation (19.1) in the form of a series in powers of the density fluctuation: $\boldsymbol{E} = \boldsymbol{E}^e + \boldsymbol{E}' + \cdots$.

Having determined the field $\boldsymbol{E}$ when $z < 0$ we can find the Poynting vector component normal to the boundary and average it with respect to the plasma fluctuations, thus finding the reflected flux of the energy which takes the form of an integral over the wave vectors $\boldsymbol{k}'$ of the reflected waves. Dividing the fluctuation-averaged energy flux dS of the reflected waves whose wave vectors lie between $\boldsymbol{k}'$ and $\boldsymbol{k}' + d\boldsymbol{k}'$ by the incident energy flux S_0 we obtain the differential coefficient of reflexion dR

$$dR = dS/S_0.$$

If there were no fluctuations in the plasma the field $\boldsymbol{E}'$ would be zero and there would be only ordinary reflexion of the electromagnetic waves from the surface, $\boldsymbol{k}'$ being unambiguously connected with $\boldsymbol{k}$ by the relations $\boldsymbol{k}'_t = \boldsymbol{k}_t$, $k'_z = -k_z$. Therefore dR contains a term proportional to $\delta(\boldsymbol{k}'_t - \boldsymbol{k}_t)\,\delta(k'_z + k_z)$. By integrating this term with respect to $\boldsymbol{k}'$ we obtain the ordinary reflexion coefficient R_0 defined by the Fresnel formulae (see, e.g., Landau and Lifshitz, 1957a). In particular, for non-polarized incident radiation R_0 is

$$R_0 = \left|\frac{k_z - g}{k_z + g}\right|^2 + \left|\frac{\varepsilon k_z - g}{\varepsilon k_z + g}\right|^2, \tag{19.2}$$

where $\varepsilon = \varepsilon(\omega) = 1 - (\Omega^2/\omega^2)(1 - i/\omega\tau)$ is the plasma's dielectric permittivity and $g = \sqrt{\varepsilon k^2 - k_t^2}$ ($\operatorname{Im} g > 0$).

Because of the fluctuations in the plasma $\boldsymbol{E}' \neq 0$ and dR, apart from the δ-type term corresponding to ordinary reflexion of the radiation from the surface, contains an additional term which, as can be shown, is of the following form in the case of a non-polarized incident wave:

$$dR' = \frac{l}{4\pi c}\left(\frac{e^2}{m\omega}\right)^2 G(\theta, \theta', \varphi)\,\Phi(\Delta\boldsymbol{k}, \Delta\omega; l)\,d^3\boldsymbol{k}'. \tag{19.3}$$

Here Φ is a Fourier–Laplace transform of the plasma electron density correlation function

$$\Phi(\Delta\boldsymbol{k}, \Delta\omega; l) = \int_0^\infty \frac{dZ}{l} \exp\left\{-\frac{Z}{l}\right\} \int d^3\boldsymbol{r}_t\, dt\, \times$$
$$\times \int_{-2Z}^{2Z} dz \exp\{-i(\Delta\boldsymbol{k}\cdot\boldsymbol{r}) + i\Delta\omega\cdot t\}\,\langle\delta n(\boldsymbol{r}_1, t_1)\,\delta n(\boldsymbol{r}_2, t_2)\rangle, \tag{19.4}$$

$\boldsymbol{r} = \boldsymbol{r}_1 - \boldsymbol{r}_2$, $Z = \frac{1}{2}(z_1 + z_2)$, $\boldsymbol{k}'$ and ω' are the wave vector and frequency of the reflected wave, $\Delta\boldsymbol{k}_t' = \boldsymbol{k}_t' - \boldsymbol{k}_t$,

$$\Delta k_z = -\mathrm{Re}(g + g'),\ \Delta\omega = \omega' - \omega,\ l^{-1} = 2\,\mathrm{Im}(g + g),$$

$g' = \sqrt{\boldsymbol{k}_t'^2 \varepsilon(\omega') - k_t'^2}$ and the brackets $\langle \ldots \rangle$ denote averaging over the fluctuations.

The function G, which depends on the angles of incidence and reflexion θ, θ' and on the angle φ between the vectors $\boldsymbol{k}_t$ and $\boldsymbol{k}_t'$, takes the form

$$\begin{aligned} G(\theta, \theta', \varphi) &= (\cos\theta)^{-1} \left|\cos\theta' \cdot b_1\right|^2 \times \\ &\times \Bigg\{ |\tilde{c}_1|^2 \cos^2\theta \cos^2\varphi + |\tilde{c}_2|^2 \sin^2\varphi + \left| \frac{\tilde{c}_3 \sin\theta \sin\theta'}{\sqrt{\varepsilon' - \sin^2\theta'}} \right|^2 \\ &- \sin 2\theta \sin\theta' \cos\varphi \,\mathrm{Re}\, \frac{\tilde{c}_1^* \tilde{c}_3}{\sqrt{\varepsilon' - \sin^2\theta'}} \Bigg\} \\ &+ (\cos\theta)^{-1} |b_2|^2 \left\{ |c_1|^2 \cos^2\theta \sin^2\varphi + |c_2|^2 \cos^2\varphi \right\}, \end{aligned} \tag{19.5}$$

where

$$\left. \begin{aligned} &\varepsilon' = \varepsilon(\omega');\quad b_1 = \frac{2g'}{g' - \varepsilon' k_z'};\quad b_2 = \frac{2\,|k_z'|}{g' - k_z'}; \\ &c_1 = \frac{2g}{g + \varepsilon k_z};\quad c_2 = \frac{2k_z}{g + k_z};\quad c_3 = \frac{2k_z}{g + \varepsilon k_z}; \\ &\tilde{c}_{1,2} = c_{1,2}\left(1 + \frac{2\Delta\omega k_t'^2}{\omega' \Delta\boldsymbol{k}^2}\right);\quad \tilde{c}_3 = c_3\left(1 + \frac{2\Delta\omega g'^2}{\omega' \Delta\boldsymbol{k}^2}\right). \end{aligned} \right\} \tag{19.6}$$

2. *Spectral Distribution of Reflected Radiation*

The differential reflexion coefficient is determined by the correlation function of the plasma electron density fluctuations. This correlation function should be calculated with allowance made for the boundary. In the case of interest to us ($ak_z \ll 1$, $ak_z' \ll 1$), however, when the long-wave fluctuations are significant, the effect of the boundary can be neglected and we can use the expression for the electron density correlator in an infinite plasma whose Fourier components have been defined in sections 14 and 15. In this case the function Φ in (19.3) becomes

$$\Phi(\Delta \boldsymbol{k}, \Delta\omega; l) = \frac{1}{\pi}\int_{-\infty}^{\infty} dq_z \frac{(2l)^{-1}\langle\delta n^2\rangle_{\boldsymbol{q},\Delta\omega}}{(2l)^{-2} + (q_z - \Delta k_z)^2}, \tag{19.7}$$

where $\boldsymbol{q}_t = \Delta \boldsymbol{k}_t$.

If $l^{-1} \ll \Delta k_z$ the reflexion coefficient is determined by the formula

$$dR' = \frac{l}{4\pi c}\left(\frac{e^2}{m\omega}\right)^2 G(\theta, \theta', \varphi)\langle\delta n^2\rangle_{\boldsymbol{q},\Delta\omega}\, d^3\boldsymbol{k}' \tag{19.8}$$

where $\boldsymbol{q} = \Delta\boldsymbol{k}$. In this case the reflected radiation spectrum (similarly to the scattered radiation spectrum, see section 17) consists of the Doppler-broadened basic line and sharply defined maxima at $\Delta\omega = \pm\Omega$. In the case of a strongly non-isothermal plasma additional sharply defined maxima appear in the reflected radiation spectrum connected with the existence of non-isothermal sound in the plasma.

If the condition $l^{-1} \ll \Delta k_z$ is not satisfied the differential reflexion coefficient is a smooth function of $\Delta\omega$.

We notice that for validity of the formula (19.8), and thus for the presence of sharply defined maxima in the spectral distribution of the reflected radiation, there is no need at all for the incident wave to be weakly damped at a wavelength into the plasma. In particular if a wave with a frequency $\omega = \Omega - \xi$ $(\xi \ll \Omega)$ damped with a decrement $\operatorname{Im} g = c^{-1}\sqrt{2\Omega\xi}$ is incident on a non-isothermal plasma, then for a normally reflected wave the coefficient of reflexion has sharply defined maxima for $\Delta\omega = \pm V_s q$, near which

$$dR' = \frac{e^2}{32\pi m}(2\Omega\xi)^{-1/2} G(\theta, \theta', \varphi) \times$$

$$\times \{\delta(\Delta\omega - V_s q) + \delta(\Delta\omega + V_s q)\}\, d^3\boldsymbol{k}' \tag{19.9}$$

where V_s is the velocity of non-isothermal sound.

If the conditions

$$\cos^2\theta \gg |1 - \varepsilon|, \quad \cos^2\theta' \gg |1 - \varepsilon'|, \quad |\Delta\omega| \ll \omega$$

are satisfied, then

$$G(\theta, \theta', \varphi) = (\cos\theta)^{-1}(1 + \cos^2\vartheta)$$

(ϑ is the angle between the vectors $\boldsymbol{k}$ and $\boldsymbol{k}'$), and the reflexion coefficient differs only by a normalizing factor from the scattering coefficient in an infinite plasma (for angles greater than $\pi/2$),

$$dR' = \frac{l}{\cos\theta}\, d\Sigma. \tag{19.10}$$

If at least one of these conditions is not satisfied the coefficient of reflexion, in accordance with (19.3), (19.5), differs significantly from the scattering coefficient. The difference between these quantities is caused by the following two circumstances.

Firstly, on penetrating into the plasma the transverse wave when it is scattered on the fluctuations excites longitudinal as well as transverse waves. At the boundary the longitudinal waves are transformed into transverse ones, making a considerable contribution to the coefficient of reflexion when $\Delta\omega \sim \omega$.

Secondly, the incident wave, on penetrating the plasma, and the scattered wave, on leaving the plasma, is refracted; this must be allowed for if $\cos^2\theta \lesssim |1-\varepsilon|$ or $\cos^2\theta' \lesssim |1-\varepsilon'|$, i.e. if $(ak\cos\theta)^2 \lesssim (v/c)^2$ or $(ak'\cos\theta')^2 \lesssim (v/c)^2$ (v is the thermal velocity of the plasma electrons). At frequencies $\omega \lesssim \Omega$ these conditions are satisfied for all angles of incidence and reflexion, so in this frequency range the coefficient of reflexion depends essentially on the angles θ, θ' (and not only on the angle ϑ between the wave vectors of the incident and reflected waves). In particular with normal incidence ($\theta = 0$) or normal reflection ($\theta' = 0$) we obtain

$$dR' = \frac{l}{\pi c}\left(\frac{e^2}{m\omega}\right)^2 |1+\sqrt{\varepsilon}|^{-2} \times$$
$$\times \left\{\left|b_1 \frac{\tilde{c}_1}{c_1}\right|^2 \cos^2\theta' + |b_2|^2\right\} \langle \delta n^2\rangle_{q,\Delta\omega}\, d^3\boldsymbol{k}' \qquad (\theta = 0);$$
$$dR' = \frac{l}{\pi c}\left(\frac{e^2}{m\omega}\right)^2 |1+\sqrt{\varepsilon'}|^{-2} \cos^{-1}\theta \times \tag{19.11}$$
$$\times \{|c_1|^2\cos^2\theta + |c_2|^2\} \langle \delta n^2\rangle_{q,\Delta\omega}\, d^3\boldsymbol{k}', \quad (\theta' = 0).$$

In the case of grazing incidence or reflexion of the waves the boundary has to be allowed for at any frequency. In particular, if $\omega, \omega' \gg \Omega, \theta = \pi/2 - \Omega/\omega$ and $\pi/2 - \theta' \gg \Omega/\omega'$, then

$$dR' = \frac{l}{\pi c}\left(\frac{e^2}{m\omega}\right)^2 \frac{1+\cos^2\vartheta}{\cos\theta} \langle \delta n^2 \rangle_{q,\Delta\omega}\, d^3\boldsymbol{k}'. \quad (19.12)$$

We see that in this case the coefficient of reflexion is four times greater than the coefficient dR' calculated by the formula (19.10) which does not allow for the plasma boundary.

The relations (19.4)–(19.12), as has already been pointed out, determine the reflexion coefficients in the case of non-polarized incident radiation averaged with respect to the polarizations. Without examining in detail the polarization effects when the radiation is reflected from the plasma boundary we shall indicate the phenomenon of "total polarization" which appears in this case: a wave reflected at a certain angle is polarized in a plane at right angles to the plane of reflexion. In particular, if the plane of reflexion coincides with the plane of incidence ($\varphi = 0$) the angle of reflexion at which total polarization of the reflected wave is achieved is determined by the relation

$$\theta' = \psi(\theta); \quad \sin^2\psi = \varepsilon' - (\varepsilon'/\varepsilon)\sin^2\theta \quad (19.13)$$

(it is assumed that $\Delta\omega \ll \omega$).

If the incident wave is polarized in the plane of incidence a wave reflected at an angle $\theta' = \psi(\theta, \varphi)$, where

$$\sin^2\psi = \varepsilon' \frac{\varepsilon - \sin^2\theta}{\sin^2\theta\tan^2\varphi + \varepsilon}, \quad (19.14)$$

is totally polarized.

20. Scattering of Electromagnetic Waves in a Plasma in a Magnetic Field

1. Current Causing Scattered Waves

Let us now examine the effect of an external magnetic field on the scattering of electromagnetic waves in a plasma [Akhiezer, A. I., Akhiezer, I. A. and Sitenko, 1961; Farley, Dougherty and Barron, 1961; Sitenko and Kirochkin, 1963]. In Chapter II we have shown that a magnetic field leads to frequency splitting of the plasma oscillations and to the appearance of new types of eigen oscillations in the low-frequency region (Alfvén and magnetosonic waves). Therefore additional maxima connected with scattering on the

Alfvén and magnetosonic oscillations appear in the scattered radiation in a plasma when there is a magnetic field present.

Since we are as before interested in the scattering of waves whose phase velocity is considerably greater than the thermal velocity of the electrons, in the derivation of the expression for the current causing the scattered waves we shall use the hydrodynamic picture just as we did when deriving the expression for the current $\boldsymbol{J}$ when there is no magnetic field present. In other words, we shall as before start with the equations (17.15), (17.16) and (17.15′) in which $\boldsymbol{H}$ is taken as the total magnetic field in the plasma including the external magnetic field $\boldsymbol{H}_0$.

Instead of the equation (17.1) the field of the incident wave now satisfies the equation

$$\left(\delta_{ij}\Delta - \frac{\partial^2}{\partial x_i\,\partial x_j} - \frac{\hat{\varepsilon}_{ij}}{c^2}\frac{\partial^2}{\partial t^2}\right) E_j^0 = 0, \tag{20.1}$$

where $\hat{\varepsilon}_{ij}$ is the dielectric permittivity operator of the plasma in the magnetic field. The field of the scattered wave satisfies the equation

$$\left(\delta_{ij}\Delta - \frac{\partial^2}{\partial x_i\,\partial x_j} - \frac{\hat{\varepsilon}_{ij}}{c^2}\frac{\partial^2}{\partial t^2}\right) E_j' = \frac{4\pi}{c^2}\frac{\partial}{\partial t} J_i, \tag{20.2}$$

where $\boldsymbol{J}$ is the electron current caused by the field of the incident wave and the thermal fluctuations in the plasma.

By repeating the calculations leading to (17.14) we can show that the Fourier component of the current $\boldsymbol{J}(\boldsymbol{k}', \omega')$ is connected with the Fourier components of the fluctuations of the electron density, their hydrodynamic velocity and the magnetic field $\delta n^e(\boldsymbol{q}, \Delta\omega)$, $\delta \boldsymbol{v}(\boldsymbol{q}, \Delta\omega)$ and $\delta \boldsymbol{H}(\boldsymbol{q}, \Delta\omega)$ by the relation

$$\begin{aligned} J_i(\boldsymbol{k}', \omega') = \frac{-i\omega}{4\pi}\Bigg\{&(\varepsilon_{ij} - \delta_{ij})\, n_0^{-1}\,\delta n^e(\boldsymbol{q}, \Delta\omega) \\ &+ \left(\frac{\omega'}{\omega^2}(\varepsilon'_{ik} - \delta_{ik})\left[k_k\delta_{jl} - \delta_{kj}k_l - \frac{\omega^2}{\Omega^2}\times\right.\right. \\ &\times \left.(\varepsilon_{mj} - \delta_{mj})(q_m\delta_{kl} + \delta_{mk}k_l)\right] + \left.\omega^{-1}(\varepsilon_{kj} - \delta_{kj})\,k_k\delta_{il}\right)\times \\ &\times \delta v_l(\boldsymbol{q}, \Delta\omega) - \frac{ie}{mc}\frac{\omega'}{\Omega^2}(\varepsilon'_{il} - \delta_{il})(\varepsilon_{kj} - \delta_{kj})\,\varepsilon_{lkm}\times \\ &\times \delta H_m(\boldsymbol{q}, \Delta\omega)\Bigg\}\, E_j^0, \end{aligned} \tag{20.3}$$

where $\boldsymbol{q} = \boldsymbol{k}' - \boldsymbol{k}, \Delta\omega = \omega' - \omega$ and $\varepsilon_{ij} = \varepsilon_{ij}(\omega)$ are the components of the dielectric permittivity tensor of a plasma in a magnetic field defined by the formulae (4.8), $\varepsilon'_{ij} = \varepsilon_{ij}(\omega')$.

Having the expression for the current $\boldsymbol{J}$ we can, in accordance with (20.2), find the field $\boldsymbol{E}'$ and investigate the various processes of wave scattering and transformation in a plasma located in a magnetic field.

Changing in (20.2) to the Fourier components we obtain the following expression for the field of the scattered electromagnetic waves:

$$\boldsymbol{E}'_{k'\omega'} = \sum_{\lambda} \frac{4\pi i\omega'}{(ck'/n'_\lambda)^2 - \omega'^2} \frac{(\boldsymbol{e}^{\lambda *} \cdot \boldsymbol{J}(\boldsymbol{k}', \omega'))}{\varepsilon'_{ij} e_i^{\lambda *} e_j^{\lambda}} \boldsymbol{e}^{\lambda}, \tag{20.4}$$

where the $\boldsymbol{e}^{\lambda}$ ($\lambda = \pm$) are the polarization vectors of the eigen oscillations of a plasma in a magnetic field with the refractive indices $n'_{\pm} \equiv n_{\pm}(\omega', \theta')$ (the quantities $n_{\pm}$ are defined by the formulae (4.10) and (4.9)).

We can show that the mean radiation intensity of a wave with type λ polarization is

$$dI^{\lambda} = \frac{V}{16\pi^2} \left(\frac{n'_\lambda}{c}\right)^3 \frac{\omega'^2}{(\boldsymbol{e}^{*}\hat{\varepsilon}'\boldsymbol{e})} \langle |(\boldsymbol{e}^{\lambda *} \cdot \boldsymbol{J})|^2 \rangle_{k'\omega'}\, d\omega'\, do', \tag{20.5}$$

where the wave vector $\boldsymbol{k}'$ and the frequency ω' of the scattered wave are connected by the relation $\boldsymbol{k}'^2 = (\omega' n'_\lambda/c)^2$ (averaging is carried over the fluctuations of the plasma).

Dividing the radiation intensity dI^{λ} by the projection S_0 of the energy flux density of the incident wave along $\boldsymbol{k}$,

$$\left.\begin{aligned} S_0 &= \frac{c}{8\pi} n(|\boldsymbol{e}_0|^2 - k^{-2}|(\boldsymbol{k} \cdot \boldsymbol{e}_0)|^2)\, E_0^2, \\ \boldsymbol{e}_0 &= \left(1; \frac{i\varepsilon_2}{n^2 - \varepsilon_1^2}; \frac{n^2 \sin\theta \cos\theta}{n^2 \sin^2\theta - \varepsilon_3}\right), \end{aligned}\right\} \tag{20.6}$$

where ε_1, ε_2 and ε_3 are defined by the formulae (4.8), we can find the differential scattering cross section (coefficient)

$$d\Sigma^{\lambda} = \frac{dI^{\lambda}}{S_0}. \tag{20.6'}$$

2. *Spectral Distribution of Scattered Radiation*

The scattering of electromagnetic waves in a plasma located in a magnetic field, in the same way as when there is no magnetic field, occurs chiefly on the electron density fluctuations. Therefore in the expression (20.3) for the current $\boldsymbol{J}$ we need keep only the first term proportional to δn^e.

Using the formulae (20.5) and (20.6) we obtain the cross section for the scattering of electromagnetic waves on the density fluctuations

$$d\Sigma = \frac{1}{2\pi}\left(\frac{e^2}{mc^2}\right)^2\left(\frac{\omega\omega'}{\Omega^2}\right)^2 N\langle\delta n^{e^2}\rangle_{q,\Delta\omega}\,d\omega'\,do', \qquad (20.7)$$

where

$$\left.\begin{aligned} N &= n'^3\,|\boldsymbol{e}^*(\hat{\varepsilon}-1)\,\boldsymbol{e}_0|^2\,\{n(|\boldsymbol{e}_0|^2 - k^{-2}\,|(\boldsymbol{k}\cdot\boldsymbol{e}_0)|^2)\,(\boldsymbol{e}^*\hat{\varepsilon}'\boldsymbol{e})\}^{-1},\\ \boldsymbol{e} &= \left(\cos\varphi - \frac{i\varepsilon_2'}{n'^2-\varepsilon_1'}\sin\varphi;\ \sin\varphi + \frac{i\varepsilon_2'}{n'^2-\varepsilon_1'}\cos\varphi;\right.\\ &\qquad\left.\frac{n'^2\sin\theta'\cos\theta'}{n'^2\sin^2\theta'-\varepsilon_3'}\right) \end{aligned}\right\}(20.8)$$

(θ' is the angle between $\boldsymbol{k}'$ and $\boldsymbol{H}_0$; φ is the angle between the planes $(\boldsymbol{k}, \boldsymbol{H}_0)$ and $(\boldsymbol{k}', \boldsymbol{H}_0)$; ε_1', ε_2' and ε_3' are the values of the quantities ε_1, ε_2 and ε_3 at the frequency ω'; the index λ is omitted for simplicity of notation).

The factor N contained in the scattering cross section depends on the directions of propagation of the incident and scattered waves relative to the magnetic field. If the incident wave is propagated along the magnetic field, then

$$N^{\pm} = \frac{n'^3}{2n}(1-\varepsilon_1\pm\varepsilon_2)^2\left(1\pm\frac{\varepsilon_2'}{n'^2-\varepsilon_1'}\right)^2 \times$$
$$\times\left\{\varepsilon_1' + \frac{\varepsilon_1'\varepsilon_2'^2}{(n'^2-\varepsilon_1')^2} + \frac{\varepsilon_3' n'^4\sin^2\theta'\cos^2\theta'}{(n'^2\sin^2\theta'-\varepsilon_3')^2} + \frac{2\varepsilon_2'^2}{n'^2-\varepsilon_1'}\right\}^{-1}, \qquad (20.9)$$

where the + and − signs relate to clockwise and anticlockwise polarizations, respectively, of the incident wave.

We notice that the relative contribution of the terms not allowed for here in the current $\boldsymbol{J}$ is $(v_e/c)^2$ in order of magnitude in the total scattering cross section.

The electron density fluctuations δn^e are connected with the electron current fluctuations $\delta \boldsymbol{j}^e$ by the continuity relation

$$\delta n^e_{q,\Delta\omega} = \left(\frac{\boldsymbol{q}}{\Delta\omega} \cdot \delta \boldsymbol{j}^e_{q,\Delta\omega}\right). \tag{20.10}$$

By using the formula (15.21) which determines the correlation function for the electron current we can obtain the following expression for $\langle \delta n^{e^2} \rangle_{q,\Delta\omega}$:

$$e^2 \langle \delta n^{e^2} \rangle_{q,\Delta\omega} = \frac{2}{\Delta\omega} \operatorname{Im} \Big\{ T_e \boldsymbol{q} (1 - 4\pi \hat{\varkappa}^e \hat{\Lambda}^{-1}) \hat{\varkappa}^e \times$$

$$\times (1 - 4\pi \hat{\Lambda}^{-1} \hat{\varkappa}^e)^+ \boldsymbol{q} + 16\pi^2 T_i \boldsymbol{q} \hat{\varkappa}^e \hat{\Lambda}^{-1} \hat{\varkappa}^e (\hat{\Lambda}^{-1} \hat{\varkappa}^e)^+ \boldsymbol{q} \Big\}. \tag{20.11}$$

where $\varkappa^e$ is the plasma's electron susceptibility (the superscript + of the tensor denotes Hermitian conjugation).

The expression for the correlation function of the electron density becomes considerably simpler if $c^2 q^2 \gg \Delta\omega^2$. In this case $\langle \delta n_e^2 \rangle_{q,\Delta\omega}$ takes the same form as for a free plasma (in this case $\varkappa$ and ε in the formula (15.7) stand for the longitudinal components of the corresponding tensors, i.e. $\varkappa = q^{-2} q_i q_j \varkappa_{ij}$ and $\varepsilon = q^{-2} q_i q_j \varepsilon_{ij}$).

If the change $\boldsymbol{q}$ in the wave vector upon scattering is parallel to $\boldsymbol{H}_0$ the spectral distribution of the scattered radiation does not differ from the scattered radiation distribution in a free plasma. If the direction of $\boldsymbol{q}$ is not the same as the direction of $\boldsymbol{H}_0$ the magnetic field affects the scattered radiation spectrum. This effect is small in the region of small frequency shifts and only when the angles between $\boldsymbol{q}$ and $\boldsymbol{H}_0$ are close to $\pi/2$ do resonance effects appear if the frequency shift is a multiple of the ion cyclotron frequency.

For an isothermal plasma the scattered radiation spectrum for angles between $\boldsymbol{q}$ and $\boldsymbol{H}_0$ which differ from $\pi/2$ is characterized by a maximum when $\Delta\omega = 0$, just as when there is no magnetic field.

If the frequency of the incident wave ω is far greater than the frequencies $\omega_{1,2}$ of the plasma's Langmuir oscillations in the magnetic field it is easy to find the total scattering cross section for the electromagnetic waves in an isothermal plasma. In this case we replace the frequency ω' by ω in the expression for N and use the dispersion relation (14.9) to obtain

$$d\Sigma = \frac{n_0}{2}\left(\frac{e^2}{mc^2}\right)^2\left(\frac{\omega}{\Omega}\right)^4 N\bigg|_{\omega'=\omega} \frac{1+a^2q^2}{2+a^2q^2}\, do'. \quad (20.12)$$

If $aq \ll 1$ the correlation function $\langle \delta n^{e^2} \rangle_{q,\Delta\omega}$ has delta-type maxima at the frequencies corresponding to the Langmuir oscillations of the plasma in a magnetic field (see (5.3) and (5.4)),

$$\omega_{1,2}^2 = \tfrac{1}{2}(\Omega^2 + \omega_e^2) \pm \tfrac{1}{2}\sqrt{(\Omega^2 + \omega_e^2)^2 - 4\Omega^2\omega_e^2 \cos^2 \tilde{\vartheta}},$$

where $\tilde{\vartheta}$ is the angle between $\boldsymbol{q}$ and $\boldsymbol{H}_0$ connected with the angles θ, θ' and φ by the relation

$$\tan^2 \tilde{\vartheta} = \frac{k^2 \sin^2 \theta + k'^2 \sin^2 \theta' - 2kk' \sin\theta \sin\theta' \cos\varphi}{(k\cos\theta - k'\cos\theta')^2}.$$

The scattering cross section for frequency shifts $\Delta\omega$ close to the Langmuir oscillation frequencies $\omega_{1,2}$ takes the form

$$d\Sigma = \frac{n_0}{2}\left(\frac{e^2}{mc^2}\right)^2\left(\frac{\omega\omega'\Delta\omega}{\Omega^3}\right)^2 (aq)^2 N \times$$

$$\times \frac{(\omega_e^2 - \Delta\omega^2)^2}{\Delta\omega^4 \sin^2\tilde{\vartheta} + (\omega_e^2 - \Delta\omega^2)^2 \cos^2\tilde{\vartheta}} \times$$

$$\times \{\delta(\Delta\omega - \omega_1) + \delta(\Delta\omega + \omega_1) + \delta(\Delta\omega - \omega_2)$$

$$+ \delta(\Delta\omega + \omega_2)\}\, d\omega'\, do'. \quad (20.13)$$

The relative contribution of the Raman-like scattering on the Langmuir oscillations to the integral scattering cross section is $(aq)^2$ in order of magnitude.

It has been shown in section 8 that in a plasma located in a magnetic field there may exist low-frequency magnetosonic oscillations (fast magnetosonic waves can exist independently of the relation between the electron and ion temperatures, but slow magnetosonic waves only if $T_e \gg T_i$). Electromagnetic waves being propagated in a plasma are scattered on the fluctuating magnetosonic oscillations. In this case scattering on density fluctuations connected with the magnetosonic oscillations plays the major role.

The scattering cross section for electromagnetic waves in a plasma located in a magnetic field has sharply defined maxima if the frequency shift $\Delta\omega$ is the same as the frequency of a magnetosonic oscillation with the wave vector q. By using the expression for the density correlator in the low-frequency region we can determine the cross section for scattering of electromagnetic waves on fluctuating fast magnetosonic oscillations

$$d\Sigma = \frac{1}{2} n_0 \left(\frac{e^2}{mc^2}\right)^2 \left(\frac{\omega}{\Omega}\right)^4 \frac{V_s^2}{V_A^2} N\, |\eta(\tilde{\vartheta})|^2 \times$$

$$\times \{\delta(\Delta\omega - qV_A) + \delta(\Delta\omega + qV_A)\}\, d\omega'\, do', \quad (20.14)$$

where

$$\eta(\tilde{\vartheta}) = \sin\tilde{\vartheta} + \frac{\omega\omega_e}{\Omega^2 q} \frac{\boldsymbol{e}^*(\hat{\varepsilon}' - 1)\,(\hat{\tilde{\boldsymbol{q}\boldsymbol{e}}} - \hat{\tilde{\boldsymbol{e}\boldsymbol{q}}})\,(\hat{\varepsilon} - 1)\,\boldsymbol{e}_0}{\boldsymbol{e}^*(\hat{\varepsilon}' - 1)\,\boldsymbol{e}_0},$$

$$\boldsymbol{e} \equiv \left\{\frac{\Delta\omega}{\omega_i} \sin^{-2}\tilde{\vartheta};\quad i;\quad \frac{1}{2}\left(\frac{V_s}{V_A}\right)^2 \frac{\Delta\omega}{\omega_i} \sin 2\tilde{\vartheta}\right\}, \quad (\hat{\tilde{\boldsymbol{q}\boldsymbol{e}}})_{ij} = q_i \tilde{e}_j.$$

This formula is valid if $v_i \ll V_A \ll v_e$, $V_s \ll V_A$ and $\cos^2\tilde{\vartheta} \gg V_A^2/v_e^2$.

By integrating the expression (20.14) over ω' and comparing the result with (20.12) it is easy to see that the ratio of the cross section for scattering on fast magnetosonic oscillations to the total scattering cross section in an isothermal plasma is V_s^2/V_A^2 in order of magnitude.

In a strongly non-isothermal plasma ($T_e \gg T_i$) slow magnetosonic oscillations whose velocity is equal to $V_s \cos\tilde{\vartheta}$ are also possible, as has been indicated above. The cross section for scattering of electromagnetic waves by fluctuating oscillations of this type is determined by the formula

$$d\Sigma = \frac{n_0}{2} \left(\frac{e^2}{mc^2}\right)^2 \left(\frac{\omega}{\Omega}\right)^4 N\, \{\delta(\Delta\omega - qV_s\cos\tilde{\vartheta})$$

$$+ \delta(\Delta\omega + qV_s\cos\tilde{\vartheta})\}\, d\omega'\, do'. \quad (20.15)$$

This formula is valid if $1 \ll T_e/T_i \ll V_A^2/v_i^2$. The cross section (20.15) when integrated over the frequency has the same order of magnitude as the cross section (20.14).

Therefore in a strongly non-isothermal plasma the basic line in the scattered radiation spectrum is split into four lines connected with wave scattering on the magnetosonic fluctuations.

3. Scattering of Electromagnetic Waves on Alfvén Oscillations

Finally let us examine the scattering of electromagnetic waves on the Alfvén oscillations of a plasma. Since the Alfvén waves are not accompanied by a change in the plasma's density, scattering on these oscillations is caused not by density fluctuations but by fluctuations of the hydrodynamic electron velocity and the magnetic field.

The magnetic field fluctuations are the most important, so when investigating the scattering on the Alfvén oscillations we need keep only the third term in the expression (20.3) for the current $\boldsymbol{J}$, which is proportional to $\delta\boldsymbol{H}$.

Using the formulae (20.5) and (20.6) we obtain the following expression for the cross section for scattering of the electromagnetic waves by Alfvén oscillations:

$$d\Sigma = \frac{1}{2\pi}\left(\frac{e^2}{mc}\right)^2\left(\frac{\omega}{\Omega}\right)^6 R\,\frac{n_0}{4\pi\, mc^2}\,\times$$

$$\times\, a_i a_j^* \langle \delta H_i\, \delta H_j\rangle_{q,\Delta\omega}\, d\omega'\, do', \tag{20.16}$$

where

$$R = n'^3\{n(|e_0^2| - k^{-2}|(\boldsymbol{k}\cdot\boldsymbol{e}_0)|^2)(\boldsymbol{e}^*\hat{\varepsilon}'\boldsymbol{e})\}^{-1},$$

$$a_i = \varepsilon_{ikl} e_j^*(\varepsilon'_{jk} - \delta_{jk})(\varepsilon_{lm} - \delta_{lm})\, e_m^0 .$$

By using the formula (15.23) for the magnetic field correlation function we obtain the following expression for the cross section for scattering of electromagnetic waves [Sitenko and Kirochkin, 1963]:

$$d\Sigma = \frac{n_0}{2}\left(\frac{e^2}{mc^2}\right)^2\left(\frac{\omega}{\Omega}\right)^6\frac{T_e}{mc^2}\, R\,|\zeta(\tilde{\vartheta})|^2\{\delta(\Delta\omega - qV_A\cos\tilde{\vartheta})$$

$$+\,\delta(\Delta\omega + qV_A\cos\tilde{\vartheta})\}\, d\omega'\, do', \tag{20.17}$$

$$\zeta(\tilde{\vartheta}) = \frac{1}{q \cos \tilde{\vartheta}} \{e^*(\hat{\varepsilon}' - 1)\, q \cdot \tilde{e}(\hat{\varepsilon} - 1)\, e_0$$

$$- e^*(\hat{\varepsilon} - 1)\, \tilde{e} \cdot q(\hat{\varepsilon} - 1)\, e_0\},$$

$$e \equiv \left\{1; \quad -i \frac{\Delta\omega}{\omega_i} \cot^2 \tilde{\vartheta}; \qquad -2\left(\frac{V_s}{V_A}\right)^2 \frac{\Delta\omega}{\omega_i^2} \frac{1}{\sin 2\tilde{\vartheta}}\right\}.$$

It can be shown that the total Alfvén oscillation scattering cross section is in order of magnitude T_e/mc^2 times less than the total scattering cross section (20.12).

21. Passage of Charged Particles through a Free Plasma

1. Probability of Scattering

We now move on to investigate the scattering of charged particles passing through a plasma. The scattering of the particles is determined by the level of the fluctuations in the plasma, as is the scattering of electromagnetic waves.

If a particle is scattered on a periodic (in time) fluctuation of the electric field, then, in accordance with the well-known formula from quantum mechanics (see, e.g., Landau and Lifshitz, 1958) the probability per unit time of the transition of the particle from a state with the momentum $\boldsymbol{p}$ to a state with the momentum $\boldsymbol{p}'$ is determined in the first approximation of perturbation theory by the expression

$$dw = \frac{2\pi}{\hbar} (ze)^2 \left| \int \exp\left\{-i\left(\frac{\boldsymbol{p} - \boldsymbol{p}'}{\hbar} \cdot \boldsymbol{r}\right)\right\} \delta\varphi_\omega(\boldsymbol{r}) \frac{d^3\boldsymbol{r}}{V}\right|^2 \times$$

$$\times\, \delta\left(\frac{p^2 - p'^2}{2\mu} - \hbar\omega\right) \frac{V\, d^3\boldsymbol{p}'}{(2\pi\hbar)^3}, \qquad (21.1)$$

where $\delta\varphi_\omega(\boldsymbol{r})e^{-i\omega t}$ is the scalar potential fluctuation; ze is the charge and μ the mass of the particle; V is the normalization volume (we consider the particle to be non-relativistic).

This expression must be averaged over the plasma fluctuations. Using the connexion between the potential fluctuations and the charge density fluctuations we obtain

$$dw = \left(\frac{4\pi\, ez}{\hbar q^2}\right)^2 \langle \varrho^2 \rangle_{q\omega} \frac{d^3\boldsymbol{p}'}{(2\pi\hbar)^3}, \tag{21.2}$$

where $\hbar \boldsymbol{q} = \boldsymbol{p}' - \boldsymbol{p}$ and $\hbar\omega = (p'^2 - p^2)/2\mu$ are the changes in the particle's momentum and energy.

When we take close collisions into consideration we need the expression for the correlator in the quantum region where $\hbar\omega$ and $\hbar q$ are comparable with the mean energy and mean momentum of the plasma particles. The action of the self-consistent field in this region can clearly be neglected and we can use the expression for the correlation function of the fluctuations in an ideal gas determined by the first term in (15.14). To find the correlation function for $\hbar q \sim mv$ it is sufficient to replace $\delta(\omega - (\boldsymbol{q} \cdot \boldsymbol{v}))$ in this expression by $\delta(\omega - (\boldsymbol{q} \cdot \boldsymbol{v}) + \hbar q^2/2m)$. As a result we obtain

$$\langle f(\boldsymbol{v}) f(\boldsymbol{v}') \rangle_{q\omega} = 2\pi F^0(\boldsymbol{v})\, \delta(\boldsymbol{v} - \boldsymbol{v}')\, \delta\left(\omega - (\boldsymbol{q} \cdot \boldsymbol{v}) + \frac{\hbar q^2}{2m}\right). \tag{21.3}$$

From this we find for the charge density correlator

$$\langle \varrho^2 \rangle_{q\omega} = 2\pi e^2 \int F_e^0(\boldsymbol{v})\, \delta\left(\omega - (\boldsymbol{q} \cdot \boldsymbol{v}) + \frac{\hbar q^2}{2m}\right) d^3\boldsymbol{v}. \tag{21.4}$$

Formula (21.3) means that each particle in the plasma is "correlated" only with itself; this formula, and thus also formula (21.4), is valid for any velocity distribution of the plasma particles.

As has been shown in sections 14 and 15, the charge density correlator (in the "classical" region $\hbar\omega \ll T$, $\hbar q \ll \sqrt{mT}$ which is all we are discussing) has sharply defined maxima at the frequencies of the plasma's eigen oscillations. There are therefore also sharply defined maxima in the expression for the particle scattering probability dw. The corresponding expressions can be interpreted as the probabilities of the scattering of a particle with excitation ($\omega > 0$) or absorption ($\omega < 0$) of different types of plasma oscillations.

Let us find the probability of scattering of a particle in a plasma in a state of complete thermodynamic equilibrium. Using (14.6) and using the continuity equation to express the charge density fluctuations in terms of the current density fluctuations we obtain

$$dw = \frac{8\pi}{\hbar}\left(\frac{ez}{q}\right)^2 (N_\omega + 1)\,\mathrm{Im}\,\frac{-1}{\varepsilon(q, \omega)}\,\frac{d^3p'}{(2\pi\hbar)^3}, \tag{21.5}$$

where $N_\omega = (\exp\{\hbar\omega/T\} - 1)^{-1}$ is the Planck distribution function.

We stress that this formula covers both the case of a decrease and the case of an increase in the particle energy. In the latter case $\omega < 0$ and $N_\omega + 1 = -N_{|\omega|}$.

For the probability of scattering a fast particle ($v \gg v_e$; v is the particle velocity; v_e is the mean thermal velocity of the plasma electrons), when the change in its energy is small compared with the actual energy, we find from expression (21.5)

$$dw = \frac{(2\pi ez)^2}{\hbar q^2}\{\omega(N_\omega + 1)\,\delta(\omega - \omega_L) + |\omega|\,N_{|\omega|}\,\delta(\omega + \omega_L)\}\,\frac{d^3p'}{(2\pi\hbar)^3}, \tag{21.6}$$

where

$$\omega_L = \Omega\,(1 + \tfrac{3}{2}\,a_e^2 q^2).$$

We can see that the scattering of a fast particle with a small relative change of energy occurs chiefly with the emission and absorption by the particle of longitudinal electron oscillations (the first term in (21.6) corresponds to emission and the second to absorption of oscillations).

The expression (21.6) is derived on the assumption that the plasma is in a state of thermodynamic equilibrium. However it can also be used for a plasma with a non-equilibrium distribution of the plasma waves if we replace the Planck function N_ω by the non-equilibrium plasma wave distribution function N_q.

Similarly we can find the probability of scattering of a particle on the low-frequency oscillations in a two-temperature plasma

$$dw = \frac{\pi z^2 T_e}{\hbar n_0(1 + a_e^2 q^2)}\left\{\omega(N_q + 1)\,\delta\left(\omega - \frac{V_s q}{\sqrt{1 + a_e^2 q^2}}\right) + |\omega|\,N_q\delta\left(\omega + \frac{V_s q}{\sqrt{1 + a_e^2 q^2}}\right)\right\}\frac{d^3p'}{(2\pi\hbar)^3}, \tag{21.7}$$

where V_s is the velocity of sound and N_q is the distribution function for low-frequency oscillations.

2. *Energy Losses of a Particle*

Knowing the scattering probability we can determine the energy losses when a charged particle passes through a plasma.† To do this we must multiply the expression (21.2) by $\hbar\omega$ and integrate over the momentum of the scattered particle $\mathbf{p}'$.

If the velocity of the moving particle is considerably greater than the thermal velocity of the plasma electrons ($v \gg v_e$) two regions of change in the transmitted momentum $\hbar q$ make the main contribution to the expression for the energy losses: the region $\hbar q \sim mv_e$ (large transmitted momenta, i.e. close collisions) and the region $q \ll a^{-1}$, where a is the screening radius (distant collisions).

To calculate the losses in these regions we shall select, as is generally done [Bohr, 1948], a certain value q_0 lying in the range $a^{-1} \ll q_0 \ll mv_e/\hbar$. When $q < q_0$ we shall use the formula (21.6) for the scattering probability and when $q > q_0$ we shall use the formula (21.2) in which we substitute the expression (21.4) as the correlator.

Let us first find the energy losses when $q < q_0$. Multiplying the expression (21.6) by $\hbar\omega$ and integrating with respect to $\mathbf{q}$ we obtain‡

$$\left(-\frac{dE}{dt}\right)_{q<q_0} = \frac{(ez)^2\Omega^2}{v} \ln \frac{q_0 v}{\Omega}. \tag{21.8}$$

This expression determines the energy transferred by the particle in unit time to the plasma waves whose wave vector does not exceed q_0.

We notice that the energy losses in plasma wave excitation do not depend on the number of waves N_q. This is connected with the fact that the energy losses are determined by the particle's spon-

† Various papers [Vlasov, 1950; Akhiezer and Sitenko, 1952; Pines and Bohm, 1951, 1952; Lindhard, 1954; Neufeld and Ritchie, 1955; Sitenko and Stepanov, 1958; Larkin, 1959] investigate the energy losses of a particle moving through a free plasma.

‡ The formula (21.8) can, of course, also be derived by the usual method, by substituting the high-frequency dielectric constant of the plasma $\varepsilon(\omega) = 1 - \Omega^2/\omega^2$ as the dielectric constant in the general expression for the energy losses of a particle in a medium (see, e.g., Landau and Lifshitz, 1957a, equation (84.5)).

taneous emission of waves, whilst the contributions to the energy losses of the forced emission and absorption (proportional to the number of waves N_q) cancel each other out. This cancelling out neglects the particle's recoil, i.e. neglects the third term in the equation $\Omega - (\boldsymbol{q} \cdot \boldsymbol{v}) - \hbar q^2/2\mu = 0$ which follows from the conservation laws. If the mean energy of the plasma wave $\hbar\overline{\omega} = T^*$ is very great ($T^*/T \gtrsim (\mu/m)(v/v_e)^2$) it becomes impossible to neglect the particle recoil and the quantity dw starts to depend on T^* [Tsytovich, 1962, 1963].

We can now find the energy losses of a particle in close collisions when $q > q_0$. Substituting (21.4) in (21.2) and multiplying by $\hbar\omega$ we obtain after integration over $\boldsymbol{q}$†

$$\left(-\frac{dE}{dt}\right)_{q>q_0} = \frac{(ez)^2\Omega^2}{v} \ln \frac{2m\mu v}{\hbar q_0(m+\mu)}. \tag{21.9}$$

By adding the expressions (21.8) and (21.9) we find the total energy losses of a fast particle in unit time

$$-\frac{dE}{dt} = \frac{(ez)^2\Omega^2}{v} \ln \frac{2m\mu v^2}{\hbar\Omega(m+\mu)}. \tag{21.10}$$

This formula has the structure of the well-known Bohr formula for the polarization losses [Bohr, 1948]. We notice that it does not contain the parameter q_0. This is because the region $q \sim q_0$ makes no significant contribution to dE/dt.‡

Therefore the energy losses of a fast particle depend essentially on the plasma density and do not depend on its temperature. Therefore the formula (21.10) can be used no matter what the distribution function of the particles in the plasma is provided their mean velocity is far less than the velocity of the moving particle. The energy losses do not depend on the numbers of plasma waves N_q either (on the assumption that the mean energy of a plasma wave T^* is not too great, $T^* \ll T(\mu/m)(v/v_e)^2$).

If the moving particle is an electron, then the fact that it is identical with the plasma electrons must be taken into consideration

† We notice that the formula (21.9) can be obtained if we calculate the energy losses of the particle as the result of binary Coulomb collisions in the first Born approximation.

‡ The formula (21.10) makes correct allowance not only for the terms $\sim e^4 \ln e^2$ but also of terms $\sim e^4$ [Larkin, 1959].

when calculating the contribution of close collisions. This leads, as we know (see, e. g., Landau and Lifshitz, 1958), to the additional factor $e/2\sqrt{2}$ (e is the base of natural logarithms) in the argument of the logarithm in (21.9). Therefore instead of (21.10) for the total losses we obtain

$$-\frac{dE}{dt} = \frac{e^2\Omega^2}{v}\left(\ln\frac{mv^2}{2\sqrt{2}\,\hbar\Omega} + 1\right). \tag{21.11}$$

As has already been pointed out, the expression (21.1) for the probability of scattering is valid in the first Born approximation which, as we know, can be used in the case of a fast particle ($e^2/\hbar v \ll 1$) for all q, but only for small momentum transfer in the case of a slow particle. Therefore the formula (21.9) for the energy losses in close collisions is valid only if $e^2/\hbar v \ll 1$.

For slow particles, when $e^2/\hbar v \gg 1$, the energy losses in close collisions takes the form

$$\left(-\frac{dE}{dt}\right)_{q>q_0} = \frac{(ez)^2\Omega^2}{v}\ln\frac{m\mu v^2}{ze^2 q_0(m+\mu)} \tag{21.12}$$

(this formula can be derived by the method of binary collisions; see, e.g., Fermi, 1940). Therefore the total energy losses of a slow particle are defined by the formula

$$-\frac{dE}{dt} = \frac{(ez)^2\Omega^2}{v}\ln\frac{m\mu v^3}{ze^2\Omega(m+\mu)} \tag{21.13}$$

(it is assumed, however, that $v \gg v_e$).

We notice that the formula (21.10) (in the derivation of which we neglected the terms $\sim v^2/c^2$) also defines the order of magnitude of the energy losses when $v \sim c$. When the relativistic effects are allowed for all that happens is that the expression under the logarithm sign changes but the factor in front of it ($(ez)^2\Omega^2/v$) does not change.

22. Passage of Charged Particles through a Plasma in a Magnetic Field

1. Probability of Scattering

Let us examine the interaction of a charged particle with a plasma in the presence of a constant and uniform magnetic field [Akhiezer and Fainberg, 1962; Akhiezer, 1956; Kolomenskii, 1956;

Sitenko and Kolomenskii, 1956; Sitenko and Stepanov, 1958; Gurevich and Firsov, 1960; Akhiezer, 1961; Kitsenko, 1962]. The magnetic field leads, in the first place, to a complication of the nature of the motion of the moving particle and, in the second place, alters the correlation functions of the fluctuations in the plasma.

If the direction of motion of the particle before and after scattering is close to the direction of the magnetic field the magnetic field has no effect on the particle's motion. In this case we must satisfy the condition

$$q_t v \sin\alpha \ll \omega_z, \quad \frac{\hbar q_t^2}{\mu} \ll \omega_z,$$

where $\hbar \boldsymbol{q}_t$ is the component of the transmitted momentum at right angle to the direction of the magnetic field $\boldsymbol{H}_0$; $\omega_z = zeH_0/\mu c$ and α is the angle between the direction of motion of the particle and the direction of the magnetic field.

The effect of the magnetic field on the motion of the moving particle can also be neglected in the case when the "spiralling" of the particle on the characteristic path is slight. For this we must satisfy one of the conditions

$$q_t v \sin\alpha \gg \omega_z, \quad \hbar q_t^2/\mu \gg \omega_z.$$

Let us first examine the scattering of a particle in these cases. In this case the probability of scattering is determined by the general formula (21.2) in which $\langle\varrho^2\rangle$ must be understood as the charge density correlator for a plasma located in a magnetic field.

The function $\langle\varrho^2\rangle_{q\omega}$, as has been shown in sections 14, 15 has sharply defined maxima at the frequencies of the plasma's eigen oscillations; the corresponding terms in the expression for dw can be interpreted as the probabilities of particle scattering with excitation (or absorption) of oscillations of a different type. In particular the probability of the scattering of a particle with the excitation or absorption of longitudinal electron oscillations is

$$dw = \frac{(2\pi ez)^2}{\hbar q^2} \frac{(\omega^2 - \omega_e^2)^2}{\omega^4 \sin^2\vartheta + (\omega^2 - \omega_e^2)^2 \cos^2\vartheta} \times$$
$$\times \{\omega(N_\omega + 1)[\delta(\omega - \omega_1) + \delta(\omega - \omega_2)]$$
$$+ |\omega| N_{|\omega|}[\delta(\omega + \omega_1) + \delta(\omega + \omega_2)]\} \frac{d^3\boldsymbol{q}}{(2\pi)^3}, \quad (22.1)$$

where the frequencies $\omega_{1,2}$ are determined by the relations (5.3)–(5.4) and ϑ is the angle between the vector $\boldsymbol{q}$ and the direction of the magnetic field.

2. *Energy Losses of a Particle*

By multiplying (22.1) by $\hbar\omega$ and integrating over $\boldsymbol{q}$ we can find the energy transferred by a particle to the plasma oscillations with wave vectors less than a certain value q_0

$$\left(-\frac{dE}{dt}\right)_{q<q_0} = \frac{(ze)^2\Omega^2}{v}\left\{\ln\frac{q_0 v}{\Omega} - f\left(\alpha, \frac{\Omega}{\omega_e}\right)\right\}, \quad (22.2)$$

where $\omega_e = eH_0/mc$ and

$$f(\alpha, u) = \frac{1}{2\pi u^2}\left\{\int_0^{z_1} g(z)\ln z\, dz - \int_{z_2}^{z_3} g(z)\ln z\, dz\right\} - \ln u; \quad (22.3)$$

$$g(z) = z(1-z)\,\{z(z-z_1)(z-z_2)(z_3-z)\}^{-1/2};$$

$$z_{1,2} = \tfrac{1}{2}(1+u^2) \mp \tfrac{1}{2}\sqrt{(1+u^2)^2 - 4u^2\sin^2\alpha};$$

$$z_3 = 1 + u^2.$$

We can now find the total energy losses of a fast particle in a plasma in the presence of a magnetic field. When close collisions (large transferred momenta) are taken into consideration the difference of the particle's motion from a straight line can be neglected and we can use the formula (21.9) or (21.12) for the energy losses in unit time.

If the angle α between the particle velocity and the magnetic field satisfies one of the inequalities

$$\sin\alpha \gg \frac{\omega_z}{\max\{\Omega, \omega_e\}}; \quad \sin\alpha \ll \frac{\omega_z}{\max\{\Omega, \omega_e\}}, \quad (22.4)$$

then the "spiralling" of the particle can be ignored also when distant collisions are taken into consideration. In this case (just as when there is no magnetic field) the scattering of a fast particle occurs chiefly because of the emission and absorption of plasma waves, so that formula (22.2) can be used to determine the energy losses.

Adding the contributions of the close and distant collisions we finally obtain the following expressions for the energy losses of a fast particle [Akhiezer, 1961]:

$$\left.\begin{aligned} -\frac{dE}{dt} &= \frac{(ez)^2\Omega^2}{v}\left\{\ln\frac{2m\mu v^2}{\hbar\Omega(m+\mu)} - f\left(\alpha, \frac{\Omega}{\omega_e}\right)\right\} \\ &\qquad\qquad (e^2/\hbar v \ll 1); \\ -\frac{dE}{dt} &= \frac{(ez)^2\Omega^2}{v}\left\{\ln\frac{m\mu v^3}{ze^2\Omega(m+\mu)} - f\left(\alpha, \frac{\Omega}{\omega_e}\right)\right\} \\ &\qquad\qquad (e^2/\hbar v \gg 1), \end{aligned}\right\} \tag{22.5}$$

where the function f is defined by the formula (22.3).

The first terms in these expressions are the total energy losses of a fast particle in a free plasma (compare (21.10), (21.13)). The second terms describe the effect of the magnetic field; they depend on the direction of the particle's motion in relation to the direction of the magnetic field and become zero when $\omega_e = 0$.

We can see that the total energy losses of a fast particle in a magnetic field are proportional to the density of the plasma and are comparatively weakly (logarithmically) dependent on the magnitude of the magnetic field. Just as in the case of a free plasma the losses are not temperature-dependent (if the fluctuations in the plasma do not differ too much from the equilibrium fluctuations).

In the case of a strong magnetic field ($\omega_e \gg \Omega$) the expressions (22.5) become far simpler; in this case the function f in them becomes

$$f\left(\alpha, \frac{\Omega}{\omega_e}\right) = \frac{1}{4}\sin^2\alpha\left(1 + \ln\frac{\Omega^2\sin^2\alpha}{4\omega_e^2}\right) - \ln\frac{\Omega}{\omega_e} \tag{22.6}$$

(the angle α is assumed not to be 0 or π).

As has already been indicated, the expressions (22.5) are valid if the angle α satisfies one of the conditions (22.4). This requirement is fulfilled in particular for a particle of any mass moving along the magnetic field.† In this case it follows from (22.5) that

$$-\frac{dE}{dt} = \frac{(ez)^2\Omega^2}{v} \ln \frac{2m\mu v^2}{(m+\mu)\hbar\sqrt{\Omega^2+\omega_e^2}} \tag{22.7}$$

(to fix the ideas we assume that $e^2/\hbar v \ll 1$).

In the case of a heavy particle the formula (22.5) can be used in practice for any angle α. In particular, if such a particle is moving at right angles to the direction of the field the expression for the energy losses is (it is assumed that $e^2/\hbar v \ll 1$)

$$-\frac{dE}{dt} = \frac{(ez)^2\Omega^2}{v}\left\{\ln \frac{4mv^2}{\hbar\sqrt{2\Omega\omega_e}} - \frac{1}{4}\right\}. \tag{22.8}$$

The formulae (22.5)–(22.8) determine the energy losses of a non-relativistic particle. If a relativistic particle moves through the plasma its energy losses are as before proportional to $(ez)^2\Omega^2/v$ and depend comparatively weakly on the magnetic field.

The following is the expression for the quantity

$$F(\omega_e, \beta) = -\frac{dE}{dt} - \left(-\frac{dE}{dt}\right)_{H_0=0}, \tag{22.9}$$

which characterizes the effect of the magnetic field on the energy losses of the particle [Kitsenko, 1962]. If the condition $\omega_e^2/\Omega^2 \leq 4\beta^2/(1-\beta^2)$, where $\beta = v/c$, is satisfied, then

$$F(\omega_e, \beta) = \frac{-(ez)^2\omega_e^2}{4v}(1-\beta^2)(2-\beta^2). \tag{22.10}$$

If

$$4\beta^2/(1-\beta^2) \leq \omega_e^2/\Omega^2 \leq 4\beta^2/(1-\beta^2)^2,$$

then

$$F(\omega_e, \beta) = -\frac{(ez)^2\Omega^2}{v}\left\{\frac{1}{2}\ln\frac{1+x}{1-x} + \frac{(1-\beta^2)(2-\beta^2)\,\omega_e^2}{4\Omega^2} - \frac{(1-\beta^2)\,\omega_e^2 x}{4\beta^2\Omega^2}\right\}, \tag{22.11}$$

† The contribution of distant collisions to the energy losses of a particle moving along the magnetic field is determined in a paper by Sitenko and Stepanov, 1958.

where
$$x = \sqrt{1 - \frac{4\beta^2\Omega^2}{(1-\beta^2)\,\omega_e^2}}.$$

Lastly, if $\omega_e^2/\Omega^2 \geq 4\beta^2/(1-\beta^2)^2$, then

$$F(\omega_e, \beta) = -\frac{(ez)^2\Omega^2}{v}\left\{\frac{1}{2}\ln\frac{(1+x)(1+\beta^2-y)}{(1-x)(1+\beta^2+y)}\right.$$
$$\left.+\frac{(1-\beta^2)\,\omega_e^2}{4\beta^2\Omega^2}\,[\beta^2(2-\beta^2) - x + (1-\beta^2)\,y]\right\}, \tag{22.12}$$

where $y = \sqrt{(1-\beta^2)^2 - 4\beta^2\Omega^2\omega_e^{-2}}$.

By putting $\beta \ll 1$ in the relation (22.12) and using (21.10) we can obtain the expression (22.7) for the energy losses of a non-relativistic particle moving along the magnetic field.

3. *Allowance for "Spiralling"*

Let us now briefly examine the case when the inequalities (22.4) are not satisfied and we must allow for the complication of the motion of the moving particle caused by the magnetic field [Akhiezer, 1961]. It is well known that the motion of a particle in a magnetic field is determined by the component of its momentum, p_z, along the direction of the field, the quantum number n characterizing the motion in a plane at right angles to $\boldsymbol{H}_0$, and by the coordinate of the centre of the Larmor circle. The energy of a particle in a magnetic field is $E_{n,p_z} = p_z^2/2\mu + (n + \frac{1}{2})\,\hbar\omega_z$, $\omega_z = ezH_0/\mu c$.

In the same way as when there is no field the particle scattering probability can be connected with the charge density correlation function. We shall not give the derivation here but proceed straight to the expression for the probability for the transition per unit time of a particle from a state with the quantum numbers n, p_z to a state with the quantum numbers n', p_z' (averaged over the initial values and summed for the final values of the coordinate of the centre of the particle's Larmor circle)

$$dw = W_{np_z\to n'p_z'}\,dp_z'/2\pi\hbar,$$

$$W_{np_z\to n'p_z'} = \left(\frac{4\pi ez}{\hbar}\right)^2 \int \frac{d^2\boldsymbol{q}_t}{(2\pi)^2 q^4}\,\Lambda_{nn'}\left(\frac{\hbar q_t}{\sqrt{2\mu\hbar\omega_z}}\right)\langle\varrho^2\rangle_{q\omega}, \tag{22.13}$$

where

$$\hbar\omega = (n' - n)\,\hbar\omega_z + (2\mu)^{-1}(p_z'^2 - p_z^2)$$

and

$$\hbar q_z = p_z' - p_z$$

are the changes in the particle's energy and the longitudinal component of its momentum and

$$\Lambda_{nn'}(x) = \int_0^\infty ds\, J_0(2x\sqrt{s})\, L_n(s)\, L_{n'}(s)\, e^{-s}$$

(L_n is a Laguerre polynomial, J_0 is a Bessel function). We notice that the relation (22.13) is also valid in the case of quantum plasmas.

Multiplying (22.13) by $\hbar\omega$, summing over n' and integrating over p_z' we can determine the total energy losses of a particle per unit time.

Bibliography

ABRIKOSOV, A. A. and I. M. KHALATNIKOV, 1958 *Zh. eksp. i teor. fiz.* **34,** 198. [*Soviet Phys.-JETP* **7,** 135, 1958.]

AKHIEZER, A. I., 1956 *Nuovo Cimento, Suppl.* **3,** 591.

AKHIEZER, A. I., I. A. AKHIEZER and A. G. SITENKO, 1961 *Zh. eksp. i teor. fiz.* **41,** 644. [*Soviet Phys.-JETP* **14,** 462, 1962.]

AKHIEZER, A. I. and YA. B. FAINBERG, 1949 *Dokl. Akad. Nauk SSSR* **69,** 555; 1951 *Zh. eksp. i teor. fiz.* **21,** 1262.

—, 1962 in coll. *Theory and Calculations of Linear Accelerators* (in Russian) Gosatomizdat, p. 320.

AKHIEZER, A. I., A. B. KITSENKO and K. N. STEPANOV 1961 *Zh. eksp. i. teor. fiz.* **40,** 1866. [*Soviet Phys.-JETP* **13,** 1311, 1961.]

AKHIEZER, A. I., G. YA. LYUBARSKII and R. V. POLOVIN, 1961 *Zh. eksp. i teor. fiz.* **40,** 963. [*Soviet Phys.-JETP* **13,** 673, 1961.]

AKHIEZER, A. I. and L. E. PARGAMANIK, 1948 *Tr. fiz.-matem. fak-ta Khar'k. un-ta* **27,** 75.

AKHIEZER, A. I., I. G. PROKHODA and A. G. SITENKO 1957 *Zh. eksp. i teor. fiz.* **33,** 750. [*Soviet Phys.-JETP* **6,** 576, 1958.]

AKHIEZER, A. I. and A. G. SITENKO 1952 *Zh. eksp. i teor. fiz.* **23,** 161.

AKHIEZER, I. A., 1961 *Zh. eksp. i teor. fiz.* **40,** 954. [*Soviet Phys.-JETP* **13,** 667, 1961.]

—, 1962 *Zh. eksp. i teor. fiz.* **42,** 584. [*Soviet Phys.-JETP* **15,** 406, 1962.]

—, 1963a in coll. *Plasma Physics and Problems of Controlled Thermonuclear Synthesis* No. 11, Kiev, Akad. Nauk Ukr. SSR, p. 28.

—, 1963b *Zh. tekhn. fiz.* **33,** 935. [*Soviet Phys.-Technical Phys.* **8,** 699, 1964.]

ALEKSIN, V. F. and K. N. STEPANOV, 1962 *Radiofizika* **5,** 61; 1963a *Radiofizika* **6,** 297; 1963b *Radiofizika* **6,** 480. 1964 *Zh. tekhn. fiz.* (in press). In coll. *Plasma Physics and Problems of Controlled Thermonuclear Synthesis* (in Russian) No. 4, Kiev, Akad. Nauk Ukr. SSR. [*Soviet Phys.-Technical Phys.* **9,** 938, 1965.]

ASTRÖM, E., 1950 *Nature* **165,** 1019.

—, 1951 *Arkiv. Fiz.* **2,** 443.

AUER, P. L., 1958 *Phys. Rev. Lett.* **1,** 411.

BASS, F. G. and A. YA. BLANK, 1962 *Zh. eksp. i teor. fiz.* **43,** 1479. [*Soviet Phys.-JETP* **16,** 1045, 1963.]

BASS, F. G. and M. I. KAGANOV, 1958 *Zh. eksp. i teor. fiz.* **34,** 1154. [*Soviet Phys.-JETP* **7,** 799, 1958.]

BERNSTEIN, I. B., 1958 *Phys. Rev.* **109,** 10.

Bibliography

BOGDANKEVICH, L.A., A.A.RUKHADZE and V.P.SILIN, 1962 *Radiofizika* **5,** 1093.

BOHM, D. and E.P.GROSS, 1949 *Phys. Rev.* **75,** 1851, 1864.

BOHR, N., 1948 Passage of Atomic Particles Through Matter. *D. Kgl. Vid.–Selskab. Mat.–fiz. Medd. Copenhagen.*

BRAGINSKII, S.I. and A.P.KAZANTSEV, 1958 In coll. *Plasma Physics and Problems of Controlled Thermonuclear Reactions* v. IV, Moscow, Akad. Nauk SSSR, p. 24. [Pergamon, Oxford, 1960.]

BUCHSBAUM, S.J., 1960 *Phys. Fluids* **3,** 418.

BURT, P. and E.G.HARRIS, 1961 *Phys. Fluids* **4,** 1412.

CALLEN, H.B. and T.A.WELTON, 1951 *Phys. Rev.* **83,** 34.

COURANT, R. and D.HILBERT, 1962 *Methods of Mathematical Physics* Vol. 2, Interscience.

DOUGHERTY, J.P. and D.T.FARLEY, 1960 *Proc. Roy. Soc.* **A. 259,** 79.

DOYLE, P.H. and J. NEUFELD, 1959 *Phys. Fluids* **2,** 39.

DRUMMOND, W.E. and D.PINES, 1963 *Nucl. Fusion, Suppl.* **3,** 1049.

DRUMMOND, W.E. and M.N.ROSENBLUTH, 1962 *Phys. Fluids* **5,** 1507.

FADDEYEVA, V.N. and N.M.TERENT'EV, 1954 *Tables of the Values of the Probabilities with a Complex Argument* (in Russian), Moscow, Gostekhizdat.

FAINBERG, YA. B., V.I.KURILKO, and V.D.SHAPIRO, 1961 *Zh. tekhn. fiz.* **31,** 633. [*Soviet Phys.-Technical Phys.* **6,** 459, 1961.]

FARLEY, D., J. DOUGHERTY and D. BARRON, 1961 *Proc. Roy. Soc.* **A. 263,** 238.

FEIX, M., 1963 *Nuovo Cimento* **27,** No. 5, 1130.

FERMI, E., 1940 *Phys. Rev.* **57,** 485.

—, 1950 *Nuclear Physics* (revised edition), Univ. of Chicago Press.

FRIED, B., 1959 *Phys. Fluids* **2,** 337.

GERSHMAN, B.N., 1953 *Zh. eksp. i teor. fiz.* **24,** 659.

—, 1955 in coll. *In Memory of A.A.Andronov* (in Russian) Moscow, Akad. Nauk SSSR.

—, 1956 *Zh. eksp. i teor. fiz.* **31,** 707. [*Soviet Phys.-JETP* **4,** 582, 1957.]

—, 1958a *Radiofizika* **1** (No. **4**), 3.

—, 1958b *Radiofizika* **1** (No. **5–6**), 49.

—, 1960a *Radiofizika* **3,** 146.

—, 1960b *Zh. eksp. i teor. fiz.* **38,** 912. [*Soviet Phys.-JETP* **11,** 657, 1960.]

GERTSENSHTEIN, M.YE., 1952a *Zh. eksp. i teor. fiz.* **22,** 303.

—, 1952b *Zh. eksp. i teor. fiz.* **23,** 669.

—, 1954 *Zh. eksp. i teor. fiz.* **26,** 680.

GINZBURG, V.L., 1951 *Zh. eksp. i teor. fiz.* **21,** 788.

—, 1959 *Uspekhi fiz. nauk* **69,** 537. [*Soviet Phys.-Uspekhi* **2,** 874, 1960.]

—, 1960 *Propagation of Electromagnetic Waves in a Plasma,* Pergamon, Oxford.

GINZBURG, V.L. and B.N.GERSHMAN, 1963 *Radiofizika* **6,** 440.

GINZBURG, V.L. and V.V. ZHELEZNYAKOV, 1958 *Astron. Zh.* **35,** 694. [*Soviet Astronomy* **2,** 653, 1958.]

GLAZOV, O.A., L.V.DUBOVOI, and B.N.RUTKEVICH, 1962 *Zh. tekhn. fiz.* **31,** 84. [*Soviet Phys.-Technical Phys.* **6,** 59, 1961.]

GORDEYEV, G.V., 1954a *Zh. eksp. i teor. fiz.* **27,** 19.

—, 1954b *Zh. eksp. i teor. fiz.* **27,** 24.

GROSS, E., 1951 *Phys. Rev.* **82,** 232.

GUREVICH, V. L. and YU. A. FIRSOV, 1960 *Papers Read at the Second Congress on Theoretical and Applied Hydrodynamics* (in Russian). Riga, Akad. Nauk Latv. SSR.

HARRIS, E. G., 1959 *Phys. Rev. Letters.* **2,** 34.

ICHIMURA, S., 1962 *Ann. Phys.* **20,** 78.

ICHIMURA, S., PINES, D. and N. ROSTOKER, 1962 *Phys. Rev. Lett.* **8,** 231.

KADOMTSEV, B. B., 1957 *Zh. eksp. i teor. fiz.* **32,** 943. [*Soviet Phys.-JETP* **5,** 771, 1957.]

KITSENKO, A. B. 1962 *Dokl. Akad. Nauk SSSR* **145,** 305. [*Soviet Phys.-Doklady* **7,** 632, 1963.]

KITSENKO, A. B. and K. N. STEPANOV, 1963 In coll. *Plasma Physics and Problems of Controlled Thermonuclear Synthesis* (in Russian) No. III, Kiev, Akad. Nauk Ukr. SSR, p. 5.

KLIMONTOVICH, YU. L., 1958 *Zh. eksp. i teor. fiz.* **34,** 173. [*Soviet Phys.-JETP* **7,** 119, 1958.]

KOLOMENSKII, A. A. 1956 *Dokl. Akad. Nauk SSSR* **106,** 982. [*Soviet Phys.-Doklady* **1,** 133, 1956.]

KONDRATENKO, A. N. 1963 In coll. *Plasma Physics and Problems of Controlled Thermonuclear Synthesis* (in Russian) No. II, Kiev, Akad. Nauk Ukr. SSR.

KÖRPER, K., 1957 *Zeitschrift Naturforsch.* **12a,** 815.

KOVNER, M. S. 1960 *Radiofizika* **3,** 631, 746.

—, 1961 *Radiofizika* **4,** 444.

KOVRIZHNYKH, L. M. and A. A. RUKHADZE, 1960 *Zh. eksp. i teor. fiz.* **38,** 850. [*Soviet Phys.-JETP* **11,** 615, 1960.]

LANDAU, L. D., 1937 *Phys. Zs. Soviet Un.* **10,** 154. [*Collected Papers,* Pergamon, Oxford, 1965, p. 163.]

—, 1946 *J. Phys. USSR* **10,** 25. [*Collected Papers,* Pergamon, Oxford, 1965, p. 445.]

LANDAU, L. D., and E. M. LIFSHITZ, 1957 *Zh. eksp. i teor. fiz.* **32,** 618. [*Soviet Phys.-JETP* **5,** 512, 1957, Landau's *Collected Papers,* Pergamon, Oxford, 1965, p. 747.]

—, 1958a *Quantum Mechanics,* Pergamon, Oxford.

—, 1958b *Statistical Physics,* Pergamon, Oxford.

—, 1960a *Electrodynamics of Continuous Media,* Pergamon, Oxford.

—, 1960b *Mechanics of Continuous Media,* Pergamon, Oxford.

LARKIN, A. I., 1959 *Zh. eksp. i teor. fiz.* **37,** 264. [*Soviet Phys.-JETP* **10,** 186, 1960.]

LEONTOVICH, M. A. and S. M. RYTOV, 1952 *Zh. eksp. i teor. fiz.* **23,** 246.

LINDHARD, J., 1954 *Det Kong. Danske Vid. Selskab. Mat.–Fys. Medd.* **28,** No. 8.

MACDONALD, W., ROSENBLUTH, M. and W. CHUCK, 1957 *Phys. Rev.* **107,** 350.

NEUFELD, J. and R. M. RITCHIE, 1955 *Phys. Rev.* **98,** 1632.

NOERDLINGER, P. D., 1960 *Phys. Rev.* **118,** 879.

OZAWA, Y., KAJI, I. and M. KITO, 1961 Instability Criterion for Plasma Waves in a Magnetic Field, Paper No. 70 presented for the Conference of Plasma Physics and Controlled Nuclear Fusion at Salzburg, September.

PARGAMANIK, L. E., 1948 Dissertation (in Russian) Kharkov State Univ.

PENROSE, O., 1960 *Phys. Fluids.* **3,** 258.

PINES, D. and D. BOHM, 1951 *Phys. Rev.* **82,** 625.

—, 1952 *Phys. Rev.* **85,** 338.

POLOVIN, R.V., 1961 *Zh. tekhn. fiz.* **31,** 1220. [*Soviet Phys.-Technical Phys.* **6,** 889, 1962.]
—, 1963 *Zh. tekhn. fiz.* **33,** 255. [*Soviet Phys.-Technical Phys.* **8,** 184, 1963.]
—, 1964 Kinetic Stability in a Magnetic Field, *Zh. tekhn. fiz.* **34,** 259. [*Soviet Phys.-Technical Phys.* **9,** No. 2, 1964.]
RAPPOPORT, V.O., 1960 *Radiofizika* **3,** 737.
ROSENBLUTH, M. and N. ROSTOKER, 1962 *Phys. Fluids* **5,** 776.
ROSTOKER, N., 1961 *Nucl. Fusion,* **1,** 101.
RUKHADZE, A.A. 1958 *Radiofizika* **6,** 401.
RYTOV, S.M., 1953 *Theory of Electrical Fluctuations and Thermal Emission* (in Russian) Moscow, Akad. Nauk SSSR.
SALPETER, E.E., 1960a *Geophys. Res.* **65,** 1851; 1960b *Geophys. Res.* **66,** 982.
—, 1960c *Phys. Rev.* **120,** 1528.
—, 1961 *Phys. Rev.* **122,** 1663.
SEN, H.K., 1952 *Phys. Rev.* **88,** 816.
SHAFRANOV, V.D., 1958a In coll. *Plasma Physics and Problems of Controlled Thermonuclear Reactions* v. IV, Moscow, Akad. Nauk SSSR, p. 416. [Pergamon, Oxford, 1960.]
—, 1958b In coll. *Plasma Physics and Problems of Controlled Thermonuclear Reactions* v. IV, Moscow, Akad. Nauk SSSR, p. 426. [Pergamon, Oxford, 1960.]
—, 1958c *Zh. eksp. i teor. fiz.* **34,** 1475. [*Soviet Phys.-JETP* **7,** 1019, 1958.]
—, 1963 Electromagnetic Waves in a Plasma. In coll. *Voprosy teorii plazmy* No. **3,** Moscow, Gosatomizdat.
SHAPIRO, V.D., 1963 *Zh. eksp. i teor. fiz.* **44,** 613. [*Soviet Phys.-JETP* **17,** 416, 1963.]
SILIN, V.P., 1955 *Tr. fiz. in-ta Akad. Nauk* SSSR **6,** 200.
—, 1959 *Radiofizika* **2,** 198.
SILIN, V.P. and A.A. RUKHADZE, 1961 *Electromagnetic Properties of a Plasma and Plasma-like Media,* Gordon and Breach, New York.
SITENKO, A.G. and YU.A. KIROCHKIN, 1963 *Radiofizika* **6,** 469.
SITENKO, A.G. and A.A. KOLOMENSKII, 1956 *Zh. eksp. i teor. fiz.* **30,** 511. [*Soviet Phys.-JETP* **3,** 410, 1956.]
SITENKO, A.G. and K.N. STEPANOV, 1955 *Zh. eksp. i teor. fiz.* **31,** 642. [*Soviet Phys.-JETP* **4,** 512, 1957.]
—, 1958 *Tr. Fiz. – Matem. Fak-ta Khar'k. un-ta* **7,** 5.
STEPANOV, K.N., 1958a Dissertation (in Russian) Kharkov State Univ.
—, 1958b *Zh. eksp. i teor. fiz.* **34,** 1292. [*Soviet Phys.-JETP* **7,** 892, 1958.]
—, 1958c *Zh. eksp. i teor. fiz.* **35,** 283. [*Soviet Phys.-JETP* **8,** 195, 1959.]
—, 1958d *Zh. eksp. i teor. fiz.* **35,** 1155. [*Soviet Phys.-JETP* **8,** 808, 1959.]
—, 1959a *Ukr. fiz zh.* **4,** 678.
—, 1959b *Zh. eksp. i teor. fiz.* **36,** 1457. [*Soviet Phys.-JETP* **9,** 1035, 1959.]
—, 1960 *Zh. eksp. i teor. fiz.* **38,** 265. [*Soviet Phys.-JETP* **11,** 192, 1960.]
—, 1962 In coll. *Plasma Physics and Problems of Controlled Thermonuclear Synthesis* (in Russian) No. 1, Kiev, Akad. Nauk Ukr. SSR, p. 45.
—, 1963 *Radiofizika* **6,** 403.
STEPANOV, K.N. and PAKHOMOV, V.I., 1960 *Zh. eksp. i teor. fiz.* **38,** 1564. [*Soviet Phys.-JETP* **11,** 1126, 1960.]
—, 1962 *Zh. eksp. i teor. fiz.* **43,** 2153. [*Soviet Phys.-JETP* **16,** 1522, 1963.]

STEPANOV, K. N. and A. B. KITSENKO, 1961 *Zh. tekhn. fiz.* **31,** 167. [*Soviet Phys.-Technical Phys.* **6,** 120, 1961.]
STIX, T. H. 1957 *Phys. Rev.* **106,** 1146.
—, 1958 *Phys. Fluids* **1,** 308.
STURROCK, P. A., 1959 *Phys. Rev.* **112,** No. 5, 1488.
—, 1960 *Phys. Rev.* **117,** No. 6, 1426.
TAMM, I. YE. and I. M. FRANK 1937 *Dokl. Akad. Nauk. SSSR* **14,** 107.
TOLMACHEV, V. V., 1957a *Dokl. Akad. Nauk SSSR* **112,** 842. [*Soviet Phys.-Doklady* **2,** 85, 1957.]
—, 1957b *Dokl. Akad. Nauk SSSR* **113,** 301. [*Soviet Phys.-Doklady* **2,** 124, 1958.]
TONKS, L. and I. LANGMUIR, 1929a *Phys. Rev.* **33,** 195.
—, 1929b *Phys. Rev.* **33,** 990.
TSYTOVICH, V. N., 1962 *Zh. eksp. i teor. fiz.* **42,** 803. [*Soviet Phys.-JETP* **15,** 561, 1962.]
—, 1963 *Zh. eksp. i teor. fiz.* **44,** 946. [*Soviet Phys.-JETP* **17,** 643, 1963.]
—, 1962 *Dokl. Akad. Nauk SSSR* **142,** 319. [*Soviet Phys.-Doklady* **7,** 43, 1962.]
TYABLIKOV, S. V. and V. V. TOLMACHEV, 1957 *Dokl. Akad. Nauk SSSR,* **114,** 1210. [*Soviet Phys.-Doklady* **2,** 299, 1958.]
VEDENOV, A. A. 1962 *Atomn. energiya* **13,** 1, 5. Engl. translation in *J. Nucl. Eng.*
VEDENOV, A. A., YE. P. VELIKHOV and R. Z. SAGDEYEV, 1962 *Nucl. Fusion, Suppl.* **2,** 465.
VLASOV, A. A., 1938 *Zh. eksp. i teor. fiz.* **8,** 291.
—, 1945 *Uch. zap. Mosk. Gos. Un-ta* **75,** No. 2.
—, 1950 *Theory of Many Particles,* Gordon and Breach, New York.
WALKER, L. R., 1955 *J. Appl. Phys.* **25,** 131.

Index

Index

 MADE IN GREAT BRITAIN